WATER IS ...

THE MEANING OF WATER

Nina Munteanu

PIXL PRESS

Praise for *Water Is...*

"This book leaves me impressed. Impressed by the variety of approaches, sources, ideas and philosophies that are assembled, discussed and spiced up by comparisons to personal experience. From science to science fiction, from philosophy to religion, from history to fairytale, the role of water is illustrated and illuminated. Water is probably the best investigated and least understood substance on this world, yet we still don't know how to describe it in a better way than calling it H_2O. This book tries to zero in on the missing part, the great unknown of water, and it does that in a very intelligent and charming way."
—Elmar C. Fuchs, WETSUS Program Manager

"Kudus to Nina Munteanu for sharing her deep wisdom, experience and knowledge of humanity's greatest natural resource! As Leonardo da Vinci said, "We forget that the water cycle and the life cycle are one." We forget at our own peril and so I am deeply grateful for this book by so highly qualified an author!"
—Elisabet Sahtouris, evolution biologist, futurist,
author of *Gaia's Dance: The Story of Earth & Us*

Water is … what an astounding journey!
Nina Munteanu takes you on a giant trip of wonderful phenomena, of experiences, of scientific insight, of wisdom, and of the beauty of what "water is". A journey, as it seems to me, that will never end—somehow like that of water itself. The author uniquely combines the merits of a scientist with those of a writer with an artistic spirit. It is a joy to be taken by the insightful and elegantly written chapters to so many and so different scientists, philosophers, writers, artists and pioneers of wisdom such as Leonardo da Vinci, Albert Einstein, or Paul Feyerabend, who declared war on the dogma of the scientific method.
In "Afterthoughts", the author hopes that somewhere among these pages the reader may have emotionally connected with water, as she has. Yes, indeed, I have. And I wish this image-rich book to provide the opportunity of such an experience to many readers, who too may wonder what water is.
—Michael Jacobi, physicist, Institute of Flow Sciences Herrischried, Germany

"A sumptuous collection of treasures...from the basics of matter itself to the social and spiritual aspects of this substance, which touches our lives so much and is still not really understood."
—Dr. B. Kröplin and Regine C. Henschel, "World in a Drop", Germany

A percentage of the proceeds of book sales will be donated to a water charity.

Table of Contents

Water Is…
The Meaning of Water
Copyright © 2016 Nina Munteanu

Cover Design / Typography and Interior Design: Costi Gurgu
Published in Canada by Pixl Press, Vancouver, B.C., Canada

ISBN 978-0-9811012-4-8 Trade paperback (alk. paper)
ISBN 978-0-98-11012-5-5 Digital

Library and Archives Canada Cataloguing in Publication

Munteanu, Nina, author
Water is… : the meaning of water / Nina Munteanu.
Co-published by: Starfire World Syndicate.
Includes bilbiographical references.
Issued in print and electronic formats.
ISBN 978-0-9811012-4-8 (pbk.)
1. Water. 2. Fresh water. I. Title.
GB661.2.M86 2015   551.48   C2014-901367-1   C2014-901368-X

We acknowledge the kind support of Writer's Trust of Canada
and the Woodcock Fund in the publication of this book.

Printed in the United States of America on acid-free paper

For Kevin.
The future is yours…

Foreword

In July 2015 an email from my agent dropped into my inbox. It was a forwarded message from Nina Munteanu, a name I recognised from my Twitter timeline, asking if I might be interested in reading her upcoming non-fiction book *Water Is... The Meaning of Water* and possibly writing a foreword for it.

The timing was not what you would call ideal: I was wading — or rather, swimming — neck-deep in the final chapters of my second novel, with a deadline looming over my head like a giant icicle ready to drop at the slightest disturbance. Nevertheless, my immediate instinct was to say yes. I had written my first novel *Memory of Water* about an imaginary future world haunted by climate change and water shortages, and had researched the topic thoroughly. I was fascinated by the promise of Nina Munteanu's approach to the subject matter, to which I had never stopped feeling close. I responded that I would be interested in reading the book, at the very least, but a lot depended on the schedule. When would she need my contribution?

Luckily, things tend to work themselves out when something good is on the way. By the time I received the manuscript from Nina Munteanu, I had finished my own and happily moved on from the constraint of immediate deadlines, which meant I was able to give *Water Is...* the attention it deserved. I had the privilege of reading this book during a residency in Northern California in February 2016, and everything about it felt pressingly timely: California was in its fifth year of drought, and while the El Niño weather phenomenon had brought some much-needed relief to the area, throughout my stay I felt a pervasive sense of living on borrowed time — or water. What had once been the odd news article in the "Environment" section of papers had become a mainstay, with new studies and information about droughts as part of man-made climate change appearing in the mainstream media on an almost-daily basis.

If ever there was an urgent time to write and read about water, it is now.

Nina Munteanu is a science fiction author and creative writing instructor. She is also a scientist, with a background specifically in the field of limnology, or the study of inland waters. In *Water Is...*, she brings together her expertise in all these areas, creating an imaginative and informative portrait of the meaning of water in our world and beyond. The book begins as a study of the history and properties of water, but it is by no means simply another scholarly textbook. In a lyrical vein reminiscent of Rachel Carson's nature writings, Munteanu takes us on an absorbing journey, a kaleidoscopic, ever-changing look at the interaction between not just water and human life, but water and all life in our known universe. She writes about water through the changing prisms of movement and rhythm, harmony and vibration, communication, memory and spiritual significance. We see the image shift and ripple before our eyes, watch a portrait emerge that holds more than the measurable qualities of water as a natural element.

I would go as far as calling it a biography: probably the very first biography of Water you will ever read.

The originality of Nina Munteanu's writing lies in the fact that she treats water as a living being, a character in its own right, rather than a lifeless resource, let alone something to exploit or profit from. For her, water is a trickster, a wizard, a teacher, a quantum shape shifter deserving of our love and respect; after all, our entire existence depends on it. Munteanu's approach is decidedly poetic and holistic, and the argument she develops throughout the book is, first and foremost, a philosophical and spiritual one. Drawing from such diverse fields as limnology, anthropology, Jungian psychology, quantum physics, music and religion – to mention but a few – Munteanu observes the qualities

and meanings of water from different perspectives, giving it its own Hero's Journey in an adaptation of Joseph Campbell's work on archetype and monomyth. Against this backdrop, human history appears as a small but significant part of the picture, something that has changed the course of water's flow and consequently the surrounding landscape, but may also hold the potential for restoring it to its natural state. In this view, we are on the edge of a new awareness of our responsibility to our environment on a global scale.

The overarching notion — message, if you will — that emerges from *Water Is...* is deceptively simple on the surface, yet radical at a deeper level. In a world where the value of nearly everything is measured by profitability, it is nothing short of revolutionary to suggest that we should perhaps not see ourselves as separate from our environment and as entitled to exploiting it, but instead consider our lives to be an inseparable part of an intrinsic and complex network, an interconnected web where all living things share one thing in common: water.

"Water's journey is really our journey, and it is ultimately our journey home," Nina Munteanu writes.

I encourage you to embark on the journey and let the flow of this book sweep you away. It is an adventure through landscape, time and thought, to the very core of human spirit and what makes life possible on our shared Earth.

Emmi Itäranta
Author of *Memory of Water*
February 2016
Silicon Valley

Author's Preface

Photo 1: Wave pattern in flowing water of the Upper Credit River, Ontario, Canada.

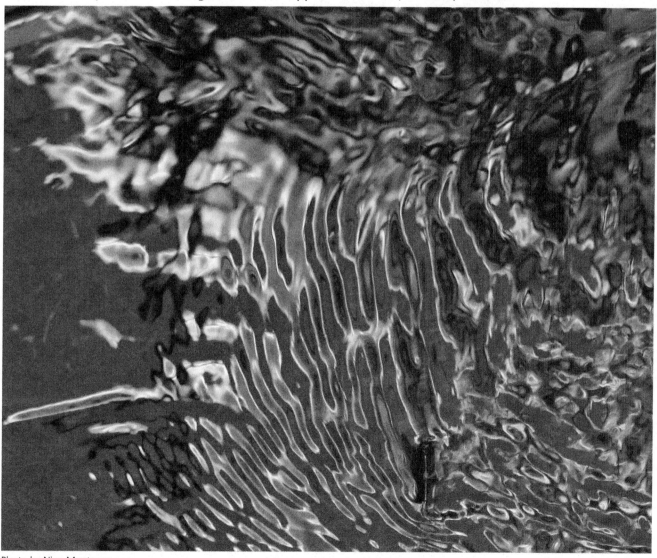

"Water is the driving force of all nature."
—Leonardo da Vinci

I'm a limnologist. Like other water scientists, I study the properties of water; how it behaves in a watershed. I help manage water in our environment; its flow, distribution, storage and quality. I look at how water changes the landscape, carving out huge valleys, forming deltas at river mouths, and polishing pebbles smooth on a lakeshore. I investigate the effects of its contamination by toxins, organic pollutants and disrespect. In its solid form, water has scraped out huge swaths of land and formed some of our largest lakes, dropping moraine in places and melt water from ice blocks elsewhere. In its gaseous form, water controls climate and weather.

And yet, what do we really know about water?

Water is the most common substance on Earth. Chemically, the water molecule is basically two atoms of hydrogen joined to one of oxygen. Simple. Not so simple.

For something so "simply" made, water is pretty complex. Its unique properties make water possibly the most important element of our existence and in ways most of us can't possibly imagine. Without water no life form could exist. Water is a universal solvent. It transports all kinds of things from the sediment of the Nile River to the oxygenated blood cells in your arteries. Water stores energy and heat. It responds to and changes the properties of all manner of things.

Photo 2: Nina Munteanu and friend Oli in Mahone Bay, Nova Scotia, Canada.

Photo by Kate Wylde

Scientific studies have begun to show some astonishing properties and behaviours of water. One is that water reacts to—and may even drive some—cosmic phenomena. Laboratory studies with water have shown that it is not always the same. Studies have revealed that water is influenced by shifts in the Earth's magnetic field or by explosions on the Sun. Of course, most of us know about how the Earth's great water bodies respond to the movements of the Moon around the Earth in the oceanic tides and the seiches of the Great Lakes. But we are learning that water is far more sensitive and responsive than most people ever imagined. And some suspect that water responds to and is interconnected in some way with all that exists in the cosmos.

While Earth is blessed with copious amounts of water, 97% is salty and 2% is locked up in snow and ice. That leaves 1 percent for us to drink, bathe, and grow our crops. Less, really, because some of that water is contaminated.

Since the dinosaurs quenched their thirst in the soupy marshes of the Triassic Period millions of years ago, to the rain falling on your house today, the amount of moisture on Earth hasn't changed. However, scientists predict that by 2025, 1.8 billion people will live where usable water is scarce.

"Water is life," says author Barbara Kingsolver in an article in the 2010 Water Issue of *National Geographic*. "It's the briny broth of our origins, the pounding circulatory system of the world. We stake our civilizations on the coasts and mighty rivers. Our deepest dread is the threat of having too little—or too much."[1] North Americans use about 100 gallons of water at home every day, yet the world's poorest subsist on less than 5 gallons, many walking miles to get their water.

One of humanity's greatest crimes is that we don't treat water respectfully and with gratitude. It's free, after all (unless it isn't, that is). It's everywhere, isn't it? "Water is the ultimate commons," says Kingsolver. All life is made up of from 50 to 95 percent water, with humans averaging 70 percent (babies generally containing more, close to 80%); this

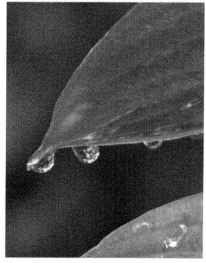

Photo 3: Water drop on a hosta leaf.

Photo by Merridy Cox

ironically reflects the proportion of water on the planet. Some scientists now tell us that—although an adult human contains generally two-thirds water—on a molecular level, our water content is much higher. Water occupies over 98% of a human cell molecule.[2]

We are water.

What we do to water we do to ourselves.

Which leads me to one of the greatest ironies of human health: many of us blessed with living in a place where water is plentiful and readily available, simply don't drink enough—by choice. We starve our bodies of this miraculous elixir by choosing instead to drink other beverages (such as coffee, tea, juice or pop). We pollute our fresh drinking water sources, then buy bottled water that comes from somewhere else to drink. Instead of petitioning governments to protect the drinking water resources near our homes for free consumption, we let others put a price tag on it and take it elsewhere; we watch something that sustains us—that we can't live without—turn into something that some of us can't afford.

In choosing to buy bottled water, you are implying a choice against tap water. In doing that, you support the implication that water is a commodity to buy and sell, rather than a global heritage and the right of all citizens of this planet—with an associated individual, national and global responsibility to keep clean and sustain for our future generations and the planet's well being.

"Water must be seen as a commons that belongs to the Earth and all species alike," says Maude Barlow, Senior Advisor on Water Issues to the President of the United Nations and National Chairperson of the Council of Canadians. "It must be declared a public trust that belongs to the people, the ecosystem and the future and preserved for all time and practice in law."[3] In fact, water belongs to no one; it is a gift from the universe, for all to use with gratitude and return in as good, if not better, condition. Like the air we breathe. Like the love we freely bestow and are, in turn, gifted with.

Photo 4: Ice formation on the shore of Lake Ontario, Toronto, Ontario, Canada.

Photo by Nina Munteanu

In a recent unprecedented move, Ecuador became the first nation on Earth to put the rights of Nature in its constitution; under their new laws, rivers and forests maintain their own right to flourish. "Under these laws, a citizen might file suit on behalf of an injured watershed, recognizing that its health is crucial to the common good,"[1] writes Kingsolver. She adds that other nations may follow Ecuador's lead. "Just as legal systems once reeled to comprehend women or former slaves as fully entitled, law schools in the U.S. are now reforming their curricula with an eye to understanding and acknowledging Nature's rights."

In the foreword to his book *Understanding Water*, Andreas Wilkens writes that water is "a substance which so well hides the consequence of our actions upon it. And which is seemingly so plentiful."[4] The consequences of our actions simply flow away. It is an unfortunate reality that most of us have remained indifferent to the effects of our actions on water. Perhaps this is because water, according to Wilkens, "is a master of concealment, withdrawing from so many phenomena, appearing in that which it simultaneously transforms: in the colors of the heavens, or the reflection of a shore on the surface of a lake. The more intensely it participates in a particular phenomenon, the more hidden it remains." [4]

If things are defined by their behaviour, then water is an altruist.

Many researchers, scientists and wellness practitioners agree that frequency affects—if not in fact directs—the manifestation and eradication of disease. Beneficial frequencies have been identified, the same ones found in the Earth and in the Earth's minerals. Just sitting on a granite boulder on a sunny day radiates frequencies flowing through your body. Water intensifies the flow and can heal.[5]

So, what is water, really? And what does it mean to you and your loved ones?

Some see water as a commodity like everything else that can make them rich; they will claim it as their own to sell. Yet it cannot be "owned"

or kept. Ultimately, water will do its job to energize you and give you
life, bring beauty to the world, then quietly take its leave.

Water is magic.

Water is you.

Photo 5: Ski hut near the Matterhorn, Zermatt, Switzerland.

Photo by Nina Munteanu

Ecology, Schrodinger's Cat & the Holo-Universe

"Discovery consists of seeing what everybody has seen and thinking what nobody has thought."
—Albert Szent-Györgyi, *Nobel laureate*

Ecologists and environmental activists provide eloquent and convincing reasons for the preservation and conservation of pristine natural water in aquatic ecosystems and watersheds throughout the world. Excellent works devoted to water's rights and people's rights to water have followed humanity's journey with water throughout the ages; others have documented our social, political and economic struggles that have impacted water in many ways.

It's been my experience, however, that *knowing* and *feeling* a truth are not the same; one leads to vehement agreement but seldom to action; the other leads to quiet resonance and often to quiet action. Before you act you have to care. A lot.

Some will argue that the best way to solicit an appreciation for something is to give it an economic value. My experience with this argument is that it's a slippery road. Some suggest that the only way to protect water is to treat it as a commodity—to put a price on it. However, when something is assigned an economic value, its value becomes relative and compartmentalized; it loses an essential part of its perceived intrinsic value.

Scholar and writer Charles Eisenstein gives us four good reasons to shy away from evaluating anything—particularly Nature and water—economically.[6] First, this view favours competition within a perception of scarcity as individuals seek to maximize self-interest. Second, competition and a perceived need for growth promotes the objectification of Nature as something separate from us, leading to abuse and the "Tragedy of the Commons".[7] Third, valuing all things in a utili-

tarian and self-serving frame instils a dominating worldview through a "Conquest of Nature" ethic. And finally, this value system "echoes science's onward march of quantification by converting a multiplicity of often qualitative values into a single metric of value called money."[6] It applies a reductionist approach to a holistic phenomenon. When that happens, we lose the meaning of the thing that we've turned into an object.

For most of us, perhaps chemists aside, when we think "water" we envision its archetype of liquid flowing in rivers, brooks, gurgling springs and surging oceans. We envision myths from the ancient creation stories to the current thoughts of today or of sacred rituals of which it plays an integral part. We think of its refreshing crystal clarity as the matrix of life. Water is "not a personality but more like a culture to itself, with laws, arts, and a unique history and geography,"[8] says science writer Philip Ball in the preface to his book, *H2O: A Biography of Water*. Water's "public persona" has co-evolved with humanity through our various cultures and philosophical beliefs, fashion, and political and social change.[8] Yet, throughout the millennia, water has remained water; it is we who have changed.

Water is a catalyst.

"We cannot avoid the conclusion that for humankind water is a force of social change—a precious resource to be treasured, nurtured and used wisely,"[8] adds Ball. But water is far more than this; it is far more than "resource", as Ball himself acknowledges in the very last page of his book, where he writes, "understanding water's physics, chemistry, geology and biology can provide only a part of the answer,"[8] and speaks to the wisdom of a relationship with water that lies outside science.

In that vein, I ask you to keep an open mind when reading these chapters. Some of what I write about may present itself with an appearance of what some call soft science, fringe science or even pseudo-science. Read these pages equally with your soul and heart as with your mind. Read the words as they flow along the pages and let them touch

Photo 6: British Columbia west coast stream, Canada.

Photo by Nina Munteanu

your heart with deeper truths felt in your soul. I'm asking you to turn off your phones and calculators and listen with your heart for what is deep inside you.

The Scientific Method &"Weird Water"

The ongoing evolution in scientific reasoning and investigation has spanned centuries, from the empirical measurements and observations of Aristotle and early Islamic hypothesis–experimentation, to the rationalism advocated by René Descartes and the inductivism of Isaac Newton and Galileo, to the hypothetico–deductivism of Popper and Kuhn in the 19th and 20th centuries.

Controlled experiments using "double-blind studies" were developed to compensate for "epistemic feedback" and "observer–expectancy effect" (or placebo effect) or other experimenter biases that would otherwise skew an objective experiment toward an "agenda" that was often hidden. The *observer effect* (Hawthorne effect) describes a type of reactivity in which individuals modify or improve an aspect of their behaviour in response to their awareness of being observed. This is something that, if taken into account, can be in of itself revealing; but if not, can bias the results toward erroneous conclusions.

Scientific archivist and professor at UC Berkleley, Paul Feyerabend, shared that many discoveries would not have come about had they been constrained by the limitations of the methodolical monism prevailing at that time. Feyerabend suggested that some of the greatest scientific leaps ignored the current scientific method. He suggested that scientists adapt their methods to tackle new discoveries that could not be examined without breaking established rules.[9]

Biochemist Gerald Pollack of the University of Washington describes the "schizophrenic" nature of the current field of water science in his 2013 book, *The Fourth Phase of Water*. On the one hand, "mainstream scientists employ computer simulations and technologically sophisticated approaches to learn more about water molecules and their immediate neighbours. Their results more or less define the field," says Pollack. "On the other side are the scientists who explore the more provocative phenomena, dismissed by mainstreamers as 'weird water'."[10] Consigned to fringe science, weird water phenomena are often placed in the same category as "cold fusion, UFOs and subtle energies," adds Pollack, who includes an 'out-on-a-limb-meter' to some theories and discussions he forwards in his book.

Goethe, an accomplished polymath and scientist, said of the conventional approach in science: "Whatever you cannot calculate, you do not think is real."[11]

I believe that the mavericks of the scientific community, like our artists—because they have one foot inside and one foot outside—provide a wide and highly relevant perspective, unencumbered by tradition and the need for acceptance. So many Nobel laureates have chosen to follow untraditional paths in their pursuits—as if finally freed to pursue their imagination and dreams—that traditional science has given it a term: *Nobel disease*. But it was Einstein who said in 1929 that imagination is more important than knowledge: "Knowledge is limited; imagination encircles the world."[12] While shared knowledge is valuable in forming a stable culture or tradition, imagination through creativity and art—while it may threaten an established hegemony—creates opportunity and needed change.

"In some cases, a new branch of the sciences ... can begin with a few mavericks (with a high Intelligence/Knowledge [I/K] ratio) whose research is initially dismissed as speculative,"[12] writes Kathleen Taylor, research scientist at Oxford University. "As their way of thinking gradually wins acceptance, it attracts recruits at an increasing rate until a paradigm shift occurs and allegiances transfer wholesale from the old establishment to the new. A period of growing stability follows in which knowledge is assembled (with a decrease in I/K ratio) which

Song of the Spirits over the Waters

The human soul
Is as water:
From heaven it comes
To heaven it rises,
And down again
To earth it must,
Ever charging.

The pure jet
Streams from the high
Steep cliff.
It sweeps sweetly
In cloudwaves
To the smooth crag,
And, gently taken,
It flows down,
Veiling all,
Gently murmuring
Into the depths.

When rocks jut out against its fall
it foams dissatisfied
step by step
into the abyss.

In the flat bed
It steals its way to valley
meadows,
And in the smooth lake
All starry constellations
Delight their countenance.

Wind is the wave's
Sweet lover
Wind mixes foaming billows
From the very bottom.

Human soul
How like water you are!
Human fate
How like wind you are!

J.W. von Goethe

supports the new ideas. Creative output falls, stagnation gradually sets in. Problems begin to emerge, which are ignored by all but a few ... and so the cycle begins again."[13]

Despite the mandate of exploration and discovery in science, the scientific community can be rather harsh with those who threaten its established hegemony. Many scientists have been ridiculed and marginalized by their peers only to have their findings and conclusions vindicated much later. Sometimes, after they themselves have perished. I call it *artist syndrome*.

I provide two examples that involve water research, which remain controversial after decades of debate.

The first was the discovery in the late 1960s by Russian scientists, led by surface physicist Boris Derjaguin, of "polymeric water molecules" found adjacent to surfaces. This "new phase of water"—water with higher stability, such as in a polymer—they called "polywater". Water that was confined within narrow capillary tubes appeared to behave differently than surrounding bulk water, demonstrating a lower freezing point, higher boiling point, and much higher density and viscosity. When it was shown that the capillary tubes contained salts and silica leached from the surrounding glass tubes, the discovery was rejected by the scientific community and the Russians accused of careless experimentation. The significance of the results was abandoned in the hubbub of scientific embarrassment. "Contaminants" are natural features of water, given its impeccable universal solvent characteristics, and their presence in limited quantities does not necessarily imply that observed features are not relevant to water's behaviour. The natural question abandoned by the community was this: *In the presence of contaminants, why does water take on the interesting features described by Derjaguin's team?* Earlier work by Henniker and Szent-Györgyi had established that water organized itself close to surfaces such as cell membranes.[14,15] This was later demonstrated by Gerald Pollack and his team at the University of Washington.[16] Forty years after the polywater debacle, Pollack and

Photo 7: Windsurfers on Lake Ontario off Cherry Beach, Toronto, Ontario, Canada.

Photo by Nina Munteanu

other scientists discussed a fourth phase of water, an interfacial water zone that Pollack calls *Exclusion Zone water* or *EZ water*,[10,17,18,19] given that it excludes materials. Interfacial EZ water was more stable, more viscous and more ordered, and according to biochemist Martin Chaplin of South Bank University this water was, "hydrophobic, stiffer, super-fluidic and thermally more stable than bulk water."[19] Not the same as "polywater" but certainly related.

The second example of controversial research was the proposed ability of water to retain a memory of substances previously dissolved in it, undertaken by the late French immunologist Jacques Benveniste. Reported in a paper published in *Nature* in 1988,[20] Benveniste and his research team dissolved biologically active substances in water and successively diluted them until there was nothing left except water. The researchers demonstrated that both concentrated and diluted substance (essentially water) triggered the same impact, suggesting that water held information. Some of you will recognize this as the basis for the practice of homeopathy. The scientific community, while unable to fully discredit his work, rejected his conclusions and declared water memory a delusion. Thirty years later, scientists are confirming Benveniste's results and more.[16,21,22,23,24] These include, among others, Nobel laureate Luc Montagnier, who posited the transmission of information stored in water,[24] and the late materials scientist Rustum Roy in his work with epitaxy, nanobubbles and pressure effects.[26]

Photo 8: Cruise ship passes under the Lions Gate Bridge as it leaves Burrard Inlet, Vancouver, British Columbia, Canada.

Over a hundred years ago, in 1871, James Clerk Maxwell's Cambridge University inaugural lecture expressed the mood of scientific achievement at the time: "In a few years," he said rather smugly, "all the great physical constants will have been approximately estimated, and … the only occupation which will then be left to the men of science will be to carry these measurements to another place of decimals." A hundred and forty-four years later, we are far from tying off decimal points and remain poised to understand the great wonders of our universe, quantum gravity and the nature of reality. Perhaps—I say a little

Photo by Nina Munteanu

tongue in cheek—it is time for *the women of science* to forge ahead.

Which brings me to non-local phenomena, quantum entanglement and decoherence, Schrödinger's cat, and the possibility of instantaneous long-range communication. What do these quantum concepts have to do with water and this book? Nothing … Well, everything.

Entangled Life

In 1935, Schrödinger's thought exercise spoke to the collision of classical physics and quantum physics—a chaotic dark thriller with a rather macabre baroque scenario involving a cat, a box and some poison. Schrödinger invented the term "entanglement" to describe the behaviour of two previously bound-together individual particles, separated and later behaving as a single entity.[27] In 1964 John Bell proved a theorem that allowed experimental tests to establish the existence of an instantaneous connectedness, what Einstein had called "spooky action at a distance".[28,29] Freedman & Clauser[30] and the Orsay experiments of Aspect et al.[31] later demonstrated that if objects had interacted, what an observer chose to observe about one of them would instantaneously influence the result that an arbitrarily remote observer chose to observe for the other object. They were entangled.

In a 2011 article in *Scientific American* entitled "Living in a Quantum World," quantum physicist Vlatko Vedral describes how quantum mechanics no longer applies to small things—as formally thought.[32] Vedral shares how quantum phenomena such as entanglement may be nurtured and exploited in living systems through biological processes from bird migration[33,34] to photosynthesis.[35,36,37] Birds use quantum processes in compass cells to navigate by sensing the Earth's magnetic field. In 2010, a team led by Gregory Scholes at the University of Toronto in Ontario, Canada, reported coherence effects at ambient temperatures for photosynthetic cryptophyte algae.[36] Photosynthesis, the process that allows

plants and bacteria to turn sunlight, carbon dioxide and water into organic matter, is "arguably the most important biochemical reaction on Earth,"[38] says writer and former editor of *Nature* Philip Ball, who adds two other examples of quantum effects in nature. One is the movement of protons from one molecule to another in some enzyme-catalyzed reactions through a phenomenon called *quantum tunnelling*, in which a particle passes through an energy barrier rather than having to gather the energy to climb over it.[39] Another example is a controversial theory of olfaction, which claims that "smell comes from the biochemical sensing of molecular vibrations—a process that involves electron tunnelling between the molecule responsible for the odour and the receptor where it binds in the nose."[40]

According to Vedral, in quantum science it is entanglement—not time or space or even gravity—that is primary. "They interconnect quantum systems without reference to space and time."[31] Engel and other scientists predict an emerging discipline called quantum biology.[35,38,41]

Illustration 1: Photosynthetic cryptophyte alga. A) the contractile vacuole; B) mitochondrion; C) nucleus; D) eyespot; E) a plastid; and F) a flagellum.

Some of the most eminent physicists have claimed that, when a nuclear particle is observed by a scientist—or when a measurement is made of it by an automatic instrument—the observation directly affects the particle. If, for example, its position is measured, the particle acquires a definite position at that moment—having previously been in an indefinite, "spread-out" state. According to this view, scientists intervene very directly in the phenomena that they study, both creating them as well as observing them. Four hundred years earlier, medieval scientist Francis Bacon wrote, "And the human understanding is like a false mirror, which, receiving rays irregularly, distorts and discolours the nature of things by mingling its own nature with it."[42] In the 1960s, Princeton University philosopher David K. Lewis proposed a *modal realism* worldview, in which all possible worlds are as real as the actual world.[43]

What am I suggesting with this line of thought? Only that "there are more things in heaven and earth ... than are dreamt of in [our]

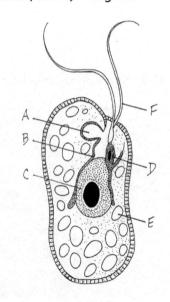

Illustration by Kerste Voute

philosophy," as Shakespeare wrote in his play *Hamlet*. Good science—and good thinking—isn't just about skepticism and proof; it starts with imagination and vision—and persistence. And who knows where our imagination—and persistence—may lead?

Symbiosis and a Cooperative Universe

Here's an example.

Eukaryotic cells, with their many intracellular organelles, were long regarded as descendants of prokaryotes that grew more complex as the result of genetic mutations. Back in 1969, when her paper on *endosymbiosis* was constantly rejected by over a dozen scientific journals (because no one knew how to evaluate it), microbiologist and evolutionist Lynn Margulis stubbornly refused to stand down when critics in her scientific community shot down her "outlandish" theory.

Briefly, her *theory of endosymbiosis* posited that primitive cells gained entry into host cells as undigested prey or as internal parasites after which the "arrangement" became mutually beneficial to both partners.[44] Chloroplasts from cyanobacteria and mitochondria from bacteria are two examples. The theory challenged Neo-Darwinism by arguing that inherited variation, significant in evolution, does not come mainly from random mutations, but that new tissues, organs and even species evolve primarily "through the long-lasting intimacy of strangers."[45]

Margulis suggested that the fusion of symbiosis followed by natural selection leads to increasingly complex levels of individuality. She contended that evolution proceeds largely through *cooperation*, not *competition*. Her persistence paid off: what was once regarded as an absurd speculation is now—thirty years later—taken as self-evident truth. The Hobbesian view that engendered the concept of the "selfish gene" programming organisms to maximize reproductive self-interest is rapidly disintegrating in the face of new science that embraces symbiosis, co-

Photo 9: Water drops on a hosta leaf.

Photo by Nina Munteanu

operation and interdependency; traits not exclusive to civilized people. For instance, researchers are finding increasing evidence that all kinds of life demonstrate qualities of empathy and altruism.[46] We just need to look for it.

Does this quality need to be confined to life?

I hope that in some chance notion, event, or experience within the pages of this book, you—like I—will discover one important thing about water and one important thing about yourself and that these will entangle, linger and resonate with all that was, is and will be.

With Gratitude,
Nina

Photo 10: Snowy mountain stream in Whistler, British Columbia, Canada.

Photo by Kevin Klassen

References:

1. Kingsolver, Barbara. 2010. "Water is Life". *National Geographic, Water Special Issue*. April 2010.
2. Freitas Jr., Robert A. 1999. "Nanomedicine: Volume I". *Landes Bioscience*. Tables 3–1 and 3–2.
3. Barlow, Maude. 2009. Address to the UN General Assembly to support the Bolivian call for an annual "International Mother Earth Day" celebration. April 22, 2009.
4. Wilkens, Andreas, Michael Jacobi, Wolfram Schwenk. 2005. "Understanding Water". *Floris Books*, Edinburgh. 107 pp.
6. Eisenstein, Charles. 2014. "Development in the Ecological Age". *Kosmos* (Spring/Summer Issue): 74–79.
7. Harden, Garrett. 1968. "The Tragedy of the Commons". *Science* 162 (3859): 1243-1248.
8. Ball, Philip. 2000. "H2O: A Biography of Water." Phoenix. London, UK. 387 pp.
9. Feyerabend, Paul. 1993. "Against Method: Outline of an Anarchistic Theory of Knowledge". *Verso*. 3rd Edition. 269 pp.
10. Pollack, Gerald. 2013. "The Fourth Phase of Water: Beyond Solid, Liquid and Vapor". *Ebner & Sons Publishers*, Seattle WA. 357 pp.
11. Goethe, J.W. Quoted In: Bartholomew, Alick. 2010. "The Spiritual Life of Water: Its Power and Purpose". *Park Street Press*. Page 10.
12. Einstein, Albert. 1929. Quote in interview/article by George Sylvester Viereck in Berlin. In: *Philadelphia Saturday Evening Post*, October 26th, 1929.
13. Taylor, Kathleen. 2002. "Is imagination more important than knowledge? Einstein". *Times Higher Education*. November 8, 2002. Online article: https://www.timeshighereducation.co.uk/features/is-imagination-more-important-than-knowledge-einstein/172613.article
14. Henniker, J.C. 1949. "The depth of the surface zone of a liquid". *Rev. Mod. Phys.* 21(2): 322–341.

15. Szent-Gyorgyi, A. 1960. "Introduction to a Supramolecular Biology". *Academic Press*, New York. 135 pp.

16. Pollack, Gerald. 2001. "Cells, Gels and the Engines of Life: A New Unifying Approach to Cell Function". *Ebner and Sons*, Seattle. 305 pp.

17. Ho, M.W. 2004. "Water forms massive exclusion zones". *Science in Society* 23: 50–51.

18. Pollack, GH and J. Clegg. 2008. "Unexpected linkage between un-stirred layers, exclusion zones, and water". In *Phase Transitions in Cell Biology* (Pollack GH, Chin WC eds.), pp 143–52, *Springer Science & Business Media*, Berlin.

19. Chaplin, Martin. 2015. "Interfacial water and water-gas interfaces". Online: "Water Structure and Science": http://www1.lsbu.ac.uk/water/interfacial_water.html

20. Dayenas, E., F. Beauvais, J. Amara, M. Oberbaum, B. Robinzon, A. Miadonna, A. Tedeschit, B. Pomeranz, P. Fortner, P. Belon, J. Sainte-Laudy, B. Poitevin and J. Benveniste. 1988. "Human basophil degran-ulation triggered by very dilute anteserum against IgE". *Nature* 333 (6176): 816–818.

21. Liu, C.S., S. Komarneni, R. Roy. 1992. "Crystallization of Anorthite Seeded Albite Glass by Solid State Epitaxy". *J Am CerSoc* 75: 2665–2670.

22. Walach, H., W.B. Jonas, R. Van Wijk, and O. Weingartner. 2005. "Research on Homeopathy: State of the Art". *J. Alt. and Comp. Med.* 11(5): 813–829.

23. Kröplin, Bernd. 2005. "Welt im Tropfen (World in a Drop)". *InstitutfürStatik und Dynamik der Luft- und Raumfahrtkonstruktionen*. Germany. 83 pp.

24. Chaplin, Martin. 2015. "Anomalous properties of water". Online: "Water Structure and Science: http://www1.lsbu.ac.uk/water/water_anomalies.html

25. Montagnier, L, J. Aissa, E. Del Guidice, C. Lavallee, A. Tedeschi and G. Vitiello. 2011. "DNA waves and water". *J. Phys. Conf. Series* 306.

26. Roy, Rustum, W.A. Tiller, Iris Bell, M.R. Hoover. 2005. "The structure of liquid water; novel insights from materials research; potential relevance to homeopathy". *Materials Research Innovations Online* 9–4: 577–608.

27. Schrödinger, Erwin. 1935. "Die gegenwärtige Situation in der Quantenmechanik (The present situation in quantum mechanics)". *Die Naturwissenschaften* 23 (49): 807–812.

28. Bell, John. 1964. "On the Einstein Podolsky Rosen paradox". *Physics* 1(3): 195–200.

29. Einstein, Albert. 1927. His quote "spooky action at a distance" in reference to the concept of quantum entanglement. Cited In: Bell, J.S. 1987. 16: "Bertlman's socks and the nature of reality", In: "Speakable and Unspeakable in Quantum Mechanics". *Cambridge University Press*. pp. 139–158 .

30. Freedman, S.J. and J.F.Clauser. 1972. "Experimental test of local hidden-variable theories". *Phys. Rev. Let.* 28 (938): 938–941.

31. Aspect, Alain, P. Grangier, G. Roger. 1982. "Experimental Realization of Einstein–Podolsky–Rosen-Bohm *Gedankenexperiment*: A New Violation of Bell's Inequalities". *Phys. Rev. Let.* 49: 91–94.

32. Vedral, Vlatko. 2011. "Living in a Quantum World". *Scientific American*, June Issue. pp. 39–43.

33. Ritz, T., Adem, S. & Schulten, K. 2000. "A model for photoreceptor-based magnetoreception in birds". *Biophys. J.* 78, 707–718.

34. Ritz, T. 2011. "Quantum effects in biology: Bird navigation". *Proc. Chem.*3, 262–275.

35. Engel, G. S. et al. 2007. "Evidence for wavelike energy transfer through quantum coherence in photosynthetic systems". *Nature* 446, 782–786.

36. Collini, Elisabetta, Cathy Y. Wong, Krystyna E. Wilk, Paul M.G. Curmi, Paul Brumer & Gregory D. Scholes. 2010. "Coherently wired light-harvesting in photosynthetic marine algae at ambient temperature." *Nature* 463 (7281): 644–648.

37. Sarovar, Mohan, Akihito Ishizaki, Graham R. Fleming & K. Birgitta Whaley. 2010. "Quantum entanglement in photosynthetic light-harvesting complexes". *Nature Physics* 6: 462–467.

38. Ball, Philip. 2011. "The Dawn of Quantum Biology". *Nature* 474: 272–274.

39. Ball, Philip. 2004. "Enzymes: By chance or by design?" *Nature* 431: 396–397.

40. Turin, Luca. 1996. "A Spectroscopic Mechanism for Primary Olfactory Reception". *Chem. Senses* 21: 443–791.

41. Keim, Brandon. 2010. "Everywhere in a Flash: The Quantum Physics of Photosynthesis". *Wired Magazine* February 3, 2010. Online website: http://www.wired.com/2010/02/quantum-photosynthesis/

42. Bacon, Francis. 1620. "The New Organon or True Directions Concerning the Interpretation of Nature", (*Aphorisms*, Book One, XLI).

43. Lewis, David K. 2001. "On the Plurality of Worlds". *Wiley–Blackwell*. 288 pp.

44. Margulis, Lynn. 1981. "Symbiosis in Cell Evolution: Microbial Communities in the Archean and Proterozoic Eons". *W.H. Freeman & Co Ltd.* New York, NY. 419 pp.

45. Mazur, Suzan. 2010. "The Altenberg 16: An Exposé of the Evolution Industry (Chapter 18, Lynn Margulis: Intimacy of Strangers and Natural Selection)". *North Atlantic Books*. Berkeley, California. 376 pp.

46. de Waal, Frans. 2010. "The Age of Empathy: Nature's Lessons for a Kinder Society". *Broadway Books*. 304 pp.

1. Water is Magic

Photo 1.1: Wave patterm in flowing water of the Credit River, Ontario, Canada.

Photo by Nina Munteanu

"If there is magic on this planet it is contained in water."
—Loren Eiseley

Water is the essence of life on Earth and dominates the chemical composition of all organisms. It is considered by many to be the most important substance in the world.

"The ubiquity of water in biota as the fulcrum of biochemical metabolism rests on its unique physical and chemical properties,"[1] says Robert G. Wetzel, limnologist and author of the textbook *Limnology*. Water is unique. And mysterious. Most typically occurring in its liquid form, water as liquid behaves far from "typically."

Life cannot evolve or continue without liquid water. Liquid water serves as a solvent, a solute, a reactant and a biomolecule; it helps structure proteins, nucleic acids and cells, and helps control our consciousness. Water is made of the first and third most common elements in the universe, hydrogen and oxygen. As ice, water is apparently the most abundant solid material out there, found on comets, planets and moons throughout the universe. Water is fundamental to star formation. According to the Weizmann Institute of Science, who provided experimental evidence in 1997, our billions of stars had a watery birth.[2] In June 2011, the Herschel telescope spotted a young star 750 light years away, spewing powerful water jets into space at 124,000 miles an hour.[3] Deep oceans of liquid water occur on Europa and Titan, Jupiter's

Photo 1.2: Melting ice on LaHave River near Bridgewater, Nova Scotia, Canada.

Photo by Nina Munteanu

and Saturn's moons, outstripping the amount on Earth from two to eleven times. Scientists have postulated that liquid water on Mars and Enceladus, a moon of Saturn, is significant. Recent evidence from the NASA rover *Curiosity* of a giant ancient sea on Mars corroborates those earlier postulations.[4] And even more recent evidence (see Chapter 2) has identified evidence of surface water on Mars currently.

"There are a hundred times as many water molecules in our bodies than the sum of all the other molecules put together,"[5] writes biochemist Martin Chaplin of London South Bank University.

Chaplin describes several dozen anomalous properties of water including phase, density, material, thermodynamic and physical anomalies.[6] According to Nobel laureate and physiologist Albert Szent-Györgyi, "Water is the most extraordinary substance. Practically all its properties are anomalous."[7]

Water, adds Chaplin, is the most studied material on Earth; yet the science behind its behaviour and function is poorly understood, not only in general, but by scientists whose work is its focus. According to several scientists, this is largely because of cooperative hydrogen bonding—the binding energy of two H-bonded molecules is modified by the presence of a third molecule[8,9]—and to nuclear quantum effects.[10]

Water is the only natural substance found in all three physical states (liquid, solid and gas) at temperatures normally found on Earth. Recent work has shown that, in fact, a fourth state exists, crystalline–liquid water, which I talk more about in Chapter 2, *Water Is Life*.

Water's unique—and anomalous—properties, such as its thermal density, high specific heat, viscosity, and liquid–solid characteristics ensure that life thrives. If not for these anomalous properties, north temperate lakes would ice up completely in winter, killing virtually all their aquatic life; lakes and oceans around the world would not mix and stratify, and would fail to provide essential nutrients to aquatic biota. As a gas, water is the lightest known. As a liquid, it is much denser than expected; and as a solid, it is much lighter than expected, compared with

its liquid form. Water can be very sticky and very slippery at the same time. Its high surface tension and its expansion on freezing help erode rocks and create soil for plant growth.

Water can exist in its liquid form, freeze, melt, evaporate, heat, sublimate and combine with many elements.

> *Water cannot be grasped in the same way as other things in the world. It is a master of concealment, withdrawing from so many phenomena, appearing in that which it simultaneously transforms: in the colours of the heavens, for example, or the reflection of a shore on the surface of a lake. Often, the more intensely it participates in a particular phenomenon, the more hidden it remains.*
> —**Wilkens, Jacobi, and Schwenk, "Understanding Water."**[11]

"Some substances become mythical," writes science writer Philip Ball of water in his book, *H2O: a Biography of Water*. Water, says Ball, transcends its physical and chemical materiality and manifests itself in our minds as a symbol. Even "when we remove its symbolic trappings, its association with purity, with the soul, with the maternal and with life and youth, when we reduce it to a laboratory chemical or a geological phenomenon, water continues to fascinate."[12]

Photo 1.3: The Credit River at Bricklane, Ontario, Canada.

"The thing no one can ignore about water," continues Ball, "is that it seems unique. Other stuff of the world is endlessly varied, but of a comparable stamp. Typically opaque, its shapes have some permanence—a leaf, a rock, an animal are comprised of fabrics that do not part before a probing finger. Water is the opposite of all that. It is compliant, mobile, transparent, tasteless. It's not hard to form the impression that, in comparison with the rest of reality, water is somehow unearthly."[12]

Ultimately, water and our relationship with it is a curious gestalt of magic and paradox. Like the *Suntelia Aion* described by the Greeks, water cuts recursive patterns of creative destruction through the landscape, an Ouroboros remembering. It changes, yet stays the same, shifting its

Photo by Nina Munteanu

face with the climate. It wanders the earth like a gypsy, stealing from where it is needed and giving whimsically where it isn't wanted; aggressive yet yielding. Life-giving yet dangerous. Water is the well-spring of life. Yet, it is the River Styx that leads the dead to Hades. The annual flooding of the Nile River served as an ancient Egyptian archetype for resurrection, and was represented by Osiris, the god of death and regeneration. Christian baptism by full immersion, then being raised out of the water of a river or pool, symbolizes burial (with the Lord) and rebirth.

Water is a shape-shifter.

Illustration 1.1: Chemical composition of a water molecule, showing slightly negative charge at oxygen end and slightly positive charge at hydrogen end of water dipole structure, with tetrahedron-shaped electrostatic interactions (van der Waals forces) or hydrogen bonds.

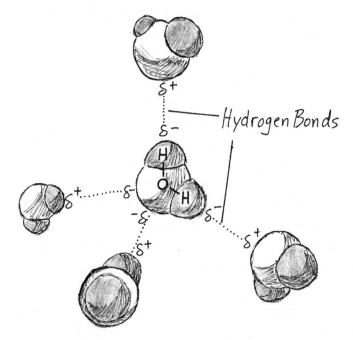

Illustration by Nina Munteanu

Properties of Water

Chemically, water is simply two atoms of hydrogen joined in covalent bonds to one of oxygen. For something so "simply" made, water is pretty complex; the configuration of its building blocks produces a molecule with unusual and almost magical properties.[13,14] Water scientists have been disagreeing for the past fifty years over how water molecules arrange themselves in a liquid drop.

Despite its ubiquity and pervasive study, water remains one of our least understood substances[15,16,17] and our most anomalous.[18,19,20] Attempts by scientists to measure and calculate the structure of water beyond the H2O molecule have been difficult, due to the hydrogen bond (H–bond) network, which can be formed by two or more water molecules. These bonds are characterized by a binding energy between 1 and 50 kJ/mol, depending on the type of strength of interaction and the local geometry.[10] This network (i.e., water's structure, more than its composition) is nowadays held responsible for many of water's weird properties[21] and is also the reason why water cannot be treated as a "simple liquid."[22,23]

According to Elmar C. Fuchs, scientist at the Centre of Excellence for Sustainable Water Technology in the Netherlands (WETSUS), the description of this substance by its chemical formula—H2O—reflects a reductionist approach of the current scientific paradigm and fails to do justice to the structure and properties of water.[10]

Water transports, lubricates, reacts, stabilizes, signals, transforms, structures, and partitions. Water is a universal solvent. It can dissolve a large variety of chemical substances like salts, other ionic compounds, and polar covalent compounds such as alcohols and organic acids. It transports all kinds of things from the sediment of the Nile River to the oxygenated blood cells in your arteries. It is the most cohesive among the non-metallic liquids. "On a molecular level [water] creates the

"Water is H2O, hydrogen two parts, oxygen one, but there is also a third thing that makes it water and nobody knows what it is."

—D.H. Lawrence

structure of DNA,"[25] Martin Chaplin of Southbank University shared in a 2006 interview. "We wouldn't have the DNA helix without water."

Water is a fractal.

Molecular Structure, Density & Viscosity

At the heart of water's unique properties lies its atomic structure, how it bonds and aggregates. The nuclei of water molecules vibrate constantly, forming isosceles triangles at equilibrium. Water is a dipole and acts like a magnet to form a quasi-stable polymer with oxygen having a slightly negative charge and the hydrogen end having a slightly positive charge. The charged ends attract other water molecules and other polar molecules, which is how substances become dissolved in water. Hydrogen's weak coulombic bonds to the weakly electronegative oxygen atom create both ionized and covalent states, simultaneously maintaining the integrity of water.[1] Water molecules form a tetrahedron shape, with oxygen at the centre, two one-electron pairs and two hydrogen bonds at the corners. Water is pretty well the only known compound that possesses these characteristics.

Most transformative matter contracts when cooled and becomes denser in its solid state. Water does the opposite; it expands below 4°C and in its solid state (as ice) becomes less dense, which is why ice floats over liquid water. When liquid water freezes, it forms an open latticework of tetrahedrons, with every oxygen atom at the center of four oxygen atoms. Every water molecule is hydrogen-bonded to its four nearest neighbours, forming "holes" with intermolecular cohesion. The increased volume decreases the density, which allows ice to float on liquid water. When ice melts, the bonds rupture and fill in the open spaces, increasing the density. Maximum density is reached at 4°C. At higher temperatures the liquid expands enough to lower density again. This is why lakes don't freeze through completely; the denser water

sinks before it can reach zero degrees, the temperature for ice to form.

Water's boiling point is also much higher than most compounds of similar weight. Water packs and stores energy and heat extremely well, which helps moderate the temperature on Earth. Large water bodies, like the Great Lakes or the oceans, influence climate. They provide heat reservoirs and exchangers and act as the source of moisture that falls as rain and snow over land.

The association and transformation of water molecules through its solid, liquid and gaseous phases is still not entirely understood. Water molecules are stabilized by strong hydrogen bonds, accounting for water's high boiling point and its ability to absorb heat. Water absorbs and releases more heat than most substances for each degree of temperature increase or decrease.

Differences in density largely govern the regulation of physical and chemical dynamics of lakes and their metabolism. Planktonic and floating aquatic organisms and nutritive particles depend on water movement for their passive locomotion. Much of a lake's water movement—and its planktonic life—is influenced by temperature-mediated density-related changes in viscosity.[1]

The viscosity of water increases near springs; lower viscosity water is more wetting and more easily absorbed.

Photo 1.4: Lake Lucerne at Merlischachen, Switzerland.

Photo by Nina Munteanu

Specific Heat (Cp)

The *specific heat* (the amount of heat in calories required to raise the temperature of a unit weight of a substance by 1°C) of liquid water is very high at 1.0.[1] This means that it can absorb a lot of heat before it begins to get hot. Its high heat-requiring and heat-retaining characteristics make water more stable than terrestrial environments and contribute to the thermal inertia of the hydrosphere. An example of this is the Gulf Stream's tempering effects on climate in Europe.

Surface Tension & Adhesion

Water has a very high surface tension. In other words, it's sticky and elastic and tends to clump together in drops rather than spread out in a thin film (like rubbing alcohol). Surface tension measures the strength of the water's surface film. The strong attraction between the water molecules creates a strong film. It's what makes water want to form a sphere. Water's surface tension allows water to hold up substances heavier and denser than itself. It can support many types of creatures, from tiny water striders to considerably larger Central American lizards.

I remember watching numerous ski videos with my son as he was growing up. In one of them, ski jumpers, eager to train year round, used plastic tracks and landed in water to practise their jumps. I was later told, however, that the water needed to be pre-softened through vigorous bubbling to lower the surface tension and lessen the bone fractures.

Surface tension is essential for the transfer of energy from wind to water. Waves help oxygen rapidly diffuse through the air–water interface of lakes and seas. The air–water interface forms a unique habitat for *neuston*, organisms adapted to living on or in surface film (e.g., whirligig beetles, water striders, protozoans, spiders, bacteria, to name a few). Excessive dissolved organic material in water reduces surface tension and compromises this unique community.

Surface tension—and adhesion—is also responsible for capillary action, which allows water (and its dissolved nutrients) to move through the roots of plants and through the small blood vessels in our bodies. Water creates enormous pressure in pores and capillaries. In a seed, water pressure reaches 400 atmospheres at the moment of germination, permitting the seedling to break through asphalt.

High surface tension—one of water's anomalies—was generally attributed to hydrogen bonding with extra lateral linkages increasing the stiffness. This is not a sufficient explanation, however; recent observations of surface or interfacial water vs. bulk water point to structural

and behavioural rather than chemical bonding as explanation. Martin Chaplin, Emeritus Professor of Applied Science at London South Bank University, suggests that high surface tension is caused by the strong attraction of interfacial water molecules at the gas–liquid surface towards the bulk liquid. "They [interfacial water molecules] are hydrophobic, stiffer, superfluidic and thermally more stable than bulk water… Liquid water at liquid–solid and liquid–gas interfaces behaves as a separate thermodynamic system from bulk water,"[24] says Chaplin. Liquid water at interfaces (i.e., interfacial water) can be investigated using x-ray reflectivity, vibrational sum-frequency generation spectroscopy (VSFG), and atomic force microscopy.

Gerald Pollack, cell biologist and author of *The Fourth Phase of Water*, describes the known phenomenon of "delayed coalescence" (e.g., when a water droplet persists, floating on a larger water body's surface, before coalescing with it). He used this to argue that interfacial tension may result from the formation of what he termed an "exclusion zone." Pollack's EZ model postulates the development of a self-organized layer of structured tubular mosaic water that resembles a liquid crystal.[26] I discuss his theory and model more in Chapter 2, *Water Is Life*.

Photo 1.5: Peggy's Cove at low tide, Nova Scotia, Canada.

The inner boundary surfaces of moving water appear to act like membranes—like water's skin—with the sensitivity of sense organs. This trait inspired the philosopher Novalis to describe water as "sensitive chaos."

Photo by Nina Munteanu

Coherence

Perhaps one of our most significant discoveries in the past few decades is that water exhibits quantum properties under ambient conditions, including quantum coherence. Water exhibits "clumping," or a long-range order called "coherence." You can see an example of coherence by watching how water flows down an incline after a rain: it pulses.

"Anyone who has ever watched a school of fish in the ocean can understand what coherence is,"[27] explain science writers Pangman and Evans. "Each fish is free to move independently, yet the group responds simultaneously—as a whole. It is as though the fish follow an unseen conductor, yet no conductor exists. In the world of physics, this kind of relationship is referred to as *quantum coherence*. At the smallest (quantum) level, there is unity and cooperation (coherence). This allows individual components to respond together as a larger unit."

Nature uses a combination of forces to establish and to sustain coherence. Cyclic or spiral movement is part of it. "When water molecules cycle within natural electromagnetic fields, they are forced to align and re-align within the field,"[27] write Pangman and Evans. "This is because water is a polar substance—with a positive and a negative pole. Each cycle refines the structure of the system. Eventually, water molecules 'find their place' within the coherent domain and even though molecules may occasionally be relocated, the system is not disturbed. The same is true within a school of fish. Predators can temporarily disturb the organization. However, it does not take long before organization re-establishes itself. This is coherence."

Neither classical nor standard quantum theory predicts quantum coherence for water; this is, according to biochemist Mae-Wan Ho, because they ignore quantum fluctuations and the interaction between matter and electromagnetic fields.[28]

Emilio Del Guidice and his colleagues at Milan University showed how quantum fluctuations and coupling between matter and electromagnetic fields in quantum electrodynamics (QED) could predict quantum coherence for liquid water even under ordinary temperatures and pressures. Del Guidice and his team, who had been researching this problem since the 1990s, theorized that interaction between the ambient electromagnetic field and liquid water induces the formation of large, stable coherent domains (CDs) of about 100 nanometres in diameter at ambient conditions, and these CDs may

be responsible for many of the special properties of water including life itself.[29,30,31,32]

Voiekov and Del Guidice suggested that water exists and maintains a stable non-equilibrium dual state that involves toggling between two phases, one a low entropy coherent and excited state (referred to as *Exclusion Zone* or interfacial water[26]) and the other a high-entropy non-coherent state (called "bulk water").[33] I talk more about this below and in Chapter 2, *Water Is Life*.

Photo 1.6: Heavy rain on maples, Mississauga, Ontario, Canada.

Photo by Nina Munteanu

Structure & Behaviour of Water

When asked to describe the structure of water, many of us first think of the structure of the water molecule: the covalent bonding of hydrogen with oxygen. However the structure of water is so much more than this. Materials scientists use the word "structure" to describe the three-dimensional architecture of the whole material. In the case of water, it's not just the shape and size of the water molecule but how many of them are arranged within a community of molecules.

Traditionally, bulk liquid water at an ambient temperature is considered homogeneous by most biochemists and water scientists. Yet, close to a hundred years ago in a paper published in 1892, Nobel laureate Wilhelm von Rontgen had boldly suggested that water existed in a mixture of two states in equilibrium.[34] Considered by many as the first paper to hypothesize on the structure of water, it was largely ignored by the scientific community. Close to a hundred years later, scientists at Texas Tech University showed that water exhibited several densities and many iso-forms depending on its environment.[35,36]

Kawamoto and other researchers at Kyoto University demonstrated in 2004 that liquid water existed in different stable structures over minutes to hours, forming distinct phases with characteristic properties, and including a detectable phase boundary.[37] Materials scientist Rustum Roy and colleagues argued in 2005 that the three dimensional arrangement of water exists in aggregates or clusters.[23]

Roy and his team concluded, that:
- The nano-structure of liquid water was heterogeneous, which changed with interchanges requiring little energy; and,
- This heterogeneity is the rule rather than the exception for strongly bonded liquids.[23]

On the basis of this heterogeneity, the researchers posited a continuum of many possible structures for water. According to Roy and his colleagues, liquid water maintains a dynamic equilibrium of changing assemblages of different oligomer and polymer species. The "architecture" of these clusters, in turn, relies on temperature, pressure, and composition, including very low levels of solutes, magnetic and electric fields, and, according to Roy, *subtle energies* (chi, intention, thought energy, life force energy, etc.).[23] "If you consider a cluster as a group of specific molecules, then it can survive only a short amount of time," said Roy in an interview in 2006. "But if you consider it as a structure whereby molecules can leave and other molecules come in, the cluster can last effectively for a very long time. The stability of the cluster structures confirms the hypothesis that water is capable of recording and storing information."[38] Roy suggested that water may be the most easily changed phase of condensed matter known,[23] making it "the single most malleable computer."[38]

Community of Water

Water scientists know that every individual water molecule forms hydrogen bonds by pointing its two hydrogen atoms towards the oxygen atom of one of its neighbours. The hydrogen bonds of ice form a complete network, with each molecule donating two bonds and accepting two bonds from its neighbours.

Some scientists suggest that water molecules toggle between ice-like and broken hydrogen-bond structures. Others contend that ice-like and broken hydrogen-bond structures are not two distinctive states, but extreme examples of a smooth distribution of possible distortions. The most structurally complex model by the late materials-science pioneer Rustum Roy, embraces the heterogeneity of water structure and the ease of water-molecule interchange that requires very little energy.[23]

Dr. Martin Chaplin of South Bank University argues that, "Water molecules form an infinite hydrogen-bonded network of localized and structured clustering."[39] He adds, drawing from the work of Rustum Roy and colleagues that, "The middling strength of the connecting hydrogen bonds seems ideally suited to life processes, being easily formed but not too difficult to break. An important concept, often overlooked, is that liquid water is not homogeneous at the nanoscopic level."[39]

Roy suggests that many different structures of liquid water must exist, given the range of observations and processes encountered near ambient conditions.[23]

Figure 1.1, from the work by DeBenedetti and Stanley[40] in *Physics Today*, shows how water's changing properties differ greatly from virtually all other liquids. While other liquids show a monotonic, linear change with temperature and pressure variables, water demonstrates a distinctly non-linear relationship.[23]

According to Roy, the most distinctive feature of bonding in liquid water is not just the well-known hydrogen bonds, but the necessary presence of a wide range of van der Waals bonds (via electrostatic attraction) between and among the various clusters. It is this range of very weak bonds that may account for the remarkable ease of changing the structure of water, which in turn could help explain the well-known anomalies in its properties and the structural changes imposed by electric and magnetic fields and by radiation of all kinds, including "subtle energies."[23]

Figure 1.1: Comparison of changes in normal (dashed lines) liquids with anomalous changes in water's properties (solid lines), relating: a) isothermal compressibility (Kt) to temperature; b) isobaric heat capacity (Cp) to temperature; and c) thermal expansion cooefficient (αp) to temperature (in Kelvin), (Modified from DeBenedetti and Stanely, 2003)

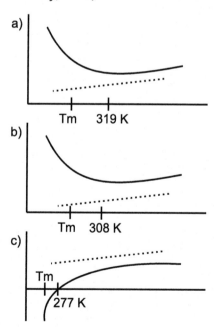

Illustration by Kerste Voute

The Free Standing "Water Bridge"

In 2007, Dr. Elmar C. Fuchs and Professor Jakob Woisetschläger demonstrated at the University of Technology in Graz, Austria, that when they subjected two adjoining beakers of water to a high voltage charge (15 kV), the water climbed the sides of each beaker to meet.

When they moved the beakers apart, the water "stuck," forming a cylindrical water bridge that stretched over 2.5 centimetres (1 inch) across. The video of the experiment is stunning. Once "jolted," the two water bodies appeared to grope for one another, trembling like two shocked children holding hands.

Publishing their findings in several journals, the scientists described a macroscopic, rotating cylinder with special optical properties through which two water currents ran. [41,42,43,44,45] They demonstrated that the water showed a well-defined operational stability, possessed complex flow patterns, and emitted thermal radiation. When the researchers added tracer particles both for flow measurements using a laser Doppler anemometer and for visualization, the floating water bridge revealed a rotating outer layer (or shell).[10] The particles of the outer layer rotated in a clockwise direction toward the "cathode" beaker with a backflow toward the "anode" beaker. Fuchs and his team discovered that the hydrogen bonds in the floating water bridge are stronger than those in liquid water at any temperature. [10A] They also found that the bridge is a proton semi-conductor with higher proton mobility than bulk liquid water, again showing that the water bridge differs from the bulk liquid state on a molecular level. [10B]

Scientists used spectroscopic, optical and neutron scattering techniques to suggest that the bridge was associated with an aligned electric field.[46] Lawrie B. Skinner and his team at the University of California, Berkeley, CA, used the evidence of two-dimensional X-ray scattering measurements in 2013 and concluded that the bulk water molecules did in fact not exhibit any significant orientation along the electric field.[47] So, how did they think the bridge formed? The authors suggested that the answer lay not with an alignment of bulk water molecules, per se, but in an increase of the already mysterious surface tension of water. How this was achieved also remained a mystery.

Gerald Pollack, at the University of Washington, observed that the bridge hardly drooped, exhibiting "an almost ice-like rigidity" despite

Photo 1.7: Free-standing water bridge.

Photo by Elmar C. Fuchs

being at room temperature. Pollack also describes an inner, or core, zone of mostly protonated water flowing from the positively charged beaker toward the negatively charged beaker and an outer annular zone with EZ-like features (see Chapter 2). This outer layer bears a negative charge, because it comes from the negatively charged beaker. And its birefringence "implies order," says Pollack.[26]

Photo 1.8: Free-standing water bridge extending 3 cm.

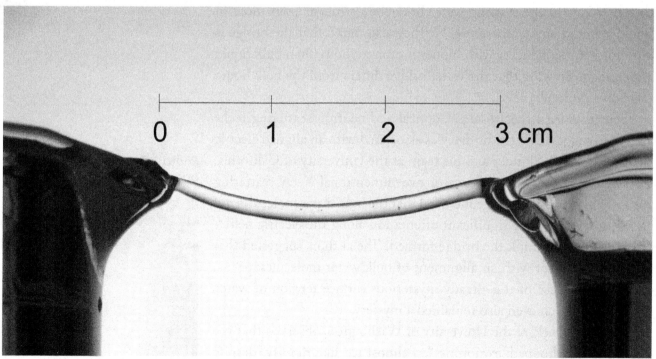

Photo by Elmar C. Fuchs

Origins of Water

The amount of moisture on Earth hasn't changed from the time the dinosaurs quenched their thirst in the soupy marshes of the Triassic Period, millions of years ago, to the rain falling on your house today. This is interesting, considering that scientists have determined that some water is continually lost to the upper atmosphere, releasing hydrogen into space, through the sun's ionizing action, in a process called photolysis. How is it getting replaced? Part of the answer lies in its origins and water's role in a much larger cycle.

Water's Cosmic Origins

According to a theory first proposed in 1986 by physicist Louis A. Frank at the University of Iowa, water arrived on Earth after travelling through space. Only three years before, scientists at the Goddard Space Center discovered an astonishing array of molecules in interstellar space that included those found in living tissue.

Using NASA's Polar Visible Imaging System (VIS), a research team led by Frank in 1996 detected objects that streaked toward Earth, disintegrated at high altitudes and deposited large clouds of water vapour in the upper atmosphere. The images showed that Earth is being bombarded by five to thirty small comets per minute, or thousands per day, according to Frank. Called "dirty snowballs" these small comets, the size of a small house, break up in the upper atmosphere some 600 to 15,000 miles above the Earth. Frank posited that "this gentle cosmic rain—which possibly contains simple organic compounds—may well have nurtured the development of life on our planet."[48]

"It is a shocking notion," writes *Washington Post* correspondent

"Surely this is a great part of our dignity... that we can know, and that through us matter can know itself; that beginning with protons and electrons, out of the womb of time and the vastness of space, we can begin to understand; that organized as in us, the hydrogen, the carbon, the nitrogen, the oxygen, those 16 to 21 elements, the water, the sunlight—all, having become us, can begin to understand what they are, and how they came to be."

**—George Wald,
Nobel Laureate in Medicine, 1964**

Kathy Sawyer in an article in *Astronomy*. "Radiation-blasted, black-jacketed snowballs the size of houses swarming out of the cosmic void every day, ploughing into Earth's atmosphere and pancaking explosively into clouds of vapour that fall as gentle rains. Over billions of years, these invaders might have filled Earth's oceans and provided the seeds of life."[49]

While Frank's theory was met with great skepticism by the scientific community, it was later confirmed by Robert Conway, planetary physicist at the Naval Research Laboratory, who announced on August 11, 1997, that his ultraviolet telescope on the *Discovery* Space Shuttle had detected unexpectedly high levels of hydroxyl in the upper atmosphere. NASA's *Polar* spacecraft also provided evidence in May 1997 that Earth's upper atmosphere is being sprayed by a steady stream of water-bearing objects.[50] Many meteorites contain frozen water, along with frozen carbon dioxide, ammonia and other volatile compounds. Meteorites called "carbonaceous chondrites" can harbour up to twenty percent water, either as ice or locked up in the crystal structures of minerals.

In December 1998, a specially designed satellite called the *Submillimeter–Wave Astronomy Satellite* (SWAS) was launched to detect radio waves emitted by water molecules in space. In an interview with water researcher William E. Marks, the project's chief scientist Gary Melnick of the Harvard–Smithsonian Astrophysical Observatory in Cambridge admitted that, "we're seeing water everywhere. Every region we've looked at so far contains water."[51] To date, evidence of water has been discovered on our Moon, the Sun, Mars, Jupiter's moon Europa, Pluto and in the "empty" spaces between the stars (interstellar space). In addition, the Oort Cloud, a huge watery cloud surrounding our solar system and made of trillions of comets that contain ice and gases, is thought to be at least as old as the solar system. This suggests that water was present at or before the creation of our solar system.

Researchers at the University of Chicago reported water-soluble salt in a meteorite that fell near Monahans Texas in 1999.[52] The mete-

orite contained purple crystals of halite (rock salt) that contained minuscule pockets of water with bubbles, which, according to planetary scientist Michael Zolensky at NASA's Johnson Space Center, "indicated that water flowed on whatever parent body spawned the meteorite. It is possible," he added, "that the water… could date back to 4.5 billion years or perhaps before the creation of our solar system."[49] Zolensky worked with other scientists on another chrondite meteorite discovered on Tagish Lake, a frozen lake in British Columbia, Canada. According to Peter G. Brown of the University of Western Ontario, the Tagish Lake meteorite "may be one of the most primitive solar system materials yet studied."[51]

During the European Space Agency (ESA) landing of the craft *Philae* on Comet 67P on November 12, 2014, instruments detected organic compounds and confirmed that the comet's surface was largely water-ice covered with a thin dust layer.[53] Scientists expect to gain insights into the possible role of comets to the chemical building blocks of the primordial mix from which life evolved on Earth. Water, of course, will play a key role.

Photo 1.9: Meandering Upper Credit River through Dragonfly Marsh near source waters, Ontario, Canada.

Earth's water and its connection to the cosmos can be inferred through the meteor trails we see blazing across the night sky. Scientists have estimated through satellite observations that from five to a hundred tons of cosmic dust and litter enter the Earth's atmosphere every day. "Cosmic dust is associated with the formation of 'noctilucent' clouds—the highest clouds in the Earth's atmosphere,"[54] says John Plane from University of Leeds in the UK. "The dust particles provide a surface for the cloud's ice crystals to form."

Since we are mostly water, you could say that we all come from outer space.

Recently, when I was driving to my home on a quiet Nova Scotia coastal road, in the pitch-black night I felt compelled to stop the car and look out at the night sky. I remember stopping in the middle of the road, turning off my headlights and sliding open the ceiling window

Photo by Nina Munteanu

of my Jetta and poking my head out to gaze straight up. The heavens beamed with stars. I saw the Milky Way, its girdle stretching across the dark expanse from horizon to horizon. I saw pin pricks of red, green, blue and purple. I even glimpsed a shooting star; it streaked across the sky like a comet. I can't explain exactly how I felt, except that I too was beaming for no reason, that I was mesmerized by the grandness of it all. And, somehow, it felt like home.

Ten years before Frank's discovery, I participated in a meditative session inside a desensitization tank at the Bodhi Tree Wellness Centre in Vancouver, B.C. The tank was just big enough for me to fit into and filled with a saturated Epsom salt solution that kept me afloat. The water was as warm as my body and the chamber was pitch dark. I also wore earplugs to dampen any sound. In this "zero gravity," I felt my muscles and ligaments relax one by one. I'm told that in this relaxed state, the brain generates low frequency range theta-waves that let you enter a state that Buddhist monks achieve only from long years of constant meditation. Blissful endorphins were released, and I felt a great peace well up inside me. I don't know how much time actually passed, but I soon felt as if I was floating in space, revolving and twirling in all directions (when I was in fact perfectly still). In my mind's eye, I bore witness to fantastic galaxies and nebulae. They surrounded me in a splendour of incredible emotion and abiding greatness. It was spectacular, and I knew that in some form I was actually there and that I belonged. I knew I was "home."

Was I water, remembering?

The Watery Birth of Stars

"Logically, stars should not exist," scientists at the Weizmann Institute for Science shared in a February 1997 article. Stars "are born when clouds of interstellar gas collapse inwardly under their own weight, growing denser and hotter until nuclear fusion causes them to emit energy in the form of light. However, since heat forces matter to expand, this hot contracting gas could be expected to immediately move outward again, preventing star formation from ever reaching completion."[2] To resolve this paradox, scientists postulated the existence of a water-based *cooling system* that regulates the temperature of interstellar clouds, enabling the contraction to continue. Drs. Daniel Zajfman and Oded Heber of the Weizmann Institute's Particle Physics Department simulated the physical and chemical conditions in interstellar clouds and showed that water is formed there in a reaction between a charged hydronium molecule (aqueous cation H_3O^+) and a single electron. They also found that a permanent ratio between water and hydronium molecules is maintained in these clouds.

A group of scientists at Japan's Institute of Low Temperature Science at Hokkaido University came to the same conclusion through their work in 2008: "Since the solar system evolved from an interstellar molecular cloud, icy objects in the solar system originated from the water ice formed in the interstellar molecular cloud."[55] The scientists concluded that water must form when atomic hydrogen interacts with frozen solid oxygen on a solid surface, such as dust grains in interstellar clouds.

Photo 1.10: Small falls at the lower Humber River, Toronto, Ontario, Canada.

In 2001, NASA's *Submillimeter Wave Astronomy Satellite* (SWAS) detected a huge amount of water vapour around the star CW Leonis, 650 light years away;[56] they also discovered a swarm of comets evaporating around the aging red giant star. The six-year SWAS mission confirmed what scientists had already surmised: that water is prevalent in the universe.

Water was detected in almost every dust cloud observed, with highest amounts found as warm gas. During a three-month reactivation in 2005 the spacecraft recorded the effects of the *Deep Impact* probe's collision with Comet P/Tempel 1. The SWAS measured 730 pounds of water per second ejected from the comet.[57]

Photo by Nina Munteanu

With the launch of the Spitzer and Keplar space transit telescopes and the continued work of radial velocity, direct imaging, timing and microlensing telescopes, water is being discovered everywhere and in the strangest forms. In June 2011, researchers at ESA's Herschel Space Observatory identified a protostar or quasar, 750 light years away. The young star was blasting jets of water into interstellar space from its poles at 124,000 miles per hour. The telescope was able to trace where hydrogen and oxygen, two of the most popular elements in the universe, formed water on and around the star. Close to the star, its heat and pressure vaporize the water into jets of gas. But farther away the water cools into droplets that move like bullets at "80 times faster than the average round fired from a rifle,"[3] writes Clay Dillow in *Popular Science Magazine*. The speedy spray is "equal to the amount that flows through the Amazon every second," researchers said. This suggests two things: (1) that young protostars may be distributing vast quantities of water, potentially seeding life elsewhere in the universe; and (2) that water may have played a significant role in the formation of our own sun and solar system. "Stars are the alchemists of the Universe,"[12] Philip Ball writes in *H2O: A Biography of Water*. Engines of creation, "out of their hearts come the elements needed to make worlds."

In July 2011 scientists discovered a huge reservoir of water in the "early universe." Teams at the California Institute of Technology, using the Z-Spec instrument at the Caltech Submillimeter Observatory in Hawaii, and the Combined Array for Research in Millimeter-Wave Astronomy in the Inyo Mountains of Southern California found water surrounding a quasar some 12 billion light years away (and therefore 12 billion years ago). *Quasars* are bright and violent galactic nuclei, fuelled by a supermassive black hole at the centre, and this one holds some 140 trillion times the amount of water on Earth. Researchers claim that this discovery shows that water has been prevalent in the universe for nearly its entire existence.[58]

The APM 08279+5255 quasar gobbles dust and gas, then spews out

the energy of a thousand trillion suns. Water vapour spreads around its central black hole in a disk that spans hundreds of light years. "Because the light we are seeing left this quasar more than 12 billion years ago, we are seeing water that was present only some 1.6 billion years after the beginning of the universe," said study co-author Alberto Bolatto, of the University of Maryland, in a statement. "This discovery pushes the detection of water one billion years closer to the Big Bang than any previous find."

"The environment around this quasar is unique in that it's producing this huge mass of water," added Matt Bradford at NASA's Jet Propulsion Laboratory. "It's another demonstration that water is pervasive throughout the universe, even at the very earliest times."

Water is a wizard.

Extraterrestrial Liquid Water

Liquid water is commonly believed to be a prerequisite for extraterrestrial life. Given that liquid water is essential to all known life forms, its presence is one of the major criteria for determining a planet's potential to harbour life. Water's presence is a product of its atmospheric pressure and a stable orbit in a star's circumstellar habitable zone. Scientists have been using infrared spectroscopy to detect the presence of hydrous minerals called *phyllosilicates*, whose structure includes water.

Professor Drake Deming, an expert in the study of "exoplanets" that orbit suns outside our solar system, shared that, "the water molecule is widespread in the universe. Wherever you have hydrogen and oxygen it naturally forms."[59]

Astrophysicist Natalie Betalha, Mission scientist for Keplar's space telescope at the Ames Research Center shared that, "the one ingredient that we think is common to all life forms is this requirement of liquid water. We look for planets that have rocky surfaces where water can pool and are receiving the right amount of energy from the star where the water wouldn't be locked up in a frozen state because the planet is so cold. Nor would it be evaporated away because the planet is too hot. We call it the Goldilocks zone where liquid water could potentially exist."[60] By early January 2015, scientists using the Keplar telescope had identified more than 1,000 exoplanets since its launch in 2009. Several are within the "habitable zone" (Goldilocks zone), with Kepler 186f (490 light years away) and Kepler 438b (475 light years away) being most Earth-like.

When I was a child—and to this day—I would look up at the deep night, dressed in sparkling stars, and let my mind and heart wander. If given the choice to explore the deep sea or the deep of space, I'd instantly reply: space, of course. I used to wonder why I chose to look away, beyond my home, to the far reaches of the unknown blackness of space, and find some thrilling element that provided an abiding fulfillment. Why did I abandon my home? Maybe I didn't…

Earth's Watery Birth

In late 2014, a study by the Woods Hole Oceanographic Institution (WHOI) makes a strong case for Earth's waters having likely existed since our planet's birth. While many have gravitated to the idea of water arriving later via comet impact, WHOI headed by Adam Sarafian, found that our seas may have arrived much earlier than previously thought. Around 4.6 billion years ago, in fact. This was when all the worlds of the inner solar system were also forming. "Scientists had suspected that our planet formed dry, with high-energy impacts creating a molten surface on the infant Earth,"[61] writes Andrew Fazekas in his 2014 article in *National Geographic*. "Water came much later, went the thinking, thanks to collisions with wet comets and asteroids."

Sarafian and his colleagues at WHOI studied carbonaceous chon-

drite meteorites, which formed around the same time as the sun, before the first planets. They then compared them with meteorites from the asteroid Vesta, which formed in the same region as Earth (about 14 million years after the birth of our solar system) and contained a lot of water. The Vesta chondrites had the same chemistry as Earth's chondrites, suggesting a common source of water.

"The study shows that Earth's water most likely accreted at the same time as the rock," said Horst Marschall, geologist at WHOI. "The planet formed as a wet planet with water on the surface."[61]

"Knowing that water came early to the inner solar system also means that the other inner planets could have been wet early and evolved life before they became the harsh environments they are today,"[61] explained Sune Nielsen, study co-author.

These findings sync with recent evidence provided by NASA for a vast ancient ocean on Mars.[62] In March of 2015, NASA reported that a massive primitive ocean covered one-fifth of the red planet's surface, creating a warm, wet and ideal place for life to gain a foothold. The evidence provides an emerging picture of Mars as warm and wet in its youth. Evidence for a vast ancient freshwater lake uncovered by the *Curiosity* rover in Gale Crater in late 2013 had demonstrated that Mars had been wet for about 1.5 billion years.[4] The recent findings, using three of the most powerful infra-red telescopes in the world, and discoveries of how different forms of water molecules varied from place to place in the Martian air have demonstrated that Mars had been wet 4.5 billion years ago, closer to the time when the solar system was being formed.[62] In September 2015 NASA revealed that Mars still contains surface and subsurface liquid water, flowing along its steep slopes. Evidence had come from the High Resolution Imaging Science Experiment (HiRISE) aboard the *Mars Reconnaissance Orbiter* (MRO).

As for why Mars pretty much dried up and froze over, when Earth didn't; Bruce Jakosky and his team at the University of Colorado at Boulder are using the *MAVEN* orbiter (short for Mars Atmosphere and Volatile Evolution) to figure out the reasons for the dramatic climate change on Mars and its loss of a thick atmosphere of carbon dioxide. Some propose that an asteroid impact blew most of the atmosphere into space in a cataclysmic event. Others suggest that the planet's surface may have absorbed the CO_2 and locked it up in minerals such as carbonate. "Either [the water] went up or went down," said Dave Brain of UC Berkeley. By down he means subsurface, where water ice is known to lurk. Either way, whatever happened to Mars didn't happen to Earth—thankfully.

Illustration 1.2: Earth's hydrological cycle

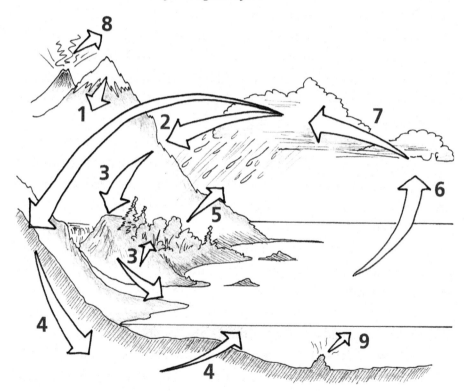

1. Snow melt/runoff
2. Precipitation
3. Infiltration / plant uptake
4. Ground water flow
5. Evapo-transpiration
6. Evaporation
7. Condensation
8. Volcanic steam
9. Vents

Illustration by Nina Munteanu

Water's Journey on Earth

"Water circulates around the globe," Japanese researcher Masaru Emoto shares in *The Secret Life of Water*, "flowing through our bodies and spreading to the rest of the world. If we were capable of reading this information contained in the memory of water, we would read a story of epic proportions."[63]

Water circulates on Earth through the global water or hydrological cycle. Its balance on the planet is expressed through constant input, output, storage and transformation. Precipitation, evaporation, transpiration, freezing, melting and condensation circulate water and energy in a never-ending global process that flows from clouds to land, to the ocean, and back to the clouds. Income from precipitation, surface influents, and groundwater sources is balanced by outflow from surface effluents, seepage to ground water and evapo-transpiration. Limnologists use the term *watershed* or *catchment basin* to describe the area of land defined by topography that aggregates surface material (and groundwater) associated with pooled surface water, such as a river, lake or sea. Each income and loss varies seasonally and geographically and is governed by climate, watershed characteristics and the morphology of water bodies.[1,64]

"The hydrological cycle emphasizes the dynamic nature of the Earth's environment,"[12] Philip Ball shares. "Water," he adds, "is the lubricant for biochemical cycling." For instance, carbon dioxide in the atmosphere is taken up by plants, in turn consumed by animals and broken down as organic debris. It is eventually carried into the deep oceans and is incorporated through marine photosynthesis, thus driving the rest of the carbon cycle, then recycled into the atmosphere by various emissions and movements. Water, according to Ball, "makes the

"Behold the element of water in its undifferentiated state! And see how all the metals, all the stones, all the glittering rubies, shining carbuncles, crystals, gold, and silver are derived from it; who could have recognized all these things in water?"
—Paracelsus c. 1531

world go round."

Pangman and Evans describe the Earth's hydrological cycle as two polar cycles comprising a "masculine" and a "feminine" aspect. "The masculine cycle occurs above ground under the influence of the Sun while the feminine counterpart occurs in the quiet, dark womb of the Earth."[27] These correspond to the Chinese philosophy of yin/yang, which I discuss more in Chapter 6, *Water is Rhythm*. Unless the "masculine" water is infused with enough invigorated "feminine" water from below, it becomes tired and lifeless and devoid of creative energy, say Pangman and Evans. They posit that, based on the abundance of hydrogen at the Earth's core and the availability of oxygen inside the Earth, the Earth itself may be a great water generator. "The core of the Earth may eventually be determined to be like a huge hydrogen fuel cell, continually producing water as a by-product."[27] The water then rises as vapour, circulates through layers of rock, flows as underground streams and eventually rises to the surface.

Scientists recently discovered a vast ocean of water bound in the rock of the Earth's mantle, hundreds of miles down.[65] The water exists not as liquid, ice or vapour, but as a hydroxyl radical, bound up in the mantle rock containing the mineral called ringwoodite. "Ringwoodite is like a sponge,"[66] said geophysicist Steve Jacobsen in a press release in June 2014. "There is something very special about the crystal structure of ringwoodite that allows it to attract hydrogen and trap water. This mineral can contain a lot of water under conditions of the deep mantle." Scientists had speculated that water is trapped in a rocky layer of the Earth's mantle between the lower mantle and upper mantle, some 250 miles to 410 miles deep. Jacobsen and his colleagues were the first to provide direct evidence that there may be water in this area of the mantle, known as the "transition zone," on a vast scale. "The weight of 250 miles of solid rock creates such high pressure, along with temperatures above 2,000 degrees Fahrenheit, that a water molecule splits to form a hydroxyl radical (OH), which can be bound into a mineral's

crystal structure,"[66] writes Megan Fellman of Northwestern University News. Schmandt and Jacobsen's findings build on a discovery reported in March in the journal *Nature* in which scientists discovered a piece of the mineral ringwoodite inside a diamond brought up from a depth of 400 miles by a volcano in Brazil. That tiny piece of ringwoodite—the only sample in existence from within the Earth—contained a surprising amount of water bound in solid form in the mineral. Jacobsen adds, "I think we are finally seeing evidence for a whole-Earth water cycle, which may help explain the vast amount of liquid water on the surface of our habitable planet. Scientists have been looking for this missing deep water for decades."[66]

According to scientists, the same amount of water exists on Earth today as when Earth was formed and water came to the planet. Given that the Earth regularly loses some water as the sun ionizes water vapour in the upper atmosphere (releasing hydrogen into space), this is one of the likely sources of regeneration. The other I mention above: the influx of water from space in the form of comets, which are mostly ice, meteors (made of from 0.1% to 20% ice), and molecular clouds in space.[12,15]

Pangman and Evans describe water's journey on Earth this way: "Water's birth and her sojourn inside the Earth utilize the quiet, dark, feminine environment in conjunction with magnetic fields, vortices and silicate minerals to produce *living water*. When this water comes to the surface and when it is exposed to sun, wind, and other surface influences... it achieves balance [and] becomes *full-spectrum, living water*."[27]

Life may exert an important and dominant influence on the Earth's natural cycles, including the water cycle. Most biochemical cycles include feedback mechanisms that may enhance or dampen a disturbance, which permit the planet the potential to regulate itself and maintain a relatively constant environment, despite changing influences. "The extent to which this really does happen," says Philip Ball, "and in particular the degree to which living organisms play a part in it, is the central issue in the debate over James Lovelock's Gaia Hypothesis, the idea of a self-regulating Earth."[12]

The Magic Thread

Over two thousand years ago, Greek philosopher Thales posited that all things come from water and that all heavenly bodies, including Earth, float in water.

Influenced by the spiritual teachings of Rudolf Steiner, Theodor Schwenk suggested that flowing water acts like a sensory organ through which celestial influences enter the world.[67]

"Water," says William E. Marks, author of *The Holy Order of Water*, "may be the connecting interstellar intermediary between all matter in the universe. Just as a thrown pebble sends waves of energy rippling through every water molecule in a pond, changes in any planet or sun may also send waves of energy rippling through every water molecule throughout the universe."[51]

Magic surges with power and mystery. Magic hides in clear view; it ripples with intrigue. When you look at magic, you see only your reflection; while its depths veil immeasurable possibility.

Magic is water.

References

1. Wetzel, Robert G. 2001. "Limnology: Lake and River Ecosystems." 3rd edition. *Academic Press*, New York. 1006 pp.

2. Zajfman, Daniel. 1997. "The Watery Birth of Stars." Weizmann Institute of Science. February 1, 1997. Online: http://wis-wander. weizmann.ac.il/water-enables-star-formation#

3. Dillow, Clay. 2011. "Herschel Telescope Spots a Star Spewing Powerful Water Jets into Interstellar Space." Popular Science. June 16, 2011. Online: http://www.popsci.com/technology/article/2011-06/ herschel-spots-young-star-spewing-water-jets-interstellar-space.

4. Lemonick, Michael. 2015. "Neighborhood Watch: Life in Our Solar System." In: *Time: The Search for Life in the Universe*. June 19, 2015. 94 pp.

5. Chaplin, Martin F. 2000. "A proposal for the structuring of water." *Biophys. Chem.* 83–221.

6. Chaplin, Martin F. 2015. "Anomalous properties of water." Online: "Water Structure and Science": http://www1.lsbu.ac.uk/water/water_anomalies.html

7. Szent-Györgyi, Albert. 1972. "The Living State: With Observations on Cancer." Academic Press. New York. 124 pp.

8. Xantheas, S.S. 2000. "Cooperativity and hydrogen bonding network in water clusters." *Chem. Phys.* 258, 225–231.

9. Reed, A.E.; Weinhold, F.; Curtiss, L.A.; and Pochatko, D.J. 1986. "Natural bond orbital analysis of molecular interactions: Theoretical studies of binary complexes of HF, H2O, NH3, N2, O2, F2, CO, and CO2 with HF, H2O, and NH3 ." *J. Chem. Phys.* 84: 5687–5705.

10. Fuchs, Elmar C. 2010. "Can a Century Old Experiment Reveal Hidden Properties of Water?" *Water* 2: 381–410.

10A. Piatkowski, Lukasz, Adam D. Wexler, Elmar C. Fuchs, Hinco Schoenmaker, and Huib J. Bakker. 2011. "Ultrafast vibrational en-

ergy realxation of the water bridge". *Phys. Chem. Chem. Phys.* DOI: 10.1039/c1cp22358e.

10B. Sammer, Martina, Adam D. Wexler, Philipp Kuntke, Helmar Wiltsche, Natalia Stanulewicz, Ernst Lankmayr, Jakob Woisetschlager, and Elmar C. Fuchs. 2015. "Proton production, neutralization and reduction in a floating water bridge". *J. Phys. D: Appl. Phys.* 48: 11pp; DOI: 10.1088 / 0022-3727 / 48 / 41 / 415507.

11. Wilkens, Andreas; Michael Jacobi; and Wolfram Schwenk. 2005. "Understanding Water." *Floris Books*, Edinburgh. 107 pp.

12. Ball, Philip. 2000. "H2O: A Biography of Water." *Phoenix.* London, UK. 387 pp.

13. Brovchenko, I. and A. Oleinikova. 2008. "Multiple phases of liquid water." *Chem. Phys. Chem.* 9: 2660–2675.

14. Environment Canada. 2011. "Water Basics." Online: https://www.ec.gc.ca/eau-water/

15. Ball, Philip. 2001. "Life's Matrix: a Biography of Water." *University of California Press.* 433 pp.

16. Ball P. 2008. "Water—an enduring mystery." *Nature: 452*, 291–292.

17. Ball P. 2008. "Water as an Active Constituent in Cell Biology." *Chem. Rev. 108*: 74.

18. Chaplin, M.F. 2003."Thirty eight anomalies of water, Part 1". *Homeopath. Med. Panorama 11*: 12–19.

19. Chaplin, M.F. 2003. "Thirty eight anomalies of water, Part II". *Homeopath. Med. Panorama 11*: 22–28.

20. Cho, C.H.; S. Singh; and G.W. Robinson. 1997. "Understanding all of water's anomalies with a nonlocal potential." *J. Chem. Phys. 107*: 7979–7988.

21. Xantheas, Sotiris S. 2000. "Cooperativity and hydrogen bonding network in water clusters." *Chemical Physics 258*: 225–231.

22. Stanley, H.E. 1999. "Liquid water: A very complex fluid." *Pramana – J. Phys. 53*: 53 – 83.

23. Roy, R.; W. A. Tiller; I. Bell; and M. R. Hoover. 2005. "The structure of liquid water; novel insights from materials research; potential relevance to homeopathy." *Mat. Res. Innovat. 9–4*: 93–124.

24. Chaplin, Martin. 2015. "Interfacial water and water–gas interfaces." Online: "Water Structure and Science": http://www1.lsbu.ac.uk/water/interfacial_water.html

25. Chaplin, Martin. 2006. In: "Water, the Great Mystery." Julie Perkul and Anastasiya Popova, directors. *Intention Media*. 87 min.

26. Pollack, Gerald. 2013. "The Fourth Phase of Water: Beyond Solid, Liquid and Vapor." *Ebner & Sons Publishers*, Seattle WA. 357 pp.

27. Pangman, M.J. and Melanie Evans. 2011. "Dancing with Water: the New Science of Water." *Uplifting Press*, Inc. 255 pp.

28. Ho, Mai-Wan. 2011. "Quantum Coherent Water and Life". ISIS Report, July 25, 2011. Online: http://www.i-sis.org.uk/Quantum_Coherent_Water_Life.php

29. Arani R., I. Bono, E. Del Guidice, and G. Preparata. 1995. "QED coherence and the thermodynamics of the water." *Int J Modern Phys* B9: 1813–41.

30. Del Giudice E. 2007. "Old and new views on the structure of matter and the special case of living matter." *Journal of Physics: Conference Series* 67: 012006.

31. Del Giudice, E.; P.R. Spinetti; and A. Tedeschi. 2010. "Water dynamics at the root of metamorphosis in living organisms." *Water* 2: 566–86.

32. Del Giudice E.; M. Fleischmann; G. Preparata; and G. Talpo. 2002. "On the 'unreasonable' effects of ELF magnetic fields upon a system of ions." *Bioelectromagnetics* 23: 52–30.

33. Voeikov, V.L. and E. Del Guidice. 2009. "Water Respiration—the Basis of the Living State." *Water* 1: 52–75.

34. vonRöntgen, W.K. 1892. "The Structure of Liquid Water." *Annu. Phys.* 45: 91.

35. Robinson, G.W.; H. Cho; and J. Urquidi. 1999. "Isosbestic points in liquid water: further strong evidence for the two-state mixture model." *J. Chem. Phys.* 111: 698–702.

36. Chaplin, M.F. 2014. "Water's Two-State Cluster History." Online at "Water Structure and Science": http://www1.lsbu.ac.uk/water/cluster_history.html

37. Kawamoto, Tatsuhiko; Shukichi Ochiai; and Hiroyuki Kagi. 2004. "Changes in the structure of water deduced from the pressure dependence of the Raman OH frequency." *J. Chem. Phys.* 120: 5867–5870.

38. Roy, Rustum. 2006. In: "Water, the Great Mystery." Julie Perkul and Anastasiya Popova, directors. *Intention Media*. 87 min.

39. Chaplin, M.F. 2001. "Water: its importance to life." *Biochem. Mol. Bio. Educ.* 29: 54–59.

40. DeBenedetti, Pablo G. and H. Eugene Stanley. 2003. "Supercooled and Glassy Water." *Physics Today.* June Issue: 40–46.

41. Fuchs, E.C.; J. Woisetschläger; K. Gatterer; E. Maier; R. Pecnik; G. Holler; and H. Eisenkölbl.2007. "The floating water bridge." *J. Phys. D: Appl. Phys.* 40: 6112–6114.

42. Fuchs, E.C.; K. Gatterer; G. Holler; and J. Woisetschläger. 2008. "Dynamics of the floating water bridge." *J. Phys. D: Appl. Phys.* 41: 185502–7.

43. Fuchs E.C.; B. Bitschnau; J. Woisetschläger; E. Maier; B. Beuneu; and J. Teixeira.2009. "Neutron scattering of a floating heavy water bridge." *J. Phys. D: Appl. Phys.* 42: 065502–6.

44. Fuchs, E.C.; P. Baroni; B. Bitschnau; and L. Noirez. 2010. "Two-Dimensional Neutron Scattering of a Floating Heavy Water Bridge." *J. Phys. D: Appl. Phys.* 43: 105502–7.

45. Fuchs, E.C.; Luewton L.F. Agostinho; Mathias Eisenhut; and Jakob Woisetschläger. 2010. "Mass and charge transfer within a floating water bridge". Proceedings of SPIE Vol. 7376. Online: http://www.researchgate.net/publication/233740568_Mass_and_charge_transfer_within_a_floating_water_bridge.

46. Ponterio R.C.; M. Pochylski; F. Aliotta; C. Vasi; M.E. Fontanella; and F. Saija. 2010. "Raman scattering measurements on a floating water bridge." *J. Phys. D: Appl. Phys.* 43: 175405

47. Skinner, Lawrie B.; Chris J. Benmore; Badri Shyam; J.K.R. Weber; and John B. Parise. 2012. "Structure of the floating water bridge and water in an electric field." *PNAS* 109(41): 16463–16468.

48. Frank, L. A.; J. B. Sigwarth; and J. D. Craven. 1986. "On the influx of small comets into the Earth's upper atmosphere, 1. Observations." *Geophysical Research Letters*, 13: 303–306.

49. Sawyer, Kathy. 1998. "Seeing Spots." *Astronomy*, October, 1998.

50. Young, Steven. 1997. "Satellite Backs Comet Bombardment Theory." *Reuters*, August 11.

51. Marks, William E. 2001. "The Holy Order of Water." *Bell Pond Books.* 256 pp.

52. Sawyer, Kathy. 1999. "A Meteoric Discovery: Extraterrestrial Water." The Washington Post, August 27, 1999. Online: http://www.washingtonpost.com/wp-srv/national/daily/aug99/water27.htm

53. Rincon, Paul. 2014. "Comet Landing: Organic Molecules Detected by Philae." BBC News Website, November 2014: http://www.bbc.com/news/science-environment-30097648.

54. Atkinson, Nancy. 2012. "Getting a Handle on How Much Cosmic Dust Hits Earth." Universe Today, March 30. Online: http://www.universetoday.com/94392/getting-a-handle-on-how-much-cosmic-dust-hits-earth/

55. Atkinson, Nancy. 2008. "Water in Interstellar Space". Universe Today, May 6. Online: http://www.universetoday.com/14075/water-in-interstellar-space/

56. NASA. 2001. "Sizzling Comets Circle a Dying Star." NASA website: http://science.nasa.gov/science-news/science-at-nasa/2001/ast11jul_1/

57. Cain Fraser. 2005. "Spacecraft Wakes Up for Comet Collision." *Universe Today*, June 28. Online: http://www.universetoday.com/10639/spacecraft-wakes-up-for-comet-collision/

58. NASA. 2011. "Astronomers Find Largest, Most Distant Reservoir of Water." NASA Website: http://www.nasa.gov/topics/universe/features/universe20110722.html

59. Mack, Eric. 2014. "Scientists Find Water in the Atmosphere of a Distant Exoplanet". *Forbes*, September 24.

60. Betalha, Natalie. 2014. Interview in: "The Science of Interstellar," Gail Willumsen, director. *Gemini Productions*. Discovery Channel Documentary, November 25. 40 min.

61. Fazekas, Andrew. 2014. "Mystery of Earth's Water Origin Solved." *National Geographic*, October 30. Online: http://news.nationalgeographic.com/news/2014/10/141030-starstruck-earth-water-origin-vesta-science/

62. Sample, Ian. 2015. "NASA finds evidence of a vast ancient ocean on Mars." *The Guardian*, March 5. Online: http://www.theguardian.com/science/2015/mar/05/nasa-finds-evidence-of-a-vast-ancient-ocean-on-mars

63. Emoto, Masaru. 2005. "The Secret Life of Water." Atria Books. 178 pp.

64. Environment Canada. 2010. "The Hydrological Cycle." Environment Canada Website: https://www.ec.gc.ca/eau-water/

65. Schmandt, Brandon; Steven D. Jacobsen; Thorsten W. Becker; Zhenxian Liu; and Kennith G. Dueker. 2014. "Dehydration melting at the top of the lower mantle". *Science* 13, Vol. 344 No. 6189: 1265–1268.

66. Fellman, Megan. 2014. "New evidence for oceans of water deep in the earth" In: *Northwestern University News*, June 12, 2014: http://www.northwestern.edu/newscenter/stories/2014/06/new-evidence-for-oceans-of-water-deep-in-the-earth.html

67. Schwenk, Theodor. 1996. "Sensitive Chaos." *Rudolf Steiner Press*, London. 232 pp.

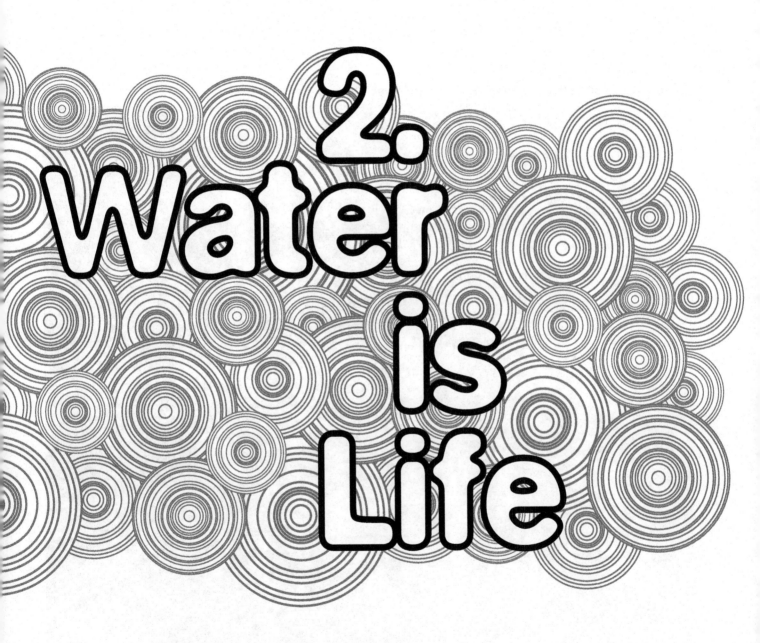

2. Water is Life

Photo 2.1: Vortex pattern of water in the Credit River, Ontario, Canada.

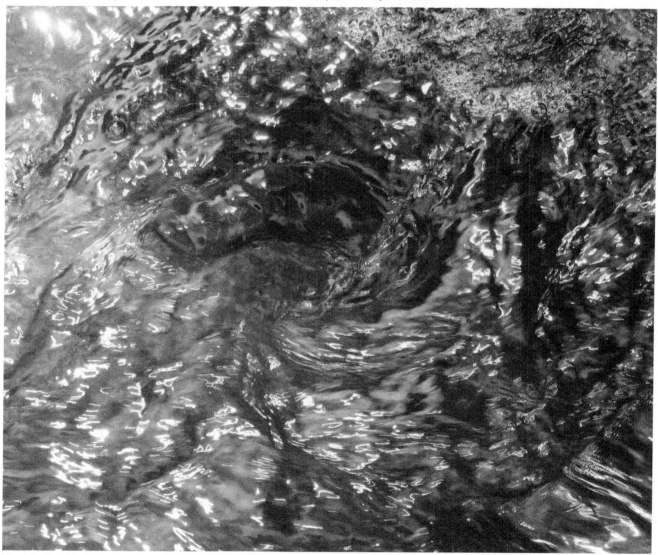

Photo by Nina Munteanu

"Why, then, does water, which has no life-characteristics of its own, form the very basis of life in all life's various manifestations? Because water embraces everything, is in and all through everything; because it rises above the distinctions between plants and animals and human beings; because it is a universal element shared by all; itself undetermined, yet determining; because, like the primal mother it is, it supplies the stuff of life to everything living."
—**Theodor Schwenk**

I n 1969, a meteor fell to Earth near the town of Murchison, Australia. Together with water, which was trapped inside the meteor for possibly billions of years, a range of amino acids linked to the precursors of life were discovered inside the carbon-rich meteorite. This led to the conjecture that cosmic forces help create the building blocks of life.[1] Forty-five years later, life's building blocks such as organic compounds and water were confirmed in many other extraterrestrial phenomena such as comets, quasars and even stars.

"Water is one of the planet's weirdest liquids,"[2] writes Lisa Grossman in the *New Scientist*, "and many of its most bizarre features make it life-giving." For instance, because water is denser as a liquid than as a solid, ice floats; this permits fish and other aquatic biota to live under partially frozen rivers and lakes. Water—unlike most other liquids—also needs a lot of heat to warm up even a little, which allows mammals to regulate their body temperature. Life's cellular processes rely on water's ability to act as a universal solvent. The high diffusion rate of water helps transport critical substances in multicellular organisms and allows unicellular life to exist without a circulatory system. One important result is that the viscosity of blood, which behaves in a non-Newtonian way (its viscosity decreases with pressure), will drop when the heart beats faster.[3]

Photo 2.2: Fresh snow with ski tracks and "snow ghosts" at First Peak, Whistler, BC, Canada

Photo by Kevin Klassen

Water and the Creation of Life

Dr. William A. Bonner of Stanford University speculated in the 1980s that the creation of life-forming amino acids may have been influenced by the vortex-like radiation generated by a neutron star.[4,5] Bonner had been intrigued with the question of how amino acids developed the consistent structural asymmetry (*homochirality*) that allows proteins to fold themselves into the living structures that form the basis for all life on Earth. Organic molecules that are asymmetric can be described as either left-handed or right-handed. Essential amino acids exist almost exclusively in a left-handed configuration. Bonner and colleague Edward Rubenstein theorized that circularly polarized light (CPL) from a giant star collapse or supernova (e.g., a neutron star) selectively eliminated one enantiomer, while blasting the surviving mirror-form out into space (where it could potentially end up on a planet, perhaps by hitching a ride on a comet or carbonaceous chondritic meteorite). Dimitar Sasselov, astronomer and director of the Harvard University Origins of Life Initiative, suggests that water plays a role in favouring the left-handed molecule on a water world such as Earth. In experiments he conducted at Harvard, Sasselov determined that, in the presence of water, 10 to 20 percent more left-handed amino-acid molecules formed.[4]

Water was identified as having played a key role in the formation of organic molecules in a meteorite of Martian origin discovered in Antarctica in 1984 (called Allan Hills 84001). Racemic α-amino acids may be created from a carbonyl compound, ammonia, hydrogen cyanide and water, all of which have been detected in interstellar space. Electricity is generated and enhanced by the presence of water, and

"By means of water, we give life to everything."

—*Koran 21:30*

Stanley Miller demonstrated in the 1950s how electricity contributes to the creation and motion of life as we know it.[6]

Speaking of Mars, recent findings from rovers, orbiters, and powerful infra-red telescopes have provided evidence that water was prevalent on Mars from the giant freshwater lake in Gale Crater to the ancient ocean that occupied a fifth of the planet's surface 4.5 billion years ago.[7,8] NASA determined that chemotrophic bacteria may have thrived in chemical reactions between minerals in Martian lakes and seas. "This environment [Gale Crater] would have been almost Earth-like in terms of geochemistry and in the presence of water," Caltech's John Grotzinger, a project scientist for NASA's *Curiosity* rover, told *Time*.[7] Grotzinger was referring to evidence gathered by the *Curiosity* mission that supports the long-hypothesized claim that Gale Crater once held a vast standing body of water for millions of years—potentially long enough for life to have formed. The sediments at the base of Mount Sharp imply that the massive crater held a vast lake; the ingredients and environment at the base of the crater were determined to have potentially supported microbial life according to Mars Exploration Program lead scientist Michael Meyer. This further implies that Mars once possessed a vigorous hydrological cycle to keep the atmosphere humid and warm enough to support such vast amounts of surface water for millions of years.[9] "Our result shows that places on Mars had the same conditions at that time [when Earth formed]—liquid water, a warm environment, and organic matter," said Caroline Freissinet in a press release from NASA's Goddard Space Flight Center.[10] More recent evidence supports the existence of a vast ancient sea that covered Mars 4.5 billion years ago (around the same time that Earth formed, with its water).[8]

The latest information from NASA—released September 28, 2015—is that water currently flows on Mars. "Mars is not the dry, arid planet that we thought of in the past," NASA's Jim Green told the Guardian. "Liquid water has been found on Mars." Michael Meyer,

lead scientist on NASA's Mars exploration program added, "Because of this, we suspect that it is at least possible to have a habitable environment today."[11]

Photo 2.3: Aerial view of Niagara Falls, Ontario, Canada

Photo by Nina Munteanu

Water's Negative Charge

As a little girl, I used to get caught in the odd thunderstorm that swept through my small town on a sudden wind. I could taste the fresh air after the storm and felt exhilarated by it. What I didn't know then was that the air was charged with negative ions from both the lightning and the rain.

In his book *The Holy Order of Water*, William Marks shares that, "In my search for the definition of life, my mind, spirit, and senses have continually guided me to see water as a loving, living, creative entity. Perhaps this is why many of us find ourselves experiencing certain emotions when approaching or passing near an ocean, a lake, waterfall, gurgling brook, or some other body of water."[12]

We are all familiar with the feeling of well-being we get from moving water—rivers, waterfalls, crashing or surging waves, thunderstorms, fresh snow, transpiration by plants, even showers and fountains. Part of this feeling comes from negative ions in the air. *Negative ions* are basically oxygen ions with an extra electron attached, produced through water molecules. As early as the 1700s, with the work of Swiss researcher Horace Bénédicte de Saussure, scientists have shown that negative ions are generated by moving water and also by plants when exposed to intense light during photosynthesis. Negative ions actually clean the air. They do this by attaching to positively charged particles such as pollen, mould, bacteria and dust, which then become too heavy to stay airborne.

A country meadow may typically contain from 2,000 to 5,000 negative ions per cubic centimetre (cc); mountains, forests and seashores may provide up to 50,000 negative ions/cc. Niagara Falls may generate anywhere from 30,000 to 100,000 negative ions/cc in its surrounding air. The negative ion concentration is well below 100/cc on a city free-way during rush hour or even in an office environment.

Rooms with air conditioners contain the lowest concentrations of negative ions. This is because they produce positive ions, as do most electrical equipment, carpets, upholstery and many synthetic materials. In an article on *Body and Soul*, Louise Deasey[13] makes suggestions for increasing the concentration of negative ions in the environment you occupy. She suggests you install a water fountain and live plants in your home and avoid the use of synthetic fibres in furniture and clothes, in favour of natural fibres such as cotton, linen, bamboo and wool. Dry your clothes in fresh air instead of using a clothes dryer, and let your hair dry naturally when you can. Replace bright fluorescent lights with low-wattage bulbs. Hand-wash clothes instead of taking them to the dry cleaners.

In a 1990 study, Dr John Ott, a US scientist who specializes in attention deficit disorder, linked fluorescent lighting—high in positive ions—with poor behaviour in schoolchildren.

Forests and the "Water Engine"

"The groves were God's first temples."
—**William Cullen Bryant**

When I was growing up in the Eastern Townships of Québec, my dad took us every spring to the local maple tree farm. I remember hiking through knee-deep snow among slim maples with buckets hanging off spiles leaking sap. Most trees had one tap but some wider trees had two. The thing to do was drip some sap onto snow and enjoy a "snow cone". I preferred to drink the sap straight, enjoying its semi-sweet complex flavour. I even preferred it to the maple syrup, made by boiling the sap in the sugar shacks, and to maple sugar—which I found far too sweet and granular for my taste. It turns out that tree sap—particularly sap from a maple, birch or walnut tree—is extremely good for you and now considered the most valuable product you can get out of a tree. The minerals, nutrients, enzymes, and antioxidants in maple sap provide a power drink that tastes delightful. Tree sap is mostly water.

Water runs this planet. Like an efficient organic "engine," it courses through the veins, arteries and capillaries of Earth, nourishing, re-cycling and communicating. At the heart of water's engine are trees, pumping, breathing, and dispersing.

Trees are highly evolved water management specialists, writes Jim Robbins, author of *The Man Who Plants Trees*. "A forest is a soft carpet on the landscape that allows a downpour to reach the ground gently rather than in a torrent."[14] This one fact reminds us of Nature's intricate fabric of intelligence and how water works with all the components of our natural world. Trees and forests are the highest functioning members of ecological society, Robbins tells us. They "create rain; render … toxic wastes in the soil harmless; neutralize harmful air pollutants in their tissue; offer shade; provide medicine. They sustain wildlife [with] food and shelter. They are the planet's heat shield, slowing the evaporation of water and cooling the earth. They generate vast clouds of chemicals that are vital to … the earth's ecosystems and … to our health and well-being. They are natural reservoirs—as much as a hundred gallons of water can be stored in the crown of a large tree. The water they release is part of a largely unrecognized water cycle."[14]

The deep roots of mature trees bring up negatively charged water along with vital minerals and trace elements, acting as bio-condensers and "harmonizing positive energy from the sun with the negative energy of the earth,"[15] writes Alick Bartholomew, author of *The Spiritual Life of Water*. Evapotranspiration from leaves of trees and shrubs is a balanced creative energy, he says.

Trees are the lungs and air conditioners of our biosphere. Scientists in Germany and the UK demonstrated that trees create and release atmospheric aerosols—biogenic volatile organic compounds such as alcohols, esters, ethers, carbonyl, terpenes, acids and other compounds—that essentially filter the sun's radiation; and they do other things we still don't understand.[14,16] Terpene aerosols help create clouds and produce an *albedo effect*, reflecting more sunlight back into space. One large tree, for instance, produces the cooling effect of ten room-sized air conditioners operating 24 hours a day.

The tree "is a chemical factory,"[17] says botanist and biochemist Diana Beresford-Kroeger. They broadcast a host of chemicals into the environment that may travel for hundreds of kilometres, as well as affect the immediate area. Researchers testing California's Sierra Nevada forest found 120 substances, of which only 70 could be identified. Aerosols released by trees are part of a sophisticated survival strategy, Beresford-Kroeger adds. Two studies published in 1983 showed that willow trees, poplars and sugar maples warn each other about insect attacks; undamaged trees then pump bug-repelling chemicals to ward off the attack.[18,19] Black walnut trees emit *juglone*, an aerosol that repels competing nearby plants and some insects. Some tree roots emit a volatile substance that attracts useful fungi. Karban and his team at the

Photo 2.4: Spiles and buckets collect maple tree sap in an Ontario forest in spring.

Photo by Merridy Cox

University of California–Davis, demonstrated that airborne communication between individual sagebrush plants (called "eavesdropping") helped neighbouring plants resist attacks.[20]

Beresford-Kroeger believes that trees help maintain the health of the natural world, as they constantly shower healing chemical mists into the air. "These substances are at the heart of connectivity in nature,"[17] says Beresford-Kroeger. For instance, during a walk through a pine forest on a warm day, the sharp pungent smell of *pinene* (a monoterpene), helps to relieve asthma. Another monoterpene aerosol, *limonene*, has an ability to fight cancer, demonstrated by Dr. Michael Gould at the University of Wisconsin.[14]

The notion that forests are linked to health is practised seriously in Europe and the East, in countries such as Japan, Russia and Korea. *Shinrin-yoku* (Japanese for "forest bathing" or "wood-air bathing") is a recognized practice in the East and is gaining interest in the West as a natural form of aromatherapy and relaxation therapy.

Photo 2.5: Mixed west coast forest in Metchosin, British Columbia, Canada

Photo by Nina Munteanu

Robbins shares the following story about Dr. A. Kukowka, a professor of medicine in Greiz, Germany, who recounted his experience beneath a crown of massive yew trees on a warm day. At first disorienting, the experience became one of exhilaration in which he envisioned paradise, angelic music, and felt "indescribably happy." Kukowka concluded that the terpene emitted from the trees had affected him.

Is this a story of fancy or does it have some validity? Why do we feel so good around trees and in the forest? And why do some forests please us more than others? When I enter a forest or woodland, a calming force descends upon me; perhaps it is the healing mist of trees. My mind quiets and embraces a state of meditative well-being, soothed by the gentle rustle of leaves or the cursive clanking of tall poplars in the wind.

Many of us feel a sense of peace in a forest. I have no doubt that this is the result of several factors including sounds and frequencies (e.g., infrasound), increased negative charge, scents, wood essential oils, genetic heritage and memory, and simple aesthetic appreciation and beauty. I write more about this in later chapters.

You don't even need to enter the forest; some of its value is in simply seeing and being near trees. Researchers in Europe and Japan found that the amount of green space and proximity to a person's home reliably predicted mental and physical health. Anxiety and depression was significantly reduced in the presence of green space. Vegetation creates "a halo of improved health."[14] Dr. Frances Kuo at the University of Illinois demonstrated that just seeing a tree helps cognition and promotes a sense of well being.[14] Kuo strongly believes that lack of trees is debilitating to general social health. "A disappearing urban forest leads to psychological, physical, and social breakdown," says Kuo, "Just as animals in unfit environments develop certain behavioural and functional pathologies, we may see more child abuse or crime or their problems when people live in unfit environments."[14]

Attention Restoration Theory suggests that a human-made environment of objects—cars and buildings—requires high-frequency processing in the brain; while a landscaped environment allows the observer to relax his or her attention, resulting in reduced muscle tension, lower heart rate, and a generally less stressful physiology.[13] What naturally appeals to us, what is considered beautiful, while subjective, also follows a kind of "universal" tendency. For instance, a Harvard Medical School study showed that people gravitated to rounded edges and that the *amygdala* (the part of our brain that registers fear) was more active when people looked at sharp-edged objects. Symmetrical shapes are generally considered more appealing than asymmetrical ones. I talk more about this in Chapter 8. Shape (e.g., symmetry), texture, tone, height and colour all play a role in determining how mind, heart and spirit function in the creative process. A study published in 2000 by environmental psychologist Nancy Wells found that ample daylight and greenery boosted attentiveness, focus, and academic performance.[21]

Photo 2.6: Bamboo forest in Kyoto, Japan

Photo by Nina Munteanu

Bartholomew describes four geologic periods when forests flourished on this planet. The first was the Carboniferous, 350 million years ago, when land vertebrates established. The second was the Jurassic, 170 million years ago, when dinosaurs flourished. The third, the Eocene epoch, 60 million years ago, witnessed the first primitive mammals. The last, the Holocene epoch, which began some 500,000 years ago, ushered in the cultures of modern humanity. "Perhaps," says Bartholomew, "in each case the forests delivered a boost in the oxygen content of the atmosphere, which may have been a trigger for an evolutionary explosion of life forms."[15]

Ten thousand years ago, the land along the Mediterranean was covered in mixed forests of conifers and oak, Bartholomew shares. Lebanon's forests provided the timber for the exploring ships of the Phoenician empire in the third century BCE. North Africa, a fertile forest two thousand years ago, is now a desert. A thousand years ago, three quarters of Europe was forest. Today forest and woodland cover only one fifth of Europe.[15]

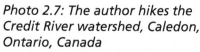

Photo 2.7: The author hikes the Credit River watershed, Caledon, Ontario, Canada

Photo by Merridy Cox

Deforestation doesn't just create erosion and loss of oxygen; it interferes with the full hydrological cycle that links precipitation with groundwater circulation, and the important energy exchange involved. A reduction in water vapour, otherwise generated by natural forests, creates an imbalance that promotes greater contrast between water-abundant areas and those without; this results in flooding on the one hand and desertification on the other. Dominick Spracklen and his colleagues suggest that, given the role of trees as the planet's "air conditioners," one of our primary climate mitigation measures should include planting indigenous trees.[16]

Russian physicists Anastassia Makarieva and Victor Gorshkov argued in 2007 that forests make rain. Their meteorological theory states that forests function as biotic pumps; they not only function as carbon sinks or havens of biodiversity, but also provide an essential role in the hydrological cycle and climate.[22] I talk more about the role of the forests, particularly the north temperate rainforest, in Chapter 9.

The proportion of the world's surface covered by forest was once close to 75 percent, Bartholomew writes. It dropped to 50 percent in medieval times and now to 25 percent.[14]

The Gaia Hypothesis

James Lovelock, co-developer of the Gaia Hypothesis and author of *The Vanishing Face of Gaia*, suggests that recent deforestation plays a significant role in climate change, given that forests are the main regulator of climate and the carbon cycle.[23,24]

Science writer and former editor of *Nature*, Philip Ball describes how water lubricates Earth's biochemical cycles. He gives the example of carbon, in which forests play a major role. Atmospheric carbon "gets woven into the fabric of plants,"[25] and consumed by animals, writes Ball. Carbon dioxide in the air also dissolves in the sea, providing a carbon source for photosynthetic marine plankton. It finally settles as dead organic debris on the ocean floor, or is carried into the deep Earth where tectonic plates meet. Carbon then recycles back to the atmosphere through volcanic and other emissions and through plant and animal respiration.

Photo 2.8: Buttressed kapok tree (Ceiba pentandra) in the Quintana Roo, Costa Maya.

According to Lovelock and others, the feedback system within each cycle gives the planet an opportunity to regulate itself. The Gaia Hypothesis proposes that living and non-living parts of our planet interact in a complex network like a super-organism; essentially the same as the feedback we use to maintain our own *homeostasis* (e.g., body temperature, blood pH and sugar levels, or water balance). The hypothesis postulates that all living things exert a regulatory effect on the Earth's environment that promotes life overall. First formulated in the 1960s during his work for NASA on methods of detecting life on Mars, Dr. James Lovelock named his notion of a self-regulating living system the Gaia Hypothesis after the Greek goddess, using the suggestion of

Photo by Nina Munteanu

novelist William Golding, who lived in the same village as Lovelock at the time.[25,27]

Lovelock published the Gaia Hypothesis in journal articles along with co-author Dr. Lynn Margulis using two fundamental precepts:

- The planet is a "super organismic system."
- Evolution results more from cooperative than competitive processes.[24,26,27,28,29,30]

"The atmosphere is … not merely a biological product, but more probably a biological construction; not living, but like cat's fur, an extension of a living system designed to maintain a chosen environment," writes Lovelock.[24] Co-theorist Lynn Margulis called Earth "a community of trust," which she referred to as "an emergent property of interaction among organisms."[30]

Their arguments included these factors:

- Constancy of global surface temperature, despite increase in the energy provided by the sun
- Constancy of atmospheric composition, even though it should be unstable
- Constancy of ocean salinity

The Gaia Theory remains accused of being teleological by critics within the scientific community, including Richard Dawkins and Ford Doolittle. Dawkins rejected the possibility of feedback loops: "There was no way for evolution by natural selection to lead to altruism on a Global scale." Other scientists rejected the implication of a "living" Gaia, as it is unable to reproduce. Both are perhaps self-limiting views.

If we view all this less literally and more metaphorically, then a remark from astronomer Carl Sagan in a 1976 NBC interview on the significance of the *Viking 1* landing on Mars both surprises and illuminates: "I can't help but think of this is as an epochal moment in planetary exploration. If you can imagine a sort of a very patient observer, observing the Earth for its four and half billion-year lifetime. For all of that period, lots of things came onto the Earth, but nothing left it. And

now just in the last 10 years, things are spewing off the Earth. It's like a dandelion gone to seed. There's little vehicles going out to Mercury to Venus to Jupiter to Saturn…"[31]

*Photo 2.9: Scanning electron micrograph (SEM) of a Tardigrade (*Paramacrobiotus craterlaki*) or water bear in moss from Crater Lake, Kenya.*

Photo by Eye of Science / Science Source

Water as the Matrix of Life

"Were water actually what hydrologists deem it to be—a chemically inert substance—then a long time ago there would already have been no water and no life on this Earth."
—Viktor Schauberger

Most of us, when asked to differentiate between "animate" and "inanimate"—something alive versus something that isn't—will readily make that distinction. A worm is alive and a rock isn't. But strictly defining the fundamental nature of this difference in biological terms escapes us still. We've defined life structurally: all living things contain specific substances such as organic macro-molecules (e.g., RNA, DNA, proteins, and polysaccharides) and smaller organics.

"But life may be—indeed should be—far more nimble than that,"[4] writes Jeffrey Kluger, senior writer at *Time*, in his article "Life as We Don't Know It." "It's vain in the extreme to assume that the entire universe is limited to the same biological cookbook we use … What's to prevent elements all over the periodic table from whipping up life-sustaining molecules we can't even contemplate?" Theoretical physicist Paul Davies posits the existence of a "shadow life," a form of life we don't recognize because it's beyond our comprehension. "We don't know how weird life could look," says Davies. "It's as wide as the imagination."[4]

We need look no further than the most inhospitable parts of our own planet to find a form of life that has adapted to extreme environmental conditions. For instance, life "thrives under the blistering sands of Chile's Atacama Desert,"[32] writes Kluger. It thrives "in the frigid permafrost that covers Antarctica; in the boiling 750° heat of hydrothermal vents at the bottom of the oceans; in the acidic hot springs of Yellowstone Park."[32] In his Time article, Klugar describes the nematode that geologist Tullis Onstott discovered two miles underground; Klugar talks about the black fungus that thrives in the Chernobyl control room with radioactivity 500 times higher than normal, following the 1986 meltdown. Klugar goes on to describe several other "extremophiles" (life that thrive in extreme environmental conditions): such as the stromat-olites of blue-green algae that cover Antartica's Lake Untersee, whose heavy concentrations of methane and an alkalinity similar to laundry detergent deter most life from flourishing. Brine shrimp hatch in the trillions every season in the endorheic salty Mono Lake in California. The bacteria of Tinto Lake in Spain, a highy acidic (pH of 2) lake affected by acid mine drainage, have adapted to the metal toxicity by using a biofilm membrane that protects them and allows them to ab-sorb nutrients. Hypolithic algae of the Atacama Salt Flats, the world's driest non-polar desert, live under quartz crystals, to photosynthesize and conserve the limited moisture beneath.[32]

Life, as it turns out, is pretty nimble; especially if you define it with an open mind. "When we speak of how unlikely it is that life exists on any alien world, we are thinking specifically of 'life' as we know it. Increasingly, however, we're learning that there is also life as we don't know it, haven't considered it, and never even imagined it before,"[32] Kluger writes.

To return to the original question—what is life?—how do we dis-tinguish that which is alive, something animate, from that which isn't?

"Living Water"

Nobel Laureate Albert Szent-Gyorgyi suggested in 1957 that a for-mal distinction by biologists between "animate" and "inanimate" was not possible because they neglected two matrices without which the substances they studied could not perform: water and electromag-netic fields. In other words, "Biology [had] forgotten water,"[33] writes Szent-Györgyi.

A system can be considered "alive," write scientists Voeikov and Del Guidice, if it is composed and participates in dynamic processes such as metabolism, multiplication, adaptability, excitability, senescence, specific reactivity to external stimuli, has the ability to grow and develop, and evolve.[34] Voeikov and Del Guidice cite the postulates first proposed by Russian biologist Erwin Simonovich Bauer[35] in 1935 to describe the properties of life.

Bauer's first principle, the Principle of Stable Non-Equilibrium, states that living systems are never in equilibrium. "At the expense of their free energy, they ceaselessly perform work against sliding toward equilibrium demanded by the physical and chemical laws." This describes a kind of negative entropy (or *negentropy*) introduced by Schrödinger in 1944.[36] According to Bauer, living systems perform work, which is executed by their excited structures or elements moving from an excited to a ground state.[34] Szent-Gyrogyi suggested bioluminescence as an example.[33] Bauer's second principle ensures that those elements that have wound down are either re-excited or substituted by new excited structures. This suggests that a living system remains intrinsically active—and coherent, which resonates with the 2010 findings of University of Toronto researchers studying *entanglement* (a reflection of coherence and self-organization) in photosynthesis. *Photosynthesis* is one of the key phenomena in the life-chain that converts Sun's energy into chemical energy using water and carbon, a process on which virtually all life on Earth depends.[37]

Most studies in experimental biology follow the premise of water as solvent in biochemical reactions and as reagent for hydrolytic reactions. However, Voeikov and Del Giudice provide some striking examples that demonstrate water being, in the widest sense, the actual basis of biological organization.

The jellyfish, for instance, is over 99 percent water by weight.[38] The "solids" of a jellyfish (bioorganic molecules, proteins, nucleic acids, carbohydrates, and so forth—the stuff we normally think of as life-sustaining, whose assemblies perform particular functions that constitute vital functions) constitute no more than a fraction of a percent of the

jellyfish's living mass. In other words, "they are 'islands' of clear 'living' water residing in a sea of 'dead' water,"[33] write Voeikov and Del Giudice, who describe water as satisfying the conditions set out by Bauer for a living system:

"Water … creates a system residing in a stable non-equilibrium state due to co-existence of its two phases that have different thermodynamic parameters. One of the phases is represented with low-entropy, coherent domains [described by biochemist Gerald Pollack as *Exclusion Zone* water][39] and the other is high-entropy 'bulk' water. This dual system can perform internal work to sustain its non-equilibrium state due to *negentropy* arousal from spontaneous non-coherent to coherent state conversion."[33]

I talk more about this below, under the heading *The Fourth Phase of Water*.

In his forward to Alick Bartholomew's book *The Spiritual Life of Water*, Chris Weedon, cofounder of the Water Association, Somerset UK, talks about the special relationship that water bears have with water. Called tardigrades, these microscopic benthic invertebrates clamber in the damp moss on eight stubby legs. When dry conditions arrive, says Weedon, water bears don't succumb to death; instead, they just dry up. "Drying to a body content of one percent water, from close to 100 percent, the creature transforms into a microscopic speck of organic dust, utterly resistant to drought, extreme cold, vacuum, and even radioactivity."[15] The water bear can survive for 200 years in this dormant state. It takes only a single drop of water to revive a water bear. That's all that's needed: just water.

Bartholomew reminds us that, "there are dozens of different roles played by liquids that are basically water, including blood, sap, and about thirty different human bodily fluids, each with its specific purpose."[15] Bartholomew calls water "the stage manager of life, communicating to our bodies' cells how to be part of a vast orchestra, distributing energy in the landscape to make it balanced and productive." He adds that, "the

Photo 2.10: Divers swim Desolation Sound, British Columbia, Canada.

Photo by Nina Munteanu

very laws that govern the harmonious movement of the planets also determine the form and behaviour of our organic life, through water." Water's part in the evolution of life comes from a discovery of quantum physics, "that we are embedded in a vast web of energy that interconnects all of creation." Bartholomew proposes that "water and the quantum field are two complementary aspects in the balanced mediation and sustenance of life."[15]

In his book *The Holy Order of Water*, science writer William Marks reminds us that even though we are made up of mostly water and water constantly flows through us, our appearance and shape remain the same; we still look human. So, too, with a whirlpool in a river. "The shape of the whirlpool retains its vortex shape even though the water forming it is constantly changing,"[12] says Marks. The physical reality of the vortex, Marks continues, is related to the spark of motion found in all life. Where does the energy come from that gives something life? Where does it go when life perishes? Marks suggests that it is "in the watery creation of protoplasm that we have the world of life being born from the world of nonlife."

Why does life exist? What is its purpose, and why do so many different forms exist?

Mythologist and scholar Joseph Campbell shared with Bill Moyers his answer: "When you really think about it, life is a lot of protoplasm with an urge to reproduce and continue being."[40] In that simple answer lies a complex panoply of interpretations and possibilities.

The Dance of Creation

Intuitive naturalist Viktor Schauberger described the attraction and repulsion of polarized forces as the dance of creation. Polarity, according to Schauberger, is Nature's engine.

Water's dipolar molecular structure and hydrogen-bonded matrix demonstrates polarity. The vortex, water's natural form of movement, is polar, cycling in a rhythm of contraction and expansion—creative destruction.

Nature's dance of creation is best illustrated through water's dance:

"Nature is balanced but never stagnant. She does not create life, wipe her hands, and walk away. If that were the case, life would spiral into oblivion. When Nature is left alone, she continually creates and re-creates—breaking down and building up again with the opportunity for each cycle to yield new and more complex life. One of Nature's greatest feats is the utilization of opposing forces and cycles for continued growth and creation."

—Pangman and Evans, *Dancing with Water*

I talk more about the energizing and creative–destructive forces of moving water, and specifically the vortex, in Chapter 3 and Chapter 6.

Photo 2.11: Boathouse perches over low tidal waters at Prospect Point, Nova Scotia, Canada.

Photo by Nina Munteanu

Water and Human Health

"Illnesses do not come upon us out of the blue. They are developed from small daily sins against Nature. When enough sins have accumulated, illnesses will suddenly appear."

—Hippocrates

The role of water in all living species, including humans, has been the same since the creation of life in salt water and its later adaptation in freshwater. Depending on age, the human body is composed of 60–75 percent water (the *solvent*), with the rest being solid matter (the *solute*). Brain tissue contains more water at 85 percent. The body prioritizes brain function over all other systems; so, while it is only two percent of total body weight, the brain receives 18–20 percent of blood circulation. Some scientists now tell us that—although an adult human contains generally two-thirds water—on a molecular level, our water content is much higher. Water occupies over 98 percent of a human cell molecule.[41]

The highest amount of biological water inside us is extracellular, in our tissues (e.g., lymph). Extracellular water is saline (like the ocean), which lets it carry an electric charge; it supplies nutrients and removes toxins. Intracellular water (water inside cells) drives the metabolism of cells. Water helps proton exchange, activates proteins, and assists cell formation.

Some thirty forms of biological water drive the various metabolic and physical processes in the body, in a kind of harmonic dance. To name a few, there are: digestive liquids (like bile and mucous), cerebrospinal fluid, amniotic fluid, breast milk, synovial fluid (surrounding the joints), sweat, and urine.

An adult drinks about 2.5 litres a day; more is absorbed through the skin by bathing, swimming or showering.

Some key life-sustaining properties of water not usually discussed in science textbooks include the following:

- Water lowers viscosity. Proteins and enzymes of the body function more efficiently in solutions of lower viscosity (a hydrated state). Examples include the command and control message systems of receptors in cell membranes.
- Water helps the body recognize thirst: recognition of thirst becomes less accurate as the body becomes more dehydrated in the interior of its cells, which happens with aging.
- Water regulates all functions of the body, including the activity of all the solutes it dissolves and circulates.[41]

Pioneer physician F. Batmanghelidj is a London-trained doctor who was imprisoned in Persia (now Iran) during the 1979 revolution. He was pardoned because he healed hundreds of fellow prisoners who were suffering from acute, stress-induced peptic ulcers. He used water.[15]

Batmanghelidj published his book *Your Body's Many Cries for Water* in 2008. The subtitle reads: *You're not sick; you're thirsty; don't treat thirst with medication*. He opens his book with this bold statement:

It is a fact that correctly prescribed and used medications make over 2 million people sicker and kill over 100,000 every year … The most fundamental mistake is the actual use of normally prescribed chemicals in standard treatment procedures … The reason is simple: when the body needs a top-up of water, it is given toxic chemicals instead.[42]

He cites the unprecedented December 2003 declaration of Dr. Allen Roses, international vice president of Glaxo–SmithKline, one of the major manufacturers of drugs in the world, in an interview with *The Independent* newspaper in London, England: "the vast majority of drugs—more than 90 percent—only work in 30 to 50 percent of the people." While Roses was quick to blame patients (e.g., having certain genes that neutralize drugs), Batmanghelidj contends that water—that is the lack of it—is the true culprit.

A year before *The Independent* interview with Roses, Jacqueline Chan published a paper in the *Journal of Epidemiology*, which established that drinking more than five glasses of water a day reduced fatal heart attack by 50 percent in both sexes.[43]

Lack of proper hydration can also affect brain function and integrity. Even dyslexia can be affected.[15]

Histamine, Allergies and Asthma

Batmanghelidj tells us that histamine formation and release is directly connected to the concentration and viscosity of the internal solutions in the body. "Histamine becomes engaged in order to correct the concentration imbalance produced by dehydration."[42]

Batmanghelidj further informs us that nerve cells contain 85 percent water. Transported in small microstreams along the length of cells, water "floats" packaged materials along microtubules for use in the brain's communication system throughout the entire body. When dehydrated, the body goes into "drought management," triggering histamine production. Excessive production and activity of the neurotransmitter histamine, along with prostaglandins, kinins and platelet activating factors (PAFs), cause allergies, asthma, and chronic pains in different parts of the body. Their excessive presence is in fact a signal of water shortage in the body and may be viewed as emergency thirst signals.

Chronic Pain

According to Batmanghelidj, chronic body pains that cannot be easily explained as injury or infection are most likely signals of chronic water shortage in the area where pain is registered—a local thirst. He recommends that non-infectious "recurring" or chronic pains be viewed as indicators of body thirst. Pain, Batmanghelidj tells us, "is a sensation that denotes chemical changes in the area around nerves that monitor the acid/alkali balance."[42] The mechanism, says Batmanghelidj, safeguards against excessive acid buildup from metabolism that could burn and eat into the cell membranes and inner structures of the cells. Water washes away the acid toxic waste of metabolism, and the nerve endings sense and report to the brain's pain centers. Pain of this kind is essentially a localized thirst signal of the body.

According to Batmanghelidj and others, pains caused by dehydration include:

- Dyspeptic pain (e.g., gastritis duodenitis, heartburn)
- Rheumatoid arthritis pain
- Angina pain (heart pain on walking, or even at rest)
- Low back pain
- Intermittent claudication pain (leg pain on walking)
- Migraine and hangover headaches
- Colitis pain and its associated constipation
- False appendicitis pain[42]

Batmanghelidj advises us to treat these pains first with improved daily water intake before resorting to medications such as antihistamines or antacids. Such medications ironically silence a cardinal signal of chronic and localized dehydration of the body, without removing the root cause of the pain. Moreover, prolonged use of analgesics may cause gastrointestinal bleeding and other side effects.

I can attest to the power of water in regulating wellness. When I feel the onset of a rare headache (I don't typically get them) or a digestive disorder, I increase my water intake; in most cases, that alone usually takes care of it in short order. When we are aware of what our body is telling us, when we recognize these symptoms as signals of water deficiencies, we can do something about them before they become chronic and develop into something more tenacious and serious.

Photo 2.12: Water drop on a hosta leaf.

Photo by Nina Munteanu

What Am I Drinking?

Bottled Water

Contrary to modern lore, bottled water may not be as clean as the tap water you can get for free from your house. Water kept in plastic bottles may accumulate plastic residue and is less regulated than public water. "No one should think that bottled water is better regulated, better protected or safer than tap," says Eric Goldstein, co-director of the urban program at the Natural Resources Defense Council (NRDC), a U.S. non-profit organization devoted to protecting health and the environment. At least 25 percent of the water sold by popular water brands take their water from public water sources, which means that you are essentially paying for tap water.[44]

Here are additional reasons why bottled water should be avoided:

- Bottles litter our environment: Billions of plastic water containers will be littering our landfills for hundreds of years. Contrary to popular belief, only 35 percent of plastic water bottles are recycled. The rest end up in our landfills.[45]
- Bottling companies overuse and deplete key watersheds: Coke, Pepsi, Nestlé and others "mine" aquifers of community watersheds for profit and often without regard for local needs. Nestlé, for example, is currently taking 3.6 million litres of groundwater per day in Aberfoyle, Ontario, depleting the resources of a nearby community at Mill Creek.[46]
- The bottling industry contributes to climate change: The production and transportation of bottled water produce greenhouse gas emissions that exacerbate climate change.

There is another reason not to buy bottled water, and it is perhaps the most important: to buy bottled water is literally to buy into a paradigm that accepts that water is not free but can be bought and sold. It makes water a commodity (see Chapter 9, *Water Is Story*).

"Water is a public trust,"[47] says Maude Barlow, Senior Advisor on Water Issues to the President of the United Nations. "No one owns water; rather it belongs to the earth and all species alike … because it is a flow resource necessary for life and ecosystem health, and because there is no substitute for it, water must be regarded as a public Commons and a public good and preserved as such for all time in law and practice."[47]

Water is an elixir.

Distilled Water

When I was in the supermarket recently, I was struck by the large proportion of shelf space for bottled water that was devoted to distilled water. I only knew about its use in my chemistry and biology experiments, where it was important to reduce variables. However, I was told that a growing number of people drink distilled water to lose weight, as part of a body-building program, and to detoxify. Some doctors even promote its frequent use, based on the fear that unfiltered water may carry parasites, chlorine, fluoride and various contaminants that find their way into our water supply. In places such as where I live, however, this is a ridiculous notion. Most municipal water in Canada is healthy and free of contamination, with no need to resort to such measures.

Distillation is the process by which water is boiled, evaporated and the vapour condensed. Because it's free of dissolved minerals, it can absorb toxic substances from the body and eliminate them. However, prolonged use can lead to rapid loss of electrolytes and trace minerals, with resulting heart beat irregularities and high blood pressure. Cooking foods in distilled water pulls the minerals out of them.

According to the U.S. Environmental Protection Agency, "Distilled water, being essentially mineral-free, is very aggressive, in that it tends to dissolve substances with which it is in contact. Notably, carbon dioxide from the air is rapidly absorbed, making the water acidic and even more aggressive. Many metals are dissolved by distilled water." Most soft drinks (with or without sugar) are made with distilled water. Heavy consumers typically spill large amounts of calcium, magnesium, and trace minerals into their urine and out of their body. Mineral loss can lead to osteoporosis, osteoarthritis, hypothyroidism, coronary artery disease, high blood pressure, and a long list of degenerative diseases generally associated with premature aging.[48,49,50,51]

Spring Water

During the summers when I was growing up in the Eastern Townships of Quebec, my father used to take my brother and my sister and me on mini-field trips to the local spring, just outside town. We walked a few miles up Mountain Road to the outskirts of town, over to Miner's farm. The spring, which ran all year round, was an unassuming seepage from a rock outcrop with a pipe attached to it by the local farmer. I remember it being very cold. Even the air around the spring was cooler than the surrounding air of the hot summer day. I remember lugging three-litre jugs full of cold clean water in the little cart that my brother and I used when we played cowboys and Indians. Even during my reckless playful days of childhood I could tell the difference. The water "tasted" better. In truth, it was partly its lack of taste that I was noticing. Its lack of chlorine and fluoride, that is. It was so refreshing. Several of my colleagues and friends share similar stories of growing up in a small town and hauling spring water to their home to drink chlorine-free vitalized water.

In the past—prior to receiving piped water from a major water supply—and in remote parts of the world today, a small village relied on spring water for drinking. Natural springs are valued for high quality water and reliability of flow, particularly in times of drought. Some springs carry a reputation for wellness and healing. I talk more about this in Chapter 10, *Water Is Prayer*. The veneration of springs is found in all cultures and major religions and as far back as prehistoric times, science author Alick Bartholomew shares. "It is not difficult to see why people invested these sites with magical powers, or saw them as inhabited by a living spirit who was guardian of … the perfect nourishing liquid issuing mysteriously from the womb of the planet."[15]

During the Age of Reason (also called the Age of Enlightenment), in which reductionist explanations for all things prevailed, philosophers and medical practitioners—rejecting the holistic "vagaries" of folklore and superstition—reasoned that the minerals contained within the spring were the true elixir. This birthed the spa culture, which flourishes today. I talk more about this in Chapter 9, *Water Is Story*.

Photo 2.13: Photo montage of an iceberg above and below the water.

Iceberg Water

When I'm in Lunenberg, Nova Scotia, I take small trips to other parts of the Maritimes on the Atlantic Ocean. Prince Edward Island. New Brunswick. Newfoundland. When I was in St. John's, Newfoundland, to give a paper at a conference on water, I looked for icebergs. Icebergs the size of a small island are known to drift past the harbour entrance. Most of them come from the glaciers of western Greenland and the rest from islands in Canada's Arctic area. I didn't spot any when I was there, but I imagined their massive structure from the pictures I'd seen. A tall iceberg would float there, revealing only its peak—the size of a house; the rest of its massive structure, the size of an apartment building, would lurk in the dark depths beneath. We're told that close to 90 percent of an iceberg remains under the surface. And we all know the

Photo by Uwe Kils and Wiska Bodo, Wikimedia Commons

story of the *Titanic*, the ocean liner that had its side ripped open like a can opener by an iceberg, just off the Newfoundland coast.

In his book *Water*, Marq de Villiers tells the story of mining for iceberg water in Newfoundland.[52] Icebergs the size of a house, called "bergy bits" by the locals, sometimes drift to shore and run aground for easy pickings. Villagers may scramble down ocean cliffs and over seaweed-covered rocks to chip away a pail full. They haul it over to the local inn and split it into cubes over a fine Scotch.

The water is literally ancient (8 to 10 thousand years old) and the cleanest water you'll ever drink, says de Villiers. "Drink it by itself," a friend of de Villiers advises, "or twelve-thousand-year-old water mixed with twelve-year-old Scotch." De Villiers reported in 2000 that local companies tried marketing "iceberg water," including towing icebergs to New York; but the business of harvesting floating ice to process vodka, beer and drinking water failed, victim of the pervasive cynicism of advertising: no one believed the claims were true. However, someday, it might not be out of the ordinary to sip iceberg beer or an iceberg martini in a hotel bar in St. John's.

De Villiers describes iceberg water as slightly acidic (with a pH of about 5.4), and traces of potassium, sodium, magnesium, calcium, chloride, sulphate and bicarbonate. "It will fizz and crack when it melts or when you drop it into a drink," de Villiers' friend remarks with a sparkle in his eye. "Crystals under pressure."

The Fourth Phase of Water

I remember how the spring water that we used to carry down to our house iced-up differently. It wouldn't "pop" out of the ice tray like tap water ice did. It clung to the tray and seemed to have a different consistency, as if it were "organized and bound" differently. The cubes seemed to form tighter yet more "friable" lattices. It was water, but it wasn't the same. When I dropped the ice into a glass of water, it cracked, popped and fizzed as it melted—more than tap water ice did, I thought. Did all this have something to do with water's transformative properties, its changing structure and interfacial properties?

I mention in Chapter 1 that water may exhibit structural and behavioural differences that do not necessarily reflect chemical bonding differences, and that these differences may result from the development of a self-organized layer of structured water that resembles a liquid crystal. Dr. Gerald Pollack, bioengineer at the University of Washington, calls this type of water *Exclusion Zone* (EZ) water, for the materials it excludes. He describes it as a "fourth phase" of water: its characteristics place it between solid and liquid. EZ water (also called crystalline water) is denser, more viscous and ordered, and more negatively charged than bulk or ordinary water; it also has a higher refractive index.[53] Pollack and others have provided evidence to suggest that liquid crystalline water is more common than previously thought and may be closely connected with the generation of life.[54]

EZ water builds millions of molecular layers, layer by layer. This is presumably how ice forms, moving from regular water to EZ water to ice. And when you melt it, it goes from ice to EZ water to regular water. So, liquid crystalline EZ water is an intermediate state.

"The living world should be thought of as an equal partnership between the biological molecules and water."
—Martin Chaplin

In his experiments with interfacial water, Pollack demonstrated that EZ water can hold and deliver energy. It builds on any hydrophilic (or water-loving) surface when infrared energy is available. According to Pollack, the key ingredient to creating EZ water is light, (i.e., electromagnetic energy), whether visible light, ultraviolet (UV) or infrared wavelengths.[53]

The higher alkalinity and negative charge of EZ water provides health benefits, given that our bodies prefer an alkaline and negatively charged environment (see the section above on negative ions).

An ideal source of EZ water for drinking is glacial melt, says Pollack. In lieu of this less available source, he suggests that another good source is water from deep sources, such as deep spring water. The deeper the better, says Pollack, given that EZ water is created under pressure. When I heard this, I knew I had my answer to my ice-cube tray anomaly.

Vortices also build crystalline water. According to Pollack, virtually any energy put into water creates or builds EZ water: "Vortexed water puts enormous energy into the water." [53]

EZ or crystalline water can be found in great abundance in nature and in biological systems, particularly. As I already mentioned, EZ water forms under pressure in springs and in the vortices of turbulent watercourses. It also fills our extracellular tissues. Components of the body, such as collagen and cell membranes, act as liquid crystals.[55] These tissues work cooperatively with water to create an informational network that reaches every cell.[56]

In 2001, Gilbert Ling suggested that water played a central role in cell function. He posited that water in human cells is not ordinary water, but something far more structured and organized: what Pollack calls EZ water. Ling showed how intracellular water adjacent to any membrane or organelle is organized very differently from bulk water. According to Ling, "structured" water plays a significant role in governing the shape and biological activity of large biopolymers (e.g., folding

proteins). He also suggested that this ordering is the reason why most solutes occur in low concentrations inside the cell; because the cell's ordered water excludes them.[57]

Crystalline water surrounds and stabilizes DNA, supporting its electromagnetic field.[58,59]

Dr. Mu Shik Jhon, a North Korean researcher states that, "all water is not created equal, and it is the structure of the water within our bodies that ultimately determines health or sickness."[59]

Jhon developed the "Molecular Water Environment Theory," which he presented in 1986 to a cancer symposium in the United States. The theory posited that replenishment of hexagonal water in our bodies can increase vitality, slow the aging process and prevent disease. Jhon verified through experiments with nuclear magnetic resonance (NMR) that what he called "structured water" or "hexagonal water" (similar if not the same as Pollack's EZ water and Chaplin's interfacial water) penetrates the cells of the human body much faster, and supplies nutrients and oxygen more efficiently than unstructured (bulk) water. When structured water replaces unstructured water in the body, cell water turnover and cellular metabolism are enhanced, argued Jhon. He concluded that structured water aids metabolic processes, supports the immune system and contributes to lasting vitality.[59]

Piezoelectricity

Piezoelectricity is a form of electricity created when non-conductive materials become polarized. Under pressure, a conductive pathway is created and a voltage forms in the direction of the polarized lattice. "Piezoelectricity is the force behind thousands of biological functions,"[60] science writers Pangman and Evans tell us. Pressure waves in the human body polarize water and other liquid crystalline biomolecules.

Water cannot be absorbed when a person is in the presence of strong, man-made electromagnetic fields. They literally short out the piezoelectric charge at the cell membrane, write Pangman and Evans.[60] There is hardly any place, other than outside, away from power lines, where we are not somehow exposed to human-made electrical fields, including electrical wiring, appliances, computers and cell phones, to name just a few common household items. Microwaves also damage water's electromagnetic field.

Drinking natural source (not bottled) water, such as spring or filtered lake water, can replenish your negative electric charge. One of the reasons why infrared saunas make you feel so good is because your body's cells are deeply penetrated by infrared energy. Light from this source, just like direct light from the sun, builds and stores EZ water, which enhances the flow of blood through your capillaries. Pollack adds that, "If you have an organ that's not functioning well—for example, it's lacking that negative charge—then the negative charge from the earth and ... [drinking] EZ water can help restore that negativity. I've become convinced ... that this negative charge is critical for healthy function."[61] You can optimize your drinking water in a variety of different ways, by injecting light energy or physical energy into the water by vortexing, for example. This is fairly easy using magnets. Reversing the vortex every few seconds may even create more energy.[60,61]

My study, twenty years ago, of algae communities settling and growing on glass slides placed in rivers, looked at the different communities that thrived in different flows, from turbulent to laminar. My paper hypothesized that the richer communities I observed in more turbulent flows resulted from increased opportunity and higher oxygen and nutrient exchange. Less interesting communities occurred in laminar flows. I remember thinking there was more to it. In hindsight, this phenomenon was likely the result of the vortexing of negatively charged EZ water in the turbulent flow.

Photo 2.14: Fresh snow covers conifer trees in Whistler, BC, Canada.

Photo by Nina Munteanu

Earthing, Lightning & Schumann Resonance

You can generate an electron surplus, or support this negative charge within your body, by spending time outside in the sun and by connecting to the Earth, which also has a negative charge. This is the basis for *Earthing* (or grounding). Earthing's significant health benefits allow negatively charged electrons from the ground to enter the soles of your feet. A good analogy is to envision your cells as batteries that are naturally recharged by spending time outdoors—whether sunny or overcast—and walking barefoot, connecting to the negative charge of the earth. Clinton Ober, Stephen Sinatra and Martin Zucker, authors of the book *Earthing*, tell us that humans, like all other living beings, are electrical creatures living on an electrical planet.[62] Just like the Earth, your body is made of mostly water and minerals, and both are excellent conductors of electrons, the authors remind us.

Tesla knew about the Earth's reservoir of energetic free electrons when he intuited that energy waves in the earth and the atmosphere could be used to transmit power to any point on the globe. Tesla understood that the surface of the Earth and the atmosphere together form a vast electrical circuit—an electrified Gaia, so to speak—and this formed the basis for his work on wireless energy transmission. "It would seem," said Tesla, "as though the Creator Himself had electrically designed this planet."

In his book *Sacred Geometry*, Robert Lawlor writes that, "The morphic similarity between lightning and the root of a plant is also functionally accurate. Science now speculates that early in earth's evolution, horrendous lightning storms in the atmosphere provided energetic ul-

tra-violet light, which transformed methane, hydrogen, nitrogen, and carbonic gases into proto-molecules for organic compounds. These molecules were deposited by torrential rains into the primal seas, out of which life arose."[63] William Marks adds, "We begin to see how a physical form that looks like a plant root, such as lightning, a river's imprint with its tributaries, or the flow of water underground are all associated in some way with water, transformation, creation, and life."[12]

Schumann Resonance (SR) is global electromagnetic resonance that occurs in the extremely low frequency (ELF) portion of the Earth's electromagnetic field spectrum, between 3 and 69 Hz. Lightning discharges excite SR in the cavity formed by the Earth's conducting surface and the ionosphere, thus replenishing the Earth with free electrons.

Tesla transmitted extremely low frequencies (ELF) through the ground and between the Earth's surface and the Kennelly-Heaviside layer of the ionosphere. He patented wireless transceivers that developed standing waves, and it was he who discovered that the resonant frequency of the Earth was about 8 Hz and in the range of the Schumann Resonance / Cavity. I talk more about Tesla's work and the Schumann Resonance in Chapter 7, *Water Is Vibration*.

Photo 2.15: Relaxing on Cherry Beach on the shores of Lake Ontario, Toronto, Canada.

Tesla was influenced by the Vedic teachings of the Swami Vivekananda and used his spiritual beliefs and the science of the ancient scriptures of the Vedas (*prana*, *akasha* and concepts of "ether") to describe the physics of the universe.

Tesla and other scientists of his time first measured the Earth's subtle ground currents, describing them as "tranquil" and "quiet." A function of radiation effects on the ionosphere, these "telluric currents" of extremely low frequency travel over large areas and help to form the larger "global electrical circuit." The global electrical circuit is powered by thunderstorms as well as precipitation, convection currents, and even blowing snow or dust.

Ancient cultures recognized the electrical potential and wellness aspects of connecting to the natural forces of earth, wind, rain and sun.

Photo by Nina Munteanu

The Chinese use the term *Qi* (or *chi*, pronounced "chee") to describe the natural force and energy that fills the universe. The Chinese practice of "growing a root" refers to opening up communication between the bottom of the feet and the Earth. *Prana*, which means "vital force," is a similar term in India's Vedic tradition. The *Tadasana* (yoga Mountain Pose), connects you from ground to sky as you stand firm and stretch up with arms aimed high above you.

Ober and his colleagues retell the ancient Greek myth of how Hercules defeated the giant Antaeus, a wrestler who remained invincible as long as his feet remained in contact with the Earth, from where he drew his strength. Hercules, who knew Antaeus's secret, lifted the giant off the ground to dispatch him.[62] In my own metaphoric science fiction tale *The Splintered Universe*, human detective Rhea Hawke visits a planet inhabited by an alien species called the Konsus. These bird-like creatures, who resemble the ancient Egyptian god Horus, are the great and wise librarians of the universe, drawing their splendid abilities from the planet's own reservoir of gentle and eternal energies. But, once a Konsus leaves his or her planet and his connection with its energy, he loses his integrity, common sense, and ultimately, his mind.[64]

Documented benefits of Earthing include improvements to afflictions such as: inflammation, chronic pain, lack of sleep, lethargy, stress, high blood pressure, muscle tension and headaches, jet lag, and abnormal body rhythms.[62]

The late Ota Kre (Luther Standing Bear), tribal leader of the Lakota Sioux, wrote: "The old people came literally to love the soil. They sat on the ground with the feeling of being close to a mothering power. It was good for the skin to touch the Earth, and the old people liked to remove their moccasins and walk with their bare feet on the sacred Earth. The soil was soothing, strengthening, cleansing and healing."[62]

"Glorious Sea, Sacred Baikal"

I remember first learning about Lake Baikal, a rift lake located in the mountains of southeast Siberia near the Mongolian border, in my introductory limnology class at university. Formed by movements of the deeper portions of the Earth's crust (faulting), limnologists classify Lake Baikal as a graben lake (other examples of *graben* lakes include Lake Tahoe in California and Pyramid Lake in Nevada).[65] Lake Baikal is the world's deepest lake and considered the world's oldest lake (at 25 million years), as well as one of the world's clearest. Lake Baikal is the seventh largest lake in the world by surface area and the largest by volume, containing about a fifth of the Earth's freshwater. The lake supports more endemic (native) species of plants and animals than any other lake on Earth—including nerpa (*Pusasibirica*), an exclusively freshwater seal—with many found nowhere else in the world. Lake Baikal was declared a UNESCO World Heritage Site in 1996.[12,65]

The lake's unusual water clarity (you can see down some 130 feet below the surface) is partly due to a large population of small crustaceans or copepods (*Epishura baikalensis*) that feed on algae and particulates in the water. Baikal's deep waters are described as deep-sea indigo that shifts to a bluish-green in the late summer, as plankton thrive. Science writer William Marks shares that people prone to vertigo are cautioned: "When taking a peek over the side of a boat, some have become nauseous at suddenly finding themselves looking down at what appears to be a drop of hundreds of feet into the depths far below the clear surface waters."[12]

Lake Baikal has been long known for its spiritual and healing qualities and these qualities have intrigued scientists and healers from around the world. It is called "Sacred Sea" and its water described as "living water," given its unusual ability to support diverse life forms to unusual depths, including larger than normal biota. This is partly because the lake remains well oxygenated to its bottom depths. In most lakes, organic build-up at the bottom takes up oxygen, often creating an anoxic or less-oxygenated profundal zone (bottom depths). Scientists have recently explained that underwater venting of hot, oxygenated water combines with Lake Baikal's horizontal and vertical currents to keep it oxygenated.

I talk more about "living water" and "sacred water" in Chapter 10, *Water Is Prayer.*

Photo 2.16: *Sand dunes of the Rub' al Khali (Empty Quarter), the largest contiguous sand desert in the world that includes Saudi Arabia, Oman, United Arab Emirates and Yemen.*

Photo by Nepenthes, Wikimedia Commons

Living Without Water

In Frank Hebert's classic ecological science fiction book *Dune*, the *Fremen* (the planet's indigenous inhabitants) had developed frugal habits to survive the harsh desert climate, particularly water conservation. To the *Fremen* water was life.[66]

Fremen wore complex full-body filtration systems called *still suits* that recycled the body's moisture. Specialized headgear prevented additional loss through the scalp and forehead through perspiration; masks and nose plugs reclaimed breath moisture. Gloves were also available, but many *Fremen* preferred to just rub the juice of the creosote bush on their hands to prevent perspiration. Inside a good working *still suit*, a *Fremen* lost only about a thimbleful of water a day. To a *Fremen*, her water belonged to her tribe. So, when a *Fremen* died, she was rendered down into water and returned to the tribe.

Desert plants and animals have formed interesting adaptations to live successfully in the desert biome. For instance, many desert plants that need to carry out photosynthesis use a process called *crassulacean acid metabolism*, which allows them to open their stomata to allow in carbon dioxide at night when it's cooler and they are less likely to lose water through evapotranspiration. Some plants, like cacti, have reduced or abandoned leaves altogether. Some desert plants produce seeds that lie dormant until rain falls; these will grow, flower, and seed rapidly before the water dries up. Many desert animals and plants have co-evolved to succeed in deserts, developing harmonizing *mutual* (both benefit) and *commensal* (one benefits and the other remains unaffected) relationships for greater success. An example of mutualism is the flycatcher (*Phainopepla*) that feeds on mistletoe berries and disperses the undigested seeds in the surroundings through its droppings. In this way, the mistletoe provides food to the bird (resource benefit), while the flycatcher helps the mistletoe spread (service benefit).

In my story *Inner Diverse* (Book 2 of *The Splintered Universe*), detective Rhea Hawke must traverse the vast desert of Upsilon 3, under the beating heat of Upsilon Andromedae. There, she uncovers a sophisticated ecological web that includes the xerophytic *cozu* bush, mice-like *cobals* and the ferocious dingo-like *blenoids*. Hawke learns that the blenoid population possess complementary physiologies in which one's waste is nutritional to the other's and the eating of each other's feces is practiced regularly.[67]

The deserts of the world have been home to humans for millennia. The Bushmen of the Kalahari, the Aborigines of Australia, and various tribes of North American Indians hunted and gathered in the desert. Like other life that was adapted to this ecosystem, these largely nomadic people were creative in using the natural environment to supply their everyday needs. They became proficient in weaponry, animal tracking, finding water and foraging for edible plants. Skills were passed down through the generations. They herded camels, yaks, llamas, and sheep and goats and traveled over vast expanses, following the erratic rains. They traded slaves, ivory, gold and salt. Berbers, who knew the African desert well, guided caravans between oases and wells.

With more and more of us dwelling in areas of precarious water supply, the threat of water-related risk encroaches. Recent droughts threatened productivity in the USA. Monsoon floods killed and displaced many in India.

Nearly a billion people don't have access to good water.

The World Resources Institute (WRI) listed the 36 most water-stressed countries in 2013, based on freshwater supply and baseline water stress (how much is withdrawn from rivers, streams, and shallow aquifers per user per year). The countries included: Antigua & Barbuda; Bahrain; Barbados; Comoros; Cyprus; Dominica; Jamaica; Malta;

Qatar; Saint Lucia; Saint Vincent and the Grenadines; San Marino; Singapore; Trinidad and Tobago; United Arab Emirates; Western Sahara; Saudi Arabia; Kuwait; Oman; Libya; Israel; Kyrgystan; East Timor; Iran; Yemen; Palestine; Jordan; Lebanon; Somalia; Uzbekistan; Pakistan; Turkmenistan; Morocco; Mongolia; Kazakhstan; and Afghanistan.[68] A similar survey in 2014 by Global Research, ranked the ten top countries with most vulnerable water supplies from pollution and depletion of natural water resources from worst to least: (1) Somalia; (2) Mauritania; (3) Sudan; (4) Niger; (5) Iraq; (6) Usbekistan; (7) Pakistan; (8) Egypt; (9) Turkmenistan; and (10) Syria. Ranking integrated elements such as access to water, water demands, and the reliance on external supplies.[69]

The WRI notes that high water-stress need not translate into severe water scarcity and collapse of public supply. They provide the example of Singapore, which scores one of the highest on their water-stress ranking system. The country is densely populated, has no freshwater lake or aquifer and its demand for water exceeds its natural supply. Yet the country's exceptional water management through technology, international agreements, and responsible allocations allow it to meet its freshwater needs. Advanced rainwater capture systems capture 20 percent, 40 percent is imported from Malaysia, grey water reuse adds 30 percent, and desalination provides the remaining 10 percent needed to meet the country's total demand.[68]

Pakistan, which appears on the water-scarce lists of both WRI and Global Research, is one of the world's most arid regions. Its public water supply is currently in a state of collapse. While the country could solve many of its problems with practical and innovative water management systems, such as collecting and storing rainwater (e.g., piped roof water collection, or building ponds or small dams to allow the water table to rise), little of this is being done. It is equally interesting that Pakistan became the test market for *Nestlé Pure Life* bottled water, marketed as a healthy alternative, but out of reach for all but its elite.[70]

Photo 2.17: Collecting water in Mwamanongu Village, Tanzania. Water that comes from open holes dug in the sand of dry riverbeds, like this one, are often contaminated.

Photo by Bob Metcalf, Wikimedia Commons

In areas of high water scarcity such as Ethiopia, Niger and Haiti, women and young girls spend a good part of their day—at the expense of education—to collect and bring 40 or 50-pound containers of water back to their village.

National Geographic and *Mother Nature Network* (MNN) describe several lakes and rivers that are literally drying up due to overuse. MNN placed the Aral Sea as the number one "poster child" for large dried up bodies of water. Others include: Lake Chad, a shallow endorheic lake in Africa, which has lost 95 percent of its volume from 1963 to 1998 due to overgrazing and deforestation; the Colorado River, which used to run from the Rocky Mountains through four other U.S. states and Mexico before emptying in the Gulf of California, but now runs dry long before its mouth due to massive diversions to grow crops and hydrate towns and cities; Owens Lake, which used to average a depth of 23 to 50 feet, but is mostly dry and averages 3 feet due to massive diversions to Los Angeles; the Indus River, which no longer flows into the ocean at the Port of Karachi in Pakistan, due to overuse for agriculture; Lake Mead, in Nevada, which has lost 60 percent of its volume, due to persistent drought and increased demand; the Rio Grande River, one of the largest rivers in North America, which has lost more than 75 percent of its flow to the Gulf of Mexico due to heavy use; the Yellow River, second longest in China, which frequently runs dry before reaching the ocean; the Teesta River, fed by snowmelt in the Himalayas, which has largely dried up from irrigation; the Murray River in Australia, which barely flows to the ocean due to heavy irrigation use.[71,72]

Sustainability & the Lesson of Angkor

The over-exploitation of water by a thirsty burgeoning civilization has been occurring for millennia and on a vast scale. The ancient Khmer Empire of Angkor, in what is now Cambodia, dug reservoirs and an underground irrigation system to store water from the monsoon rains throughout the drought season; their water-harnessing ingenuity allowed Angkor to become the largest pre-industrial city in the world.

The water system spanned over 1200 square kilometres and connected the natural lake (Tonle Sap) to the artificial reservoirs (*barays*) via a series of canals. The 12th century "temple-mountain" Angkor Wat was built as a spiritual home for the Hindu god Vishnu.

Angkor flourished for six centuries. However, the impact of water management to sustain a growing population, along with deforestation practices and other watershed alterations, eventually led to erosion, which choked the system with sediment and rendered it unmanageable. By the 15th century, Angkor collapsed—a victim of its own success. The empire had outstripped its resources. Somehow, in their success, the Khmer empire had crossed the threshold from healthy adaptation to unsustainable expansionism, to achieve the fate of all great civilizations whose mandate is to "conquer Nature": collapse.

Photo 2.18: The South Gate of Angkor Thom, Cambodia

Photo by Baldiri, Wikimedia Commons

What Was Once the Aral Sea

"Even a light wind picks up the salts and the dust and turns the air hazy, like heat shimmering in a mirage,"[52] writes Marq de Villiers in his 1999 book *Water*. "When the winds are stronger, the white clouds drift higher and deeper and the sky is opaque like milk." Farms nearby look as if they've been dusted with white snow. If you drive to Muynak, once on the shore of the Aral when it was the fourth largest lake in the world, the view from the ridge is a depressing expanse of sand. Dilapidated husks of fishing vessels and barges and bones of cattle—detritus from a once thriving fishing culture—litter the desert. The Aral Sea has shrunk to a tenth of its original size in less than five decades, through the hubristic mining of inflowing water.[73,74,75]

In the 1960s the Aral Sea, which ran the border between Kazakhstan and Uzbekistan in central Asia, was roughly half the size of England. Then the Soviet Union began diverting the two rivers that flow into the Aral Sea, the Amu and Syr, for irrigation to grow cotton and wheat. Now the Aral Sea is almost completely gone.

Aral Sea is an *endorheic* lake (a closed basin that does not flow into the sea). Watersheds of endorheic lakes are often confined by natural geologic land formations (such as a mountain range), which cut off water flow to the ocean. Since the outflow pathways of these lakes are chiefly through evaporation and seepage, endorheic lakes are usually more sensitive to environmental pollutant inputs than water bodies that have access to oceans, as pollution can be trapped in them and accumulate over time.

The Amu and Syr rivers provided the lion's share of freshwater to the Aral, in a system that covered 1.5 km^2 and supported some 35 million people. When the Soviet Union left the region, it abandoned the scattered republics (Turkmenistan, Uzbekistan, Kazakhstan, Kirgistan and Tajikistan) to wrestle with the dregs of what some are calling a "quiet Chernobyl." It is certainly one of the greatest recent ecological disasters created by humanity's greed, hubris, ignorant politics and total lack of compassion—for other humans and for the environment.

Historically, there had always been some agriculture in the region, where mostly nomadic people pursued small-scale farming with sustainable irrigation. The Aral remained untouched. In the 1930s, the Soviet Union expanded its cotton industry and within a decade, with the help of mechanized agriculture, Turkmenistan and Uzbekistan became major growers of cotton, wheat, and other food grains. Cornfields and cattle ranches appeared where nothing had grown before, with the help of massive irrigation and diversion projects. Between 1956 and 1960 major canals were built to divert water from the Amu into the Usbek and Kazakh deserts, irrigating millions of hectares. But the rivers drained to a trickle and the massive lake shrank. By 1962, the village of Muynak, once an island on the Amu Delta, had become a peninsula, fishing wharves and landing areas abandoned. A decade later, the nearest water was over 40 km away. By 1998, it was 75 km away. The Aral seabed had become a desert and 90 percent of the Aral Sea's volume had disappeared. [73,74,75]

By the late 70s, the commercial fishery had declined by over 75 percent and then collapsed a few years later. Between 1987 and 1989 the water dropped severely, splitting the sea into two: the small northern Aral and the large southern Aral. Port towns were left stranded. Ecological effects rippled throughout the entire area as oases disappeared with the dropping water table, and wildlife disappeared with them.

The local climate changed, no longer regulated by the large body of water. The Aral Sea, like all great waterbodies and their associated vegetation, had provided a buffer for seasonal temperature fluctuations, tempering the winter storms from Siberia. The climate took on an edge and became unruly—with a vengeance.

The increasingly salty water of the Aral Sea concentrated fertilizers and pesticides. Salty contaminated dust blew off the exposed lakebed, estimated at about 40 million tons every year, and settled onto fields where it degraded the soil. It turned into a public health hazard, causing respiratory illnesses and cancers. The dust was reported as far away as Belarus, 2,000 km to the west, and in Pakistan to the east, writes de Villiers.[52]

On his experience some two decades ago in Bukhara, the capital of Uzbekistan, De Villiers writes, "I flew into Bukhara from Samarkand late one October afternoon on a rattling little Aeroflot flight out of Dushanbe. There was a dust storm in the region … The air was stifled by roiling clouds of sooty dust called a 'black blizzard' by the locals. Dust choked everything in the town. There was grit on the floors, grit on the hotel beds, grit in the cars, grit on the restaurant tables, grit in the food. The sun was still up, but it was already dark, like a badly lit *film noir.*"[52]

In the early 1990s, the five Aral Basin states pledged to cooperate to save the Aral Sea, although little was actually done. However, in 2005, Kazakhstan built a dam in an attempt to refill part of the sea, which has resulted in slight rise of the water level and somewhat revived the fishing industry. If restoration efforts continue, "A substantial recovery might be achieved within 20 years," says the United Nations Environment Program, "although, it is doubtful that the Aral Sea will ever be restored to the conditions that existed before the large-scale diversion of its inflowing rivers."[73]

In 2014, Brian Clark Howard reported in the National Geographic that the Aral Sea's Eastern Basin was dry for the first time in 600 years.[73] This, thanks to continued irrigation and recent droughts—droughts partly due to local climate change as a result of human-created desertification. Recent images from NASA revealed the complete loss of the eastern lobe of the sea.[75]

Life is sacred and flows with holy expression. Energetic, invigorating, and bracing, life fertilizes all Being to become more than Itself.

Life is water.

Photo 2.19: Aerial view of the Aral Sea in 1989 and 2014

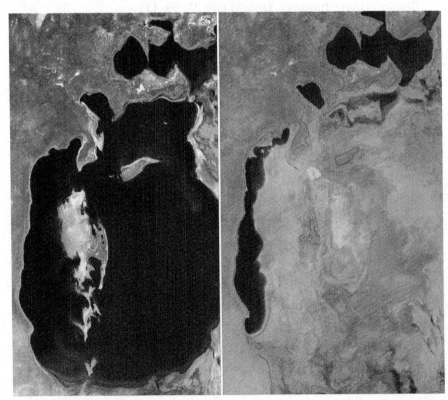

Photo by NASA, Wikimedia Commons

References

1. Cronin, J.R. and S.Pizzarello. 1997. "Enantiomeric Excesses in Meteoritic Amino Acids". *Science* 275: 951–955.

2. Grossman, Lisa. 2011. "Water's Quantum Weirdness Makes Life Possible." *The New Scientist* 2835. October 25, 2011. Online: http://www.newscientist.com/article/mg21228354.900-waters-quantum-weirdness-makes-life-possible.html#.VWKQ3Etgrlw

3. Denton, Michael J. 2002. "Nature's Destiny: How the Laws of Biology Reveal Purpose in the Universe". Free Press, New York, NY. 480 pp.

4. Kluger, Jeffrey. 2015. "Life as We Don't Know It". *Time Magazine The Search for Life in the Universe*. Single issue, June 19, 2015. 94 pp.

5. Bonner, William. 1991. "The Origin and Amplification of Biomolecular Chirality". *Origins Life* 21: 59–111.

6. Lazcano, A. J.L. Bada. 2004. "The 1953 Stanley L. Miller Experiment: Fifty Years of Prebiotic Organic Chemistry". *Origins of Life and Evolution of Biospheres* 33 (3): 235–242.

7. Lemonick, Michael. 2015. "Neighborhood Watch: Life in Our Solar System". *Time Magazine The Search for Life in the Universe*. Single issue, June 19, 2015. 94 pp.

8. Sample, Ian. 2015. "NASA Finds Evidence of a Vast Ancient Ocean on Mars". *The Guardian*, March 5, 2015. Online: http://www.theguardian.com/science/2015/mar/05/nasa-finds-evidence-of-a-vast-ancient-ocean-on-mars

9. O'Kane, Sean. 2014. "Mars' Gale Crater Once Held Massive Lake, NASA says". *The Verge*, December 8, 2014. Online: http://www.theverge.com/2014/12/8/7354299/new-nasa-findings-show-gale-crater-once-held-a-massive-lake

10. Gronstal, Aaron L. 2014. "Curiosity Detects Methane and Organic Molecules in Gale Crater". *Astrobiology Magazine*, December 19, 2014. Online: http://www.astrobio.net/news-exclusive/curiosity-detects-methane-organic-molecules-gale-crater/#sthash.9bK5BUch.dpuf

11. Sample, Ian. 2015. "Nasa scientists find evidence of flowing water on Mars". *The Guardian*. Online: http://www.theguardian.com/science/2015/sep/28/nasa-scientists-find-evidence-flowing-water-mars

12. Marks, William. 2001. "The Holy Order of Water." *Bell Pond Books*. 256 pp.

13. Deasey, Louise. 2015. "Negative Ions Are Great for Your Health". *Body and Soul*.

14. Robbins, Jim. 2012. "The Man Who Plants Trees". *Spiegel & Grau*, New York. 256 pp.

15. Bartholomew, Alick. 2010. "The Spiritual Life of Water". Park Street Press, Rochester Vermont. 338 pp.

16. Spracklen, Dominick V., Boris Bonn, and Kenneth S. Carslaw. 2008. "Boreal Forests, Aerosols and the Impacts on Clouds and Climate". *Phil. Trans. R. Soc. A* 366: 4613–4626.

17. Beresford–Kroeger, Diana. 2003. "Arboretum America: A Philosophy of the Forest." *University of Michigan Regional.* 214 pp.

18. Baldwin, Ian and Jack Schultz. 1983. "Rapid Changes in Tree Leaf Chemistry Induced by Damage: Evidence for Communication Between Plants". *Science* 221 (4607): 277–279.

19. Farmer, Edward E. and Clarence A. Ryan. 1990. "Interplant Communication: Airborne Methyl Jasmonate Induces Synthesis of Proteinase Inhibitors in Plant Leaves". PNAS 87: 7713–7716.

20. Karban, R., K. Shiojiri, M. Huntzinger, and A.C. McCall. 2006. "Damaged-induced Resistance in Sagebrush: Volatiles are Key to Intra- and Interplant Communication". *Ecol. Soc. Amer.* 87(4): 922–930.

21. Wells, Nancy M. 2000. "At Home with Nature: Effects of 'Greenness' on Children's Cognitive Functioning". *Environment and Behavior* 32 (6): 775–795.

22. Hance, Jeremy. 2012. "New Meteorological Theory Argues that the World's Forests are Rainmakers". Mongabay, February 1, 2012. Online: http://news.mongabay.com/2012/02/new-meteorological-the-ory-argues-that-the-worlds-forests-are-rainmakers/

23. Lovelock, James. 2010. "The Vanishing Face of Gaia". *Basic Books*. 278 pp.

24. Lovelock, J.E. 1972. "Gaia as Seen Through the Atmosphere". *Atmospheric Environment*, Elsevier Science 6: 579–80.

25. Ball, Philip. 2000. "H2O: A Biography of Water". *Phoenix*. London, UK. 387 pp.

26. Lovelock, J.E. and L. Margulis. 1974." Atmospheric Homeostasis by and for the Biosphere: the Gaia Hypothesis". *Tellus: a bimonthly journal of Geophysics*, Swedish Geophysical Society 26(1): 2–10.

27. Lovelock, James. 1979. "Gaia: A New Look at Life on Earth". 3rd Edition. *Oxford University Press*. 176 pp.

28. Lovelock, James. 1988. "Ages of Gaia". *Oxford University Press*. 288 pp.

29. Margulis, Lynn. 1981. "Symbiosis in Cell Evolution". *W.H. Freeman & Company*. 419 pp.

30. Margulis, Lynn. 1998. "Symbiotic Planet: a New Look at Evolution". *Weidenfeld & Nicolson*, London. 176 pp.

31. Sagan, Carl. 1976. "Astronomer Carl Sagan Describes Significance of *Viking 1* Landing on Mars". NBC Nightly News, July 20, 1976. Online: http://archives.nbclearn.com/portal/site/k-12/flatview?cuecard=60248.

32. Kluger, Jeffrey. 2015. "Extremophiles". In: *Time: The Search for Life in the Universe*. June 19, 2015. 94 pp.

33. Szent-Györgyi, Albert. 1957. "Bioenergetics". *Academic Press*. 139 pp.

34. Voeikov, V.L. and E. Del Guidice. 2009. "Water Respiration—The Basis of the Living State". *Water* 1: 52–75.

35. Bauer, E.S. 1935. "Theoretical Biology". *VIEM Publishing House*, Moscow–Leningrad.

36. Schödinger, E. 1944. "What is Life?" *Cambridge University Press*.

37. Collini, Elisabetta, Cathy Y. Wong, Krystyna E. Wilk, Paul M.G. Curmi, Paul Brumer and Gregory D. Scholes. 2010. "Coherently Wired Light-harvesting in Photosynthetic Marine Algae at Ambient Temperature". *Nature* 463 (7281): 644–648.

38. Jankowski, T. 2000. "Chemical Composition and Biomass Parameters of a population of *Craspeda custasowerbii* Lank 1880 (Cnidaria:

Limnomedusa)". *J. Plankton Res.* 22: 1329–1340.

39. Pollack, G.H. 2001. "Cells, Gels and Engines of Life". *Ebner and Sons*, Seattle. 305 pp.

40. Campbell, Joseph and Bill Moyers. 1991. "The Power of Myth". *Anchor.* 293 pp.

41. Freitas Jr., Robert A. 1999. "Nanomedicine: Volume I." *Landes Bioscience.* Tables 3–1 and 3–2.

42. Batmanghelidj, F. 2008. "Your Body's Many Cries for Water". Global Health Solutions, Inc., 3rd ed. 196 pp.

43. Chan, J. 2002."Water, Other Fluids, and Fatal Coronary Heart Disease". *Am. J. Epidem.* 155 (9): 827–833.

44. Anonymous. 2008. "Bottled Water Vs. Tap Water: Rethink What You Drink". *Reader's Digest*, February issue. Online: http://www.rd.com/ health/wellness/rethink-what-you-drink/.

45. Recycle Across America. 2014. "Recycling Facts". Online: http://recycleacrossamerica.org/recycling-facts

46. Canadian Council of Canadians. 2011. "News: Barlow challenges Nestle's 'bully tactics' in Guelph". Online: http://canadians.org/ node/6826

47. Barlow, Maude. 2007. "Our Water Commons: Toward a new freshwater narrative". The Council of Canadians. Online: http://canadians.org/sites/default/files/publications/water%20commons%20-%20 web.pdf

48. Airola, P. 1974. "How To Get Well". *Health Plus Publishers*, Phoenix, AZ. 304 pp.

49. Baroody, Dr. Theodore A. Jr. 1995. "Alkalize or Die". *Portal Books.* 242 pp.

50. Haas, Elson M. 1992. "Staying Healthy with Nutrition. The Complete Guide to Diet and Nutritional Medicine". *Celestial Arts*, Berkley, CA. 944 pp.

51. Rona, Zoltan P. and J.M. Martin. 1995. "Return to the Joy of Health". *Alive Books*, Vancouver. 407 pp.

52. de Villiers, Marq. 1999. "Water". *Stoddart*. 422 pp.

53. Pollack, Gerald. 2013. "The Fourth Phase of Water: Beyond Solid, Liquid, and Vapor". Ebner & Sons. 357 pp.

54. Pollack, G. et al. 2009. "Molecules, Water, and Radiant Energy: New Clues for the Origin of Life." *Int. Mol. Sci.* 10(4): 1419–29.

55. Ho, Mae-Wan. 1998. "The Rainbow and the Worm: The Physics of Organisms". 2nd ed. World Scientific Publishing. 380 pp.

56. Pischinger, A. 2007. "The Extracellular Matrix and Ground Regulation". North Atlantic Books. 232 pp.

57. Ling, G.N. 2001."Life at the Cell and Below-Cell Level: The Hidden History of a Fundamental Revolution in Biology". *Pacific Press*, NY. 373 pp.

58. Pal et al. 2003. "Water at DNA surfaces: Ultrafast Dynamics in Minor Groove Recognition". PNAS 100 (14): 8113–8118.

59. Jhon, M.S. 2004. "The Water Puzzle and the Hexagonal Key". Uplifting Press, Inc. 101 pp.

60. Pangman, M.J. & Melanie Evans. 2011. "Dancing with Water: the New Science of Water". *Uplifting Press, Inc.* 255 pp.

61. Mercola, Joseph. 2013. "The Fourth Phase of Water—What You Don't Know About Water, and Really Should". Mercola.com. Online: http://articles.mercola.com/sites/articles/archive/2013/08/18/exclusion-zone-water.aspx

62. Ober, Clinton, S.T. Sinatra, and M. Zucker. 2010. "Earthing." *Basic Health Publications*, Inc. 260 pp.

63. Lawlor, Robert. 1982. "Sacred Geometry". *Thames & Hudson, Ltd.* 112 pp.

64. Munteanu, Nina. 2011. "Outer Diverse". *Starfire World Syndicate*. 324 pp.

65. Wetzel, Robert. 2001. "Limnology". 3rd Edition. Academic Press. 1006 pp.

66. Hebert, Frank. 1965. "Dune". *Ace*. 896 pp.

67. Munteanu, Nina. 2012. "Inner Diverse". *Starfire World Syndicate*. 344 pp.

68. Reig, Paul, Andrew Maddocks and Francis Gassert. 2013. "World's

36 Most Water-Stressed Countries". *World Resources Institute*. December 12, 2013. Online: http://www.wri.org/blog/2013/12/world's-36-most-water-stressed-countries

69. Global Research. 2014. "Top Ten Countries at Risk of Water Shortages". Global Research, June 3, 2014. Online: http://www.globalresearch.ca/top-ten-countries-at-risk-of-water-shortages/19996

70. Schnell, Urs. 2012. "Bottled Life: Nestlé's Business with Water". Documentary by Schnell, Drewing, and Hunziker. 90 min.

71. Howard, Brian Clark. 2015. "8 Mighty Rivers Run Dry from Overuse". *National Geographic*. Online: http://environment.nationalgeographic.com/environment/photos/rivers-run-dry/

72. Mother Nature Network. 2015. "7 Lakes and Rivers that are Drying Up". August 12, 2015. Online: http://www.mnn.com/earth-matters/wilderness-resources/photos/7-lakes-and-rivers-that-are-drying-up/bone-dry

73. Schultz, Collin. 2014. "The Aral Sea is Pretty Much Gone". Smithsonian.com. Online: http://www.smithsonianmag.com/smart-news/aral-sea-pretty-much-gone-180952914/?no-ist

74. Howard, Brian Clark. 2014. "Aral Sea's Eastern Basin Is Dry for First Time in 600 Years". *National Geographic.*Online: http://news.nationalgeographic.com/news/2014/10/141001-aral-sea-shrinking-drought-water-environment/

75. Liston, Enjoli. 2014. "Satellite Images Show Aral Sea Basin 'Completely Dried'". *The Guardian*. Online: http://www.theguardian.com/world/2014/oct/01/satellite-images-show-aral-sea-basin-completely-dried

3. Water is Motion

Photo 3.1: The author photographing the rapids of the Upper Credit River, Ontario, Canada.

"I had fewer difficulties in discovering the motions of the heavenly bodies, despite their incredible distances, than I did in investigating the motion of flowing water, something that takes place before our eyes."
—Galileo Galilei

The Chinese character for water, "sui", is composed of three rippled lines that indicate flowing water. Water in Chinese always refers to flowing water or moving water, reflecting water as dynamic, moving and playing. Water is always moving, even when it isn't.

Much of water's motion is invisible to us, either by being too small to see or without the right conditions. Water constantly moves: from microscopic Brownian movement and cytoplasmic streaming to the spray and turbulence of waterfalls and surging ocean currents to the swirling vapour from a hot coffee and chaotic billows of clouds. Water moves within a phase (e.g., liquid) and between phases (e.g., liquid to vapour).

"It is the living movement of water that makes life on earth possible,"[1] say Theodor Schwenk and Wolfram Schwenk, scientists at the Institute of Flow Sciences in Herrischried, Germany. Water is dynamic, continually transforming, seemingly chaotic and always in motion. Leonardo da Vinci called rivers the blood of the Earth and commented on how the channels of a river resemble the veins of the human body.[2]

Illustration 3.1: Sui (water)—squeezing the river for water. The ancient Chinese considered that if you squeeze a river (3 swirled lines) you get water.

Illustration by Kerste Voute

"[Water] is never at rest until it unites with the sea," he said. "Without it, nothing retains its form."[3]

The movement of water in and between any of its phases is not easily described or calculated. A whole science (Fluid Mechanics) evolved and has yet to describe it fully. The science helps little to elucidate why fluids possess "such an unnerving propensity for pattern,"[2] says science writer Philip Ball, author of *Flow*. Moreover, the theory of fluid dynamics lacks a definitive understanding of turbulence.

Andreas Wilkens, Michael Jacobi, and Wolfram Schwenk, scientists at the Institute of Flow Sciences in Herrischried, Germany, and authors of *Understanding Water*, suggest that it is impossible to describe the variety of manifestations of water with static concepts. Water, they say, naturally meanders, spirals, and creates sinuous patterns in space—patterns that reflect the vortex or eddy.[4]

Flow lies at the heart of our vibrant world: the cascade of a water spout; the undulation of a woman's tresses; curling smoke and coiling vegetation; the shear flow of Jupiter's Red Eye Spot or Saturn's hexagonal storm. A correspondence pattern of flow is at work.

Chinese artists strove to imbue their art with Chi (or Qi), the vital energy of the universe.[2] Circulation of Chi produces movement of life, the 17th century painter's manual *The Mustard Seed Garden* tells us. The ancient painters of China used to teach, "Take five days to place water in a picture."[2]

"What could be more representative of the Tau (a symbol for dynamic life and resurrection, or Chi) than the currents of a river swirling around rocks?"[2] Ball shares. The universe is a turbulent place. Interstellar turbulence, for instance, causes the "twinkling" of radio sources just as turbulence in the Earth's atmosphere makes stars twinkle. Turbulence, Ball tells us, is normally associated with unpredictable chaos; and yet, he points out, from this chaotic flow emerges a kernel of order in the vortex or eddy form. A kind of self-organized stable chaos; like Kármán vortex streets (alternating swirls caused by a separation of flow around a

Photo 3.2: Patterns of water swirling around a rock, Upper Credit River, Caledon, Ontario, Canada.

Photo by Nina Munteanu

blunt body) or the Kelvin-Helmholtz instability of vortex waves when two different fluids with different velocities or directions pass each other as in Jupiter's Great Red Spot. I talk more about these features of flow in Chapter 8, *Water Is Beauty*.

Da Vinci considered the vortex a fundamental feature of flow.[2]

"The vortex is the mediator between the polarity of motion and stillness,"[4] say Wilkins, Jacobi, and Schwenk. Quiescence and motion, vortex generation, metamorphosis, decay and again quiescence, in a continual cycle of motion and transformation: it is creative destruction.

The cycling Ouroboros.

Just as non-random order emerges from the self-organized landslides of building and moving sand dunes or snow avalanches, turbulent water contains organized motion that spawns vortices. "Experiments have shown, not only that there are correlations in turbulence," Ball writes, "but that these have a remarkably long reach, generally extending over almost the entire width of the flow. It is as though individuals in a jabbering crowd were able to converse with one another from opposite sides of the room."[2] These correlations give rise to the "elegant, baroque beauty" of turbulence: from Leonardo da Vinci's scientific empiricism with eddies[2] to Van Gogh's technically accurate portrayal of the vortex form in art.

Vincent van Gogh's well-known painting *Starry Night* intuited the deep mathematical structure of turbulent flow with remarkable accuracy. A team of scientists led by physicist José Luis Aragón recently tested van Gogh's swirly style using a statistical distribution specified by Russian mathematician Andrey Kolmogorov in his 1941 theory for genuine turbulent flow.[5] Van Gogh completed *Starry Night* during his residence in a mental asylum at St-Rémy. His *Road with Cypress and Star* and *Wheat Field with Crows*, painted during his period of mental instability in the Saint-Paul Asylum, also accurately represented Kolmogorov's turbulence. His own turbulent mind had somehow tapped into the mathematical truth of turbulent flow in Nature.

Figure 3.1: The Starry Night *painted in 1889 by Vincent van Gogh.*

Museum of Modern Art, New York, NY

From Coffee to Clouds

"Everything flows, out and in; the pendulum-swing manifests in everything; the measure of the swing to the right is the measure of the swing to the left—rhythm compensates."
—Hermes Trismegistus (Thoth)

When I was growing up in the Eastern Townships of Quebec, Canada, I enjoyed lazy summer days, lying on the grass and staring up at the puffs of clouds that glided across the azure sky above me. I'd pick a favourite cloud and follow it as it shape-shifted from one form to another. I used to wonder what determined its motion-dance and often imagined myself up there, flying within the cloud, touching its fractal secrets.

High school geography taught me about the water cycle, that clouds form through condensation of water vapour and that their colour and form provide clues to their origin and to weather. (For example, dark and towering cumulonimbus clouds are formed by water vapour condensing onto organic particles carried by powerful upward air currents, and often leading to a thunderstorm. Thin, wispy cirrus clouds are clouds that condense and freeze, or nucleate, on very specific mineral and metal particles high in the atmosphere.)[6]

Some of the answers still elude me. Water is mysterious.

One of the best opportunities for me to watch rising vapour is during one of my favourite pastimes: drinking a flat white in a fine coffeehouse while writing my next novel. Have you ever noticed how the coffee-foam surface forms a mosaic pattern of light and dark swirling tones? Or how the vapour rises in a series of puffs and thin streams that coil and swirl? It's actually quite mesmerizing.

Those patterns are self-organizing non-linear "cells" that naturally form in heated fluid. The phenomenon, called Rayleigh–Bénard convection, reflects temperature gradients. The hotter liquid from beneath, being less dense, travels up toward the cooler surface. The upwelling spontaneously organizes into a regular pattern of cells as surrounding fluid cools through evaporation and falls. This happens as you heat water too, except you don't see it as you can with a cup of coffee.[7]

Gerald Pollack, professor of bioengineering at the University of Washington and author of *The Fourth Phase of Water*, provides another interpretation to the mosaic patterns: one based on order, fluid structure or boundaries, and electrostatic charge. According to Pollack, the upward force that lifts water vapour, and causes those visible puffs and streams, is not just a function of lower density (of water vapour molecules vs. air molecules), but also of electrostatic lifting. Pollack proposes that *vesicles* (a networked structure of water) self-assemble to form *tubes*, seen as mosaic cells from the surface, and once they acquire a sufficient negative charge they escape the water as emerging puffs of vapour. Given that the water vapour vesicles or clusters are negatively charged, the Earth's negative charge would repel the vesicles, pushing them upward.[8]

Photo 3.3: Cumulo-nimbus clouds in Quebec, Canada.

Photo by Nina Munteanu

Photo 3.4: Rum heating in a Lunenburg keel-laying celebration, Nova Scotia, Canada.

Photo by Nina Munteanu

Running Water

When I was ten years old, my family visited Niagara Falls. My dad found a parking spot far away from the falls and, for my little feet, it seemed as though we walked for miles to the falls. The prize was worth it, though. Our final destination was the small fenced off promontory adjacent to the Horseshoe Falls, where 2,400 m³/s of water cascade over a pressurized limestone rock cap down 670 metres, sending almost the same height of spray above it. Soaked and in pure bliss, a thrill beat inside me as I stood so close to the falls that I felt as if I could almost touch that smooth green mass of water. Inexplicably drawn to it, I watched that powerful green water spill over the edge with an absurdly calming effect. I imagined myself flying over with it—as I'm sure we all do—and felt exhilarated, terrified and somehow free in it.

I was following a river, falling.

We walked upstream from the falls, along the Niagara River, to where one-story high standing waves, whirlpools and surges equally hypnotized. The water rushed with incredible speed (actually 40 km/hr), as if in a great hurry to reach the falls, and the volume carried over the falls was beyond imagining. It's actually falling at 168,000 m³/minute at 65 km/hr, making up one-fifth of the freshwater in the world (as part of the Great Lakes basin).[9] The startling green colour of the Niagara River is a visible tribute to its erosive power; the river sweeps about 60 tons of dissolved minerals over the falls every minute. These include dissolved salts and "rock flour" (very finely ground rock), picked up mainly from the limestone, marine shale, and exposed sandstones of the riverbed laid down during the Silurian period 430–390 million years ago.[9]

What struck my ten-year old mind was that it continued without end. Running water keeps running.

An entire branch has evolved within the science of limnology to study *lotic* (flowing) waters. This branch covers the study of streams and rivers and may include human-made channels and ditches, river-run reservoirs, and even *estuaries* (where a river empties into the ocean). This study intersects the *science of hydrology*, which investigates the movement, distribution and quality of water, with a focus on the hydrological cycle.

Limnologists describe three general types of water movement: (1) laminar; (2) surge; and (3) turbulent. Other types of movement include eddy–diffusion (resulting from temperature/density gradients); surface waves (usually due to wind); standing waves (such as seiches) due to wind but also seismic events; tides; surface currents (due to the Coriolis Effect from Earth's rotation); and Langmuir circulation or streaks (also due to wind action).[10]

In flowing water—such as streams, rivers and sloughs—water is generally directed downward, based on gravity. The energy dissipated from the moving mass of water affects the morphology of the stream, how sediments flow and distribute, water chemistry, and the biology of its aquatic life.[10] The ecology of running waters differs from other aquatic ecosystems in a number of ways:

Photo 3.5: The Upper Credit River, Belfountain, Ontario, Canada.

- Running waters flow unidirectionally.
- They are continuously changing.
- They experience multi-level heterogeneity (i.e., from micro to macro scale), both spatially and temporally.
- Variability between streams is quite high.
- Running waters support a diverse life, adapted to flow conditions.

During my consulting years as limnologist in British Columbia, I had the chance to study one of Canada's largest river systems, the Fraser River Basin. The basin occupies almost a quarter of the western province, draining about 220,000 km²; it flows 1,375 km from a dripping spring in Fraser Pass and empties not far from my house in Delta, BC, into the Strait of Georgia. On its way there, the river passes through

Photo by Nina Munteanu

the Coast Mountains and through a narrow canyon known as Hell's Gate. I remember standing on the bridge constructed across the gorge for visiting tourists and peering down into the churning brown water. I'd read that the discharge that passes through that narrow canyon is twice that of Niagara Falls. The water is actually 100 m deep and at the *thalweg* (the line defining the lowest points along the length of a river bed; from German meaning "valley-way"), the discharge at high flow is the speed of a racing car at 76 m³/second.

Photo 3.6: Horseshoe Falls in winter, Niagara Falls, Ontario, Canada.

Photo by Nina Munteanu

Describing Flow

The nature of water flow, both velocity and form, varies according to the nature of the streambed, channel sides, sinuosity, obstructions, and incline gradient. The amount of water, whether from precipitation, snow-melt, or groundwater spring, will also affect the flow, which varies from riffle to glide to pool. Water moving over the Earth's natural surfaces causes whirlpools (vortices) and eddy currents (a reverse current to the main current created by water flowing past an obstacle).

Turbulence may be chaotic and destructive or chaotic and "purposeful". In shallow riffles, turbulent water brings in oxygen. A rock may create a long turbulent wake that introduces higher energy into the stream body, as well as providing a protected downstream surface for debris build-up and habitat creation for small invertebrates. When water reaches a deeper pool, it slows down and provides excellent resting and foraging habitat for fish and other aquatic life.

Rivers seldom run straight; their channels tend to meander, braid, and anastomose. Streams and rivers drain an area of land defined by geographic high points, called a drainage basin or watershed. When I look at a river drainage basin from above, with its many forks or tributaries that lead into a major system, I am reminded of lightning, the veins of a leaf, great trees, or an animal's circulatory system.

Rivers constitute an insignificant amount (0.1%) of Earth's land surface, Wetzel tells us. Yet, running waters, he reminds us, wield a major influence on humanity.[10] Rivers have been moving significant amounts of nutrients and sediment from one place to another for millennia and this determined where our ancient civilizations began. The civilization of ancient Egypt, for instance, relied on the seasonal flooding of the Nile River, rich in nutrients, to create a fertile valley that fed an empire.

There is something vital and majestic about our great rivers. "The great rivers of the world have a profound resonance, even for those who

Photo 3.7: Close-up of small cascade on the Credit River, Ontario, Canada.

Photo by Nina Munteanu

have never set eyes on them,"[11] Philip Ball, author of *H₂O: a Biography* shares. "The names alone are enough to conjure up dark tales of exploration and adventure, romance and intrigue: the Congo, the Amazon, the Nile, the Volga and Seine and Danube."[11] When I was growing up in the small town of Granby, Quebec, alongside the Yamaska River, where I used to go fishing with my older brother, I used to dream with my sister about travelling the Amazon or the Nile on a great quest. Rivers take us places in so many ways. And, as Ball shared, we don't even have to "be there" to travel with them.

Pangman and Evans, authors of *Dancing with Water* provide a wonderful analogy to water's compulsion to move: "Think of the words that have been used to describe water in nature: dancing, splashing, laughing, gurgling, frolicking … Each of these words implies not just movement, but freedom … What would happen if a child were forced to jump straight up and down when she was at play. Soon it would not be playing at all, only a tiresome exercise … With limited freedom of movement, a child would soon lose the ability to interact with the environment and would almost certainly lose zest for life. In many ways, a child would die. This is what happens when water is delivered via pressurized pipelines around the world. When it arrives at its destination, it is empty, tired, and lifeless."[12]

Photo 3.8: The River Seine, Paris, France.

Photo by Nina Munteanu

Stream Ecology & the River Continuum

During the years when I taught Limnology and Aquatic Ecology at the University of Victoria in British Columbia, one of the first things I did was take my students on a field trip to several urban streams. Usually one or two students came prepared to go into the water, bringing the requisite equipment like boots or old sneakers to change into. I would "volunteer" them to wade into the stream to examine and dislodge a few rocks for the others to see. It was so fun to witness the startled glee in my students' faces when they turned the rocks over to discover the active life that lurked there. It was one thing to know that *benthic* (bottom-dwelling) life clung to surfaces; it was quite another to be confronted with the reality of this rather bizarre community. My student Florence could hardly hold onto the rock as stunned mayflies and stoneflies scurried for cover. *Glossoma* caddisflies peered out of stone "houses" glued to the rock, no doubt hoping for reinstatement in the cool, dark streambed—which my student kindly obliged them.

I began my limnology career as a stream ecologist and the focus of my master's study included several rural and urban streams in the Eastern Townships of Quebec, Canada, not far from where I grew up. Later, as a limnologist for various environmental consulting companies in British Columbia, I studied the nature of macro-benthos communities in streams impacted by various activities from industrial discharges to agriculture and municipal development.[13,14,15] *Macro-benthos* is bottom-dwelling life you can see with the naked eye. They're made up mostly of aquatic worms and juvenile stages of insect species (*benthic invertebrates*).

Stream ecologists identify benthic invertebrates by their form, but they also recognize them by how they feed.[16] *Shredders*, such as amphi-

"Eventually, all things merge into one, and a river runs through it. The river was cut by the world's great flood and runs over rocks from the basement of time. On some of the rocks are timeless raindrops. Under the rocks are words, and some of the words are theirs."

—Norman Maclean

pods, mayflies, stoneflies, midges, and some caddisflies, use scissor-like mouths to cut and shred apart coarse particulate matter. *Collector–gatherers* (e.g., worms, nematodes, crustaceans, and gastropods) use their broom-like mouths to sweep in fine and ultra-fine organic matter. *Grazers* or *scrapers*, such as beetles, mayflies, and stoneflies, feed on attached algae and biofilms. Their mouths chisel against periphyton (attached algae) on rocks, woody debris and aquatic plants. *Filtering collectors*, such as blackfly larvae, collect suspended fine and ultra-fine organic matter, which can include phytoplankton (floating algae) in their finely spun nets. The caddisfly larva *Arctopsychegrandis*, for instance, builds a rough house made from twigs, leaf fragments, and small pebbles and spins silk nets across its threshold to capture organic matter suspended in the stream. *Predatory* benthic invertebrates, such as damselflies and dragonflies, have piercing mouth parts that act like a straw, allowing them to suck the nutrients from their prey without having to chew or shred it.[17,18]

Food sources come to the benthos externally (allochthonous), such as leaf litter, or internally (authochthonous), such as periphyton in the stream. The river continuum concept describes how these different feeders situate themselves along a river or stream based on how their food comes to them.[19] Shredders and collectors prefer headwater streams, while scrapers tend to live in mid-reaches and collectors dominate the depositional zones of large rivers. The communities basically move from a grazing-base to a detritus-base as the ecosystem matures in time and space and the materials that the community feeds upon change.[20] Environmental impacts tend to act as reset mechanisms, shifting the continuum one way or another depending on the nature of the impact.[19] I talk more about the river continuum and the three stages of river maturation in Chapter 9, *Water Is Story*.

Since 1909, when Kolkwitz and Marsson[21] demonstrated that benthic invertebrates demonstrated specific tolerances to organic enrichment and other sources of pollution, scientists have used these

Illustration 3.2: An Agrypina sp. *Caddisfly larva (Phryganeidae) that builds its case of plant material; clean water organism.*

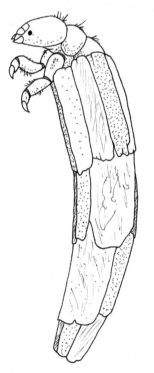

Illustration by Kerste Voute

communities to study various impacts to stream health, including chemical pollution, flow disruption and habitat destruction.[22,23,24,25] The EPT Richness Index was developed, based on the EPT groups being generally pollution-intolerant. EPT stands for Ephemoroptera, Plecoptera and Tricoptera: the index corresponds to the percentage of mayflies, stoneflies and caddisflies in the stream. They tend to disappear in areas of poor water quality, organic enrichment, low oxygen, and high metal levels.

I recently tested this in several *ad hoc* field trips I made with my naturalist friend Merridy Cox along the Credit River in Ontario. We started our explorations with the lower Credit River watershed, within the urban setting of Mississauga, Ontario, where we sampled the river and a few small tributaries in Riverwood Park, a few kilometres from where the river empties into Lake Ontario.

Illustration 3.3: A clinging Heptagenia sp. Mayfly nymph (Ephemeroptera) with characteristic three tails; clean water organism.

Originally named "trusting creek" (*Missinnihe*) by the Mississauga First Nation people, the salmon-bearing Credit River drains some 860 km^2 of Ontario and flows 90 km from its source at Orangeville, over the Niagara Escarpment, through several suburbs, and into Lake Ontario at Port Credit.

Great efforts have been made to restore and maintain the health of the Credit River and its watershed, mostly through the work of the Credit Valley Conservation Authority, together with the provincial and various municipal governments.[26]

While the water quality of the lower river is considered generally fair to poor, the river is partially saved by its gradient and turbulent flow. The length of the Credit River, up to very close to its mouth, rushes with the sound of a great storm. It tumbles and gurgles over rocks, capturing oxygen from the air; it scours gravel beds and cuts swirling eddies and creates undercut banks for foraging fish. The habitat is complex and life thrives here. Green algae cling to smooth boulders as water shears over them into pools of bubbling water. Water striders skate on the water surface in calmer backwaters.

Illustration by Kerste Voute

A cursory sampling of rocks in the river revealed a diversity of macro-benthic organisms. I spotted several species of mayfly, including rock-clinging *Heptagenids* (flat-headed mayflies) and the stone-building caddisfly *Glossoma*, all indicators of well-oxygenated turbulent flowing waters.

About 500 m from where we had sampled in the Credit River, we investigated a small tributary in the forest that led into the river. The creek obviously drained storm water runoff from the streets above; and, while the water was clear and contained riffles with a good flow, I found no macro-benthos on the rocks. Only blue-green algae populated the shoals. This was not surprising, given that storm water and street runoff generally contain contaminants (e.g., chlorides, heavy metals, organics, and oxygen-depriving materials) that susceptible organisms can't tolerate.

What struck me was the deceptive nature of this contamination. Most of us, when we think of polluted water, envision a turbid stagnating watercourse with visible garbage, bubbling with toxic algae. The pollution in this tributary was invisible; so was the life. It reminded me that the face of pollution varies and ranges from the obvious—as with most organic enrichment—to the insidiously subtle—as with heavy metal contamination or acid rain.

Water holds many secrets; some good, some not so good.

Water is an introvert.

The next day Merridy and I travelled to the rural countryside of Caledon, where we explored the middle Credit River at the Forks of the Credit, about 40 kilometres upstream of our previous sampling location. Three forks of the river meet near the village of Belfountain, a destination for touring motorcyclists and sightseers looking for ice cream. We investigated two forks nested deep in mixed forest. Water cascaded and tumbled in great waves and vortices around me as I waded in. The strong current tugged my legs in chaotic pulses. A diversity of life flourished amid boulders and cobbles and in shallow shoals:

Illustration 3.4: A Stonefly nymph (Plecoptera) with characteristic two tails; clean water organism.

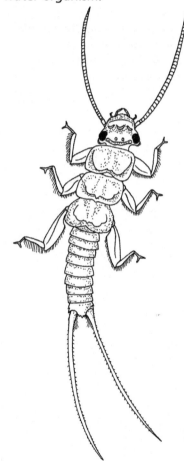

Illustration by Kerste Voute

stoneflies, dobsonflies, net-spinning caddisflies, shrimp-like amphipods and rock-clinging mayflies—all indicators of clean oxygenated flowing water.

The following day we went all the way to the source of the Credit, a marshy collection of springs, now collected in a human-made reservoir for the community of Orangeville. The Upper Credit meandered through open cattail marsh, mostly glides and riffles, and supported a rich *periphyton* (attached algae) and a benthic community of grazing mayflies and caddisflies that covered the cobble and gravel. The headwaters, located above the Niagara Escarpment, are home to native brook trout and brown trout populations. The Credit River also contains an active spawning habitat for Chinook salmon and rainbow trout.

On the larger rocks, like soldiers lined up for battle, dozens of little tubes of plant and mineral fragments (called *retreats*) fluttered in the current. At their open end intricate nets were spun, traps laid out by the net-spinner caddisfly of the family Hydropsychidae. The larvae spin silk nets to capture food particles—insects, diatoms, other algae and detritus (organic matter)—brought in by the water current. Each intricately spun net, attached to a concentric tube, resembles a tiny window screen, diligently and beautifully woven by a larva. The stronger the current, the stronger the net-spinners make their nets.

Long skeins of green macrophytes (plant-like algae that resemble seaweed), including *Elodea canadensis*, wavered in the riffles like green hair. Predatory damselflies clung to emerging grasses, as did stalking flies, mosquitoes and other small insects. We also spotted broods of young fish. The healthy population of benthic invertebrates and periphyton supports a diverse fish population of steelhead, Chinook salmon, Coho and Atlantic salmon, resident brown trout, speckled trout, and rainbow trout.

Illustration 3.5: Chironomid (midge) larva; pollution-tolerant organism. A) head; B) anterior proleg; and C) posterior proleg.

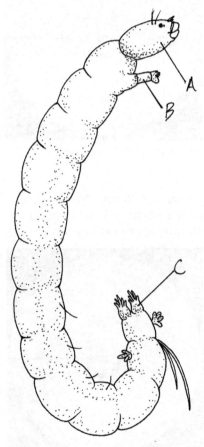

Illustration by Kerste Voute

The "Drop Picture"

Figure 3.2: Water Drop Picture of the Mettma River, upstream of brewery outflow.

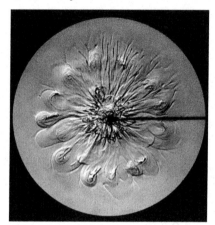

Institute of Flow Sciences, Germany

Figure 3.3: Water Drop Picture of the Mettma River, 70m downstream of brewery outflow.

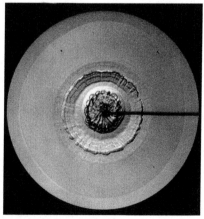

Institute of Flow Sciences, Germany

In the late 1960s Theodor Schwenk, founder of the Institute of Flow Sciences in Germany, developed the drop picture method to visually depict water quality. The method involves placing the test water in a shallow container with glycerine (to render flow motions and forms visible through its schlieren effect); distilled water is dropped into the test water, which creates an outward harmonic flow and "dendrites." In numerous experiments conducted with various water sources—including spring water, city drinking water, and water from pure forest streams to polluted rivers—Schwenk and his colleagues found that water's mobility reflected its nature.[4]

According to Wilkens, Jacobi and Schwenk, who have been continuing this work for the last forty years and have published an image-rich book entitled *Understanding Water*, the method lets you "observe the mobility of water as an expression of its central purpose: namely, to serve life by facilitating (among other things) metamorphosis, growth and decay."[4]

Wilkens, Jacobi and Schwenk provide stunning "drop pictures" of water taken from various stretches of the Mettma River, a creek in the Black Forest, which receives wastewater from a brewery. Drop pictures of water upstream of the brewery reflected a rich benthic community of plants and animals. These drop pictures showed a balanced, multifoliate spread of water from the drop point at the centre of the container (Figure 3.2). Water taken 50 m and 700 m downstream of the brewery discharge (within the impact zone) displayed small and simple concentric waves outward, with no sign of complexity (Figure 3.3). Water drop images remained simple until water sampled three kilometres downstream of the brewery, where they again resembled the complex movement and active dendrites of the upstream site.

Schwenk and his team correlated their visual drop pictures with a benthic community analysis. Upstream of the brewery, diverse and clean water communities that included clean water indicators (such as stonefly and mayfly larvae), thrived in the stream where the water drop picture demonstrated active vortex formation. Downstream of the brewery, a simpler community of organisms that indicate organic pollution (e.g., bacteria such as *Sphaeroti lusnatans* that forms a thick greyish mat or "fur" and tubificid worms) dominated stream water whose drop picture demonstrated limited vortex formation. The drop pictures reflected a gradual recovery of the stream water quality and benthic community from the far edge of the impact zone (as far as 700 m downstream). Recovery began 1,800 m downstream (with the dominant appearance of midges and blackfly larvae) to 3,000 m downstream (with fewer dominant species and the appearance of a diverse periphyton community and attendant grazers, such as amphipods and mayflies). Full recovery of the original benthic community occurred at 8,000 m.[4]

The drop picture method provides an excellent visual metric on the nature of water flow generally and can provide evidence for how subtle differences in solutes (e.g., organics, nutrients, and various pollutants) will affect it. The drop picture is a remarkable demonstration of the holistic expression of water's various characteristics.

Water is subtle.

"One drop of water contains the whole universe."

—Viktor Schauberger

Illustration 3.6: Blackfly (Simulium) larva; pollution-tolerant organism; A) head; B) thorax; C) abdomen; D) proleg (hidden beneath); and E) posterior circlet for clinging to surface in flowing water.

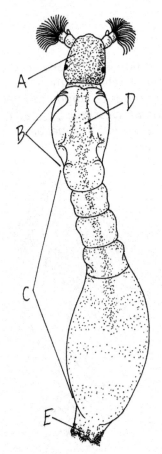

Illustration by Kerste Voute

Moving Stillness

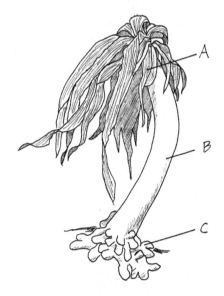

Illustration 3.7: The seaweed Postelsia palmaeformis *(sea palm) clings to craggy rock faces pf the BC west coast, Canada. A) the blades; B) stipe; and C) holdfast.*

Illustration by Nina Munteanu

While streams and rivers provide the most obvious examples of moving water, all large bodies of "standing" water such as lakes, ponds and oceans remain in constant motion. It's just that we don't always notice. It's a matter of scale.

Most of us are, of course, familiar with the tides of the oceans. Tides are driven by the gravitational pull of the Moon as it orbits Earth together with the Sun's tidal forces. When I studied and taught algal ecology at the University of Victoria and went on occasional boating trips with my family up the British Columbia coast, I learned about spring tides and neap tides. I learned that when Earth, Moon and Sun line up at the full and new moon, the solar and lunar tides reinforce each other, creating maximum tidal changes called *spring tides*. When the Earth and Moon align perpendicular to the line between Earth and Sun, there is a lower tidal change called the *neap tide*. Neap tides occur during the first and third quarters of the moon and show the least difference between low and high tide.

On a field trip to Port Renfrew on the exposed western coast of Vancouver Island, I diligently waited for the low spring tide to catch sight of my favourite seaweed: *Postelsia palmaeformis*. Known as a sea palm (it resembles a miniature palm tree), this intertidal brown alga clings tenaciously to craggy rock faces, invigorated by the rocking surf of a rough sea. It only reveals itself during low tides, and you must clamber over rocks and brave the danger of being swept to sea by oncoming swells, just to glimpse it.

Large bodies of confined water, such as freshwater lakes, reservoirs, pools, bays and harbours, also experience water level fluctuation on a seasonal to short-term basis. Short-term changes are called *seiches*, from the French word meaning "to sway back and forth." A seiche is a standing wave that oscillates in a body of water. It's basically the "sloshing" back and forth of water, like what happens when you carry a cup of coffee across the room. Seiches occur daily and are mostly so small in magnitude that they aren't noticed. Seiches are caused by strong winds and changes in atmospheric pressure or seismic disturbances. The standing wave, which can be created in just moments, sloshes between shores of the lake basin and, in the Great Lakes for example, where surges as high as ten feet have been recorded, it is often referred to as tide-like. Seiches can happen quickly: on July 13, 1995, a big seiche on Lake Superior caused the water level to fall then rise by one metre within fifteen minutes. In June 26, 1954, a 10-foot seiche hit the Chicago waterfront on Lake Michigan, sweeping eight fishermen away.[27,28]

Even still water will reveal its inner movement by reflecting the motion around and beyond it.

Photo 3.9: Net-spinning Hydropsychidae Caddisfly larva, showing the window-screen net at the mouth of its tube.

Photo by Merridy Cox

Effects of Motion

Illustration 3.8: Freshwater periphyton (mostly diatoms) colonizing a rock surface in moving water.

Illustration by Kerste Voute

I was introduced to one of the wonders of water movement over twenty years ago by accident. While fulfilling my studies for a Master's of Science degree, I made an interesting discovery. I'd chosen to study periphyton (attached algal) communities in streams affected by organic pollution and urban runoff in a rural community in the Eastern Townships of Quebec, Canada (where I'm originally from). My study involved placing glass slides in various locations in my control and experimental stream (from source to mouth) and in various orientations (parallel or facing the current), exposing the slides to colonizing algae. What I didn't expect to see, time and again, was that the community colonized the slides in a non-random way. Excited by my discovery, I asked my supervisor if we could study this diversion further. He agreed, and so began my foray into fluid mechanics, water movement and its biological manifestations. The result was a paper we published in the scientific journal *Hydrobiologia* that discussed this curious phenomenon.[29]

I discovered that periphyton, made up mostly of diatoms, preferentially colonized the two edges of the slide when oriented parallel to the current, while they colonized evenly across the slide when its flat side faced the current. There are two ways an algal community grows in a new area: (1) by initial colonization and settling and (2) by reproduction and growth. I studied both by collecting slides exposed for differing lengths of time (collecting young and mature communities) in different seasons. Following data analysis and further research and discussions with experts in fluid mechanics, I concluded that the periphyton of flowing streams thrived in turbulence. I postulated that the drift velocity was reduced on the slide's edge, where turbulence was greatest, giving drifting algae a greater chance to collide and settle on the slide over the more shear laminar flow along the slide's central face. Once settled, the community was more likely to grow with turbulence. Greater turbulence decreases the diffusion gradient of materials around algal cells, with a higher rate of nutrient uptake and respiration. Turbulence provides greater opportunity to an existing colony by increasing "chaotic" flow, potential collision and exchange. Turbulence is a kind of "stable chaos" that enhances vigour, robustness and communication.

Without quite realizing it, I'd discovered one of nature's most intriguing and fundamental qualities and a tenet in ecology: at the boundary, where two different entities meet—liquid with solid, land with water, forest with field, freshwater with salt water, fast water with slow water—life thrives most vigorously. Ecologists have a name for this zone: they call it an *ecotone*. I talk more about this in Chapter 4, *Water is Communication*. At the root of this vitality lies movement: turbulence, spiralling, swirling, vortices, flushing, and, yes, collision and excitation, exchange, learning, adaptation, change, and evolution.

What I hadn't considered at the time was the subtle connection between increased periphyton growth and production to the water's own increased vigour in the turbulent zone. Like a good traditional scientist at the time, I had restricted my observations of water to its role as a physical medium without accepting the possibility of water's own vital characteristics.

"Water is not just concerned with all life processes," write Wilkens, Jocobi and Schwenk. "It makes life possible."[4]

Alexander Lauterwasser (whose name translates to "louder water") describes water through the quality of its boundary interactions. "Contrary to the world of solid borders and bodies, in which no 'something' tolerates a different 'something', the liquid world enables a mutual penetration and overlay of very different motion–impulses. From [liquid's] weaving patterns and structures, complex and more highly organized forms can evolve, which then take lasting shape by a gradual coagulation, solidifying and crystallizing."[30]

Water is the driver of change, providing opportunity.

There is an element of cooperation and acceptance associated with opportunity. Cooperation lies at the heart of transforming existing structures, generating new forms, maintaining and moderating process, and bringing rhythm to movement. It brings to mind what happens when ideas or even worldviews are exchanged between two open-minded individuals from different cultures. Movement and change—permanent change—does not happen without some element of cooperation, whether recognized or not. Even antagonism involves cooperation of a sort.

In my writing courses, I focus part of each class on the role of setting and environment in the journey of "our hero" (see Chapter 9, *Water Is Story*). I teach that the environment is, in fact, a character with agency. Some of my students are at first surprised or puzzled by this bold personification. But all truths are best told in metaphor. To see the world—or water—as a character is to recognize that all is in motion, on a journey of interaction, relationship, and influence: all parts of a whole; a whole comprising parts.

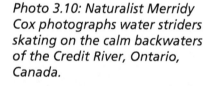

Photo 3.10: Naturalist Merridy Cox photographs water striders skating on the calm backwaters of the Credit River, Ontario, Canada.

Photo by Nina Munteanu

"By renouncing every self-quality, [water] becomes the creative substance for the generation of all forms," writes Theodor Schwenk. "By renouncing every life of its own, it becomes the primal substance for all life. By renouncing every fixed substance, it becomes the carrier of all substance transformation."[31]

The ultimate altruist, water is a herald and a mediator. It is a catalyst, championing change.

"All life flows with the flow of water,"[32] writes Japanese writer and philosopher Masaru Emoto. "The Buddha, knowing that flow is a fundamental principle of the Universe, said that all things are in flux and nothing is permanent. Water is a good example of this. Water is always flowing with life, purifying what it encounters as it travels. It carries life while also carrying away impurities, giving life to all … The act of living is the act of flowing … When your soul is allowed to flow, you feel a burden lifted from your weary body … If you have been offended, forgive the offender. If you feel oppressed for your own offenses against others, forgive yourself … Water teaches us how to live, how to forgive, how to believe. If you open your ears to the possibilities in life, you may just be able to hear the sound of the pure water that flows through your body even now. It is the sound of your life—a melody of healing."[32]

Photo 3.11: Water surging over moss-covered rocks of the Upper Credit River, Belfountain, Ontario, Canada.

Photo by Merridy Cox

Water Spiralling & the Fibonacci Sequence

"What else, when chaos draws all forces inward to shape a single leaf."

—*Conrad Aiken*

Water's movements have fascinated me since childhood, from the recursive waves lapping on Lac Boivin in my hometown of Granby, to the meandering swirls of my mother's hot coffee or the whirlpool in my emptying bath. Why did water like to form a perfect spiral?

Several years ago, when I lived in Vancouver, I accompanied my husband and son on our annual summer boating trip to Desolation Sound, British Columbia. After experiencing its untouched wilderness in 1792, explorer Captain Vancouver peevishly gave it its desolate name and wrote in his log, "There is not a single prospect that was pleasing to the eye." Desolation Sound is now far from desolate. During the summer, it offers one of the best cruising grounds in the world, drawing boaters from all over the planet to its clear and warm waters. There is exceptional scenery and a kayaker's paradise at the northern tip of the Sunshine Coast.

I remember the onslaught of stormy weather as we reached our destination. That night, I dreamt that two large vortexes opened up beside our boat. The boat broke free of its mooring and pitched toward one yawning spiral. In my dream, I surged out to grab a piling nearby to keep us from dropping down into the dark waterhole—and thankfully woke up. The next day, we reached Prideaux Haven, a protected waterway behind a cluster of islands in Humphrey Channel and a true haven for kayaking, diving and swimming. Eager to tour the scenic area with my kayak, I paddled off in search of Nature's beauty, hugging the shoreline. In one cove, I spotted an intense windfall of trees on shore that had likely been caused by a cyclone, which might have easily stirred up a waterspout. I swallowed and thought of my dream. The next day, as I was boat tending for my son and his friend, who were diving along one of the rocky islands, I noticed that two perfect spirals formed each time I drew my paddle across the water. I did a double take (pardon the pun) and decided to pay attention to this insistent form that persisted in my psyche.

What I found was that the spiral is one of the oldest symbols of human spirituality. It was found scratched into rocks from thousands of years ago, on every continent in the world. The ancient Celts used the spiral to symbolize reaching the soul and God. The Hopi Native Americans used circular and square labyrinths as symbols of Mother Earth and the emergence from her womb upon creation and spiritual awakening.

The double spiral represents balance, life, and regeneration. Like the equinoxes, the double spiral reflects the co-existence of death and life. Reflecting the yin–yang symbol, it symbolizes the polarity and balance of the two reverse streams of a unique cosmic force. Our expiration and inspiration or our diastole–systole heartbeats are good examples. The Hindu double helix of the Brahman's staff and the destructive and regenerative power of the vajra depict this polarity and balance. The double spiral is also revealed in Lorenz's *Butterfly Effect* in chaos theory.

Photo 3.12: Double eddy spiral forms behind a rock in the Credit River, Ontario, Canada.

Photo by Nina Munteanu

The spiral is thought by some to be the universal symbol of God and the Self. Is this why it is such a pleasing structure for us? The medieval mathematician Leonardo Fibonacci proposed a sequence based on the number *phi* that, when graphed, approximated what is called the Golden Mean spiral, essentially a double spiral. Ubiquitous in the natural world, this fractal phi vortex can be seen in anything from the bone structure of a human being, to the seed pattern of a sunflower, to the spiral shape of a kudu antelope horn, or a seashell and, ultimately, in the spiral shape of our own galaxy.

The Fibonacci sequence is created by adding the last two numbers in a sequence to get the next one. Based on whole numbers, not the actual numbers for *phi*, it approximates the Golden Mean spiral, which has no beginning and no end. Phi vortices are ubiquitous in Nature. If you look hard enough, you'll see them virtually everywhere. In the double helix of DNA. In the plant world, the sunflower head is often given as an obvious example. However, virtually all aspects of most plants reflect a toroid, spiral or double spiral: in the pattern of tree bark wrapping around a trunk, or of branches as they form from shoots. The phi vortex is reflected in wave patterns left in the sand as an ocean wave recedes. A double phi vortex forms in the air at the wingtip of a moving plane; it emerges on the water surface from a waterspout.

Photo 3.13: The author kayaking in Prideaux Haven in Desolation Sound off the British Columbia coast, Canada.

Photo by Herb Klassen

The Vortex

Early in 2008 I traveled to Louisville, Kentucky, to visit a friend recovering from an illness. While there, one breezy night I drove to a local store to get some supplies and, in the short while that I was inside, a severe storm swept in like an angry god. It howled outside like a train locomotive and hailed down a deluge of wind and rain that drew the attention of the shopkeepers. Just as I came to the window, the wind cast down the store's huge neon sign, smashing the car below—luckily not mine, three cars down. It proceeded to claw down trees and power lines and create flotsam out of garbage cans, chairs and such. My drive back to my friend's place was an obstacle course, as I swerved around sparking power lines on the road, fallen branches, moving debris and totally uprooted trees.

I didn't even know that I was experiencing the ripping force of a multiple-vortex tornado. One column touched down twice, blocks from my friend's house. The twister burst windows, destroyed cars and signs and buildings. It ripped off rooftops and uprooted concrete driveways and killed a few people. It left my friend's house in deep darkness, prey to the vagaries of a howling wind. I learned later that the atypical winter tornado had touched down four times in the area.

I was lucky. My friend was lucky. We had avoided the tornado's path. Some "long-track" tornadoes stay on the ground for great distances before finally lifting. I read about one tornado in Broken Bow, Oklahoma, that carried a motel sign 40 kilometres and dropped it in Arkansas. The vortex energy of a tornado is created by the water energy in the atmosphere. Tornadoes, which can produce winds exceeding 483 km/hr with a 160 km/hr updraft, are composed of super-condensed water vapour. They are a violently rotating column of air that is in contact with both the surface of the earth and a cumulonimbus cloud and are typically in the form of a visible condensation funnel.

"In the beginning was the vortex."

—Democritus

Photo 3.14: Tornado in central Oklahoma, May 3, 1999, showing tube-like condensation funnel attached to the rotating cloud base, surrounded by a translucent dust cloud.

Photo by Daphne Zaras, Wikimedia Commons

To this day I feel both cheated and blessed that I did not see the twister come through—it was dark out—and I don't know what I would have done and felt if I had. Either way, the experience gave me a new respect for the immense power—and focus—of vortex energy. It was shocking to see one house totally gutted, right next to another that was absolutely untouched.

Water is a trickster—employing some interesting minions.

In his work with tornadoes, Dr. Alexey Dmitriev of the Russian National Academy of Sciences showed that tornadoes were accompanied by very high electromagnetic fields, visible light and ball lightning. He discussed how matter became permeable to other matter within a tornado. Physical objects fused into each other: two burnt and charred wooden boards had fused; pebbles had passed through glass without breaking it; pieces of straw had penetrated a window without breaking it. Dmitriev concluded that matter was able to disappear or become permeable to other matter in the presence of a sufficiently strong field. In this case a vortex energy field.[33]

Photo 3.15: Double spiral inflo-rescence of a sunflower.

Photo by Nina Munteanu

Vortices exist everywhere in our universe, from the spiral form of our DNA and floral inflorescences to atmospheric phenomena—like tornadoes and hurricanes—and the motion of planets around a star. Even black holes spin like whirlpools.[34] NASA has been studying the coil of energy (its magnetic field) that is spiralling in what they call a *Parker Spiral* out from the Sun and carried in waves by the solar wind.[35]

Fluid mechanics shows us that vortex energy accompanies the meeting of virtually all interfaces and boundaries, creating opposite directions of movement. *Eddies* (swirling currents that run counter to the main current) are ubiquitous in moving water. Such vortices allow salmon to swim upstream and stratified lakes to turnover (e.g., vertically mix) in the fall.

During one of my field trips along the turbulent Credit River in Ontario, I decided to wade in and watch the mesmerizing flow of water around a large boulder. I noted how, at regular intervals, an eddy consistently formed in the boulder's wake, dissipated, and then formed again.

Eddies carry much of the energy of turbulent flow, Philip Ball writes in his book *Flow*. Much of the motional (or kinetic) energy of water is captured by eddies, "which fritter it away, in the end dissipating it in frictional heating as one parcel of fluid rubs against another,"[2] says Ball, who adds that this friction is the origin of viscosity. Energy fed into the flow at large scale, creating large eddies, moves along an energy cascade as big eddies transfer their energy to smaller eddies, and so on. To describe the process, Lewis F. Richardson, inspired by Jonathan Swift's doggerel about fleas, coined this rhyme that I'd learned in my introductory Ecology class:

Big whirls have little whirls
That feed on their velocity,
And little whirls have lesser whirls
And so on to viscosity.

The spiralling vortex has been expressed throughout history by various cultures through symbols and in art. Leonardo da Vinci, a true polymath who devoted much of his time to the study of water and fluid dynamics, found water paradoxical: "Water is sometimes sharp and sometimes strong, sometimes acid and sometimes bitter, sometimes sweet and sometimes thick or thin, sometimes it is seen bringing hurt or pestilence, sometimes health-giving, sometimes poisonous. It suffers change into as many natures as are the different places through which it passes."[36] On examining the motion of waves and currents, he commented on its erosive nature: "Water gnaws at mountains and fills valleys. If it could, it would reduce the earth to a perfect sphere."[36] Of bubbles, he noted that "motions of water always move in a circle from surface to bottom."[36] Da Vinci wished to understand the movement of water within water—the swirls, eddies and vortices[2]—and drew parallels between current and hair in its tendency to curl: "Observe the motion of the surface of the water which resembles that of hair, and has two motions, of which one goes on with the flow of the surface, the other forms the lines of the eddies; thus the water forms eddying whirlpools, one part of which are due to the impetus of the principal current and the other to the incidental motion and return flow."[36]

In the late 1500s, German astronomer Johannes Kepler outlined three basic laws to describe the motion of the planets. The second law described how a planet's motion, in its elliptical orbit around the sun, grew faster the closer it was to the sun. Kepler was describing a vortex.

The current thought in quantum physics suggests that sub-atomic particles are vortices of energy concentrated to such a degree that they act like a particle. "Vortices accompany every creative process,"[12] say Pangman and Evans. Vortices "initiate [and provide much of the energy for] the coherent organization capable of creating and sustaining life." Vortices, they contend, are the power of the universe—from the spinning of each quantum particle to spiralling galaxies.

The Earth's rotation causes all fluids and gases to move in spirals. Water naturally wants to spin. In fact, when forced into a straight path, water is obliged to give away energy. In a series of experiments conducted in 1952, Schauberger and Pöpel demonstrated that water flowing through a straight pipe experienced more resistance than water flowing through a spiral enclosure.[37] As water flows down a winding river, its central axis forms a horizontal vortex that interacts with numerous smaller vortices around it. At each bend of the river, the spiral reverses direction, gathering and dispensing energy throughout its journey. Wilkens and his colleagues demonstrated in a series of experiments how water naturally meandered when encountering any resistance with solid matter, even smooth surfaces.[2]

The spin of the vortex creates powerful forces that pulse in a rhythm of contraction and expansion. The layers of water in a vortex glide past each other, forming boundaries of faster and slower moving water as the vortex creates its own energetic entity. In his 1965 book *Sensitive*

Photo 3.16: The heart of the Whirlpool Galaxy (Spiral Galaxy M51) located in the Canes Venatici constellation, via Hubble Space Telescope, NASA.

Photo by N. Scoville (Caltech), T. Rector (U. Alaska, NOAO) et. al., Hubble Heritage Team, NASA/ESA

Chaos, Theodor Schwenk described vortices as being created when two streams of water move past each other at different speeds. A hollow develops, into which oxygen flows: "Boundary surfaces, with their rhythmical processes are the birthplaces of living things."[31]

The condition required to produce a vortex is turbulence, or chaotic motion. The vortex, say Pangman and Evans, is an example of polarity, combining two opposing forces: gravitational (masculine) and levitational (feminine). As the vortex spins downward, the expansion that follows draws the contents upward and outward. The levitational force re-cycles mineral-rich sediments from the ocean bottom, and it enables sap to flow, spiralling against gravity in the tallest trees. This same force propels salmon up waterfalls during their annual spawning runs. The horizontal levitational force of the vortex lets trout remain stationary with little effort in a strong current. Tornados and hurricanes use the vortex's levitational force in their highly destructive motions.[12]

Naturalist and early biomimicry practitioner Viktor Schauberger describes two basic forms of vortex motion: (1) outwardly expanding (centrifugal); and (2) in-winding (centripetal). Centrifugal motion begins slowly at the centre and increases in speed toward the periphery. Also called explosive and de-constructive motion, centrifugal motion pushes energy outward, producing heat and friction, and requiring more energy than it generates. Centripetal motion, used by Nature during the creative process, begins from the outside and winds inward, gathering and cooling and organizing, rather than breaking down and dispersing; this constructive motion generates energy. Schauberger suggested that if we used vortex motion in our energy-generating devices and technology, we would gain more energy at less cost.[37]

In the late 1800s, Lord Kelvin, accomplished scientist and founding father of thermodynamics, posited that all matter was an expression of vortex energy.[31] His colleague German scientist Herman von Helmholtz had previously suggested that vortex energy could live forever, if it existed in a frictionless fluid. James Clark Maxwell later developed the electromagnetic theory that led to the development of radio, television and radar based on vortex theory. Several years later, based on vortex energy found in the centres of cells of living organisms, Alexis Carrel won the Nobel Prize in medicine for showing that living cells could be kept alive indefinitely.[38]

The Liquid Crystal

Schauberger and Pöpel discovered that vortices cause molecules to compress. According to Schauberger, water molecules inside a vortex organize into their most energy efficient geometry, the *liquid crystal*.[37]

According to Dr. Gerald Pollack, bioengineer at the University of Washington, the liquid crystal is a fourth phase of structured water, between the solid and liquid phase.[5] Its properties of viscosity, density, order (especially, organization and "community"), negative charge, alkalinity, and optical characteristics set it apart from "ordinary" water. Water in this liquid crystalline state establishes an *exclusion zone* (EZ), which excludes things, even small molecules. Collagen and cell membranes are also considered liquid crystals.[39] These tissues work cooperatively with water to create an informational network that reaches every cell.[40] Crystalline water surrounds and stabilizes DNA, supporting its electromagnetic field.[41, 42] I talk more about this in Chapter 2 and Chapter 4.

Water's Fractal Spiral

In 2006, researchers at the University of Nebraska–Lincoln demonstrated how nanoscale ice formations, which resembled the double helices of DNA, formed when water molecules were frozen inside carbon nanotubes and subjected to high pressure. Water molecules organized themselves into "spiral staircase" arrangements similar to those of DNA.[43]

The Hindu Vedas and Puranas described our Universe as a huge spiralling wheel that contains an infinite number of wheels within wheels in an infinite cyclical oscillation of creative destruction; and itself as part of innumerable universes, all spinning and pulsing to an inner rhythm.

From atoms and orbiting electrons to spinning galaxies, the fractal nature of the Universe unfolds all around us, expressing self-similarity. We see self-similarity in objects from small to large all around us, in the clouds above us, in a piece of coastline or a river network or branching tree. Benoit Mandelbrot created the term *fractal* (from the Latin word *fractus*, which means broken or fractured) to describe his observations of the recursive form or expression of self-similarity: something that may be subdivided into parts, each of which is a smaller replica of the whole—not identical but similar in nature.[44] Because they appear similar at all levels of magnification, fractals are often considered infinitely complex. Much of nature—if not all of it—embraces this hidden order, which I describe as "stable chaos."

Examples of natural fractals include clouds, mountain ranges, lightning bolts, trees, coastlines, river networks, blood vessels, and snowflakes.

The Sanskrit concept of *chakras* (which means "wheels") was conceived in the ancient Vedic healing arts that involved the vortex. The belief is that the human body is a fractal reflection of the Universe and our seven major chakra centres contain an infinity of spinning chakras within chakras, each—if healthy—spinning synchronously in accordance with the Earth's environment and our Universe. All reflect a grand "heartbeat." Perhaps, water is that heartbeat.

Water is a fractal whole.

The Music of the Spheres
& the Whirling Dervish

In 1619, Johannes Kepler discovered that the velocities of the planets correspond to musical intervals. The *Music of the Spheres* is an ancient philosophical and mathematical concept, originated by Pythagoras, which proposes a connection between the movements of celestial bodies to music. Both Kepler and Pythagoras before him thought that the key to linking celestial and terrestrial events was through musical harmonics. I talk more about this in Chapters 6 and 8.

Kepler found that the difference between the maximum and minimum angular speeds of a planet in its orbit conforms to a harmonic proportion. He based his observations and laws on the concept of an electromagnetic solar system. According to Kepler, the symphony supplies the creative and sustaining tones of the entire universe. The tones that each celestial body expresses change with the cycling seasons and the planet's journey through space. The symphony evolves and communicates throughout the universe by vortices.[45] I talk more about this notion in Chapter 6.

A few years ago, I had the honour of attending a Sufi Whirling Dervish dance. This meditative prayer dance (*sama*) within the *sema* (worship ceremony) reflects that all beings are comprised of revolving electrons, protons, neutrons and atoms. The *sema* is a eulogy to the *music of the spheres*. The hat represents the tombstone of the ego, and the white skirt is the ego's shroud. The dervishes (*semazen*) raise their right palm to the sky and the left down as they whirl and spin. This allows them to receive the blessings of Heaven through the right hand, transferred through the body to the left hand, bringing the blessing back to the Earth. The human being has been created with love in order to love.

As above, so below.

Photo 3.17: Sufi whirling dervishes perform the Sema at the Sirkeci Railway Station in Instanbul.

Photo by Vladimer Shioshvili, Wikimedia Commons

Saturn's Hexagonal Vortex

In 1981, the *Voyager* probe discovered a persistent hexagonal cloud formation at Saturn's north pole. The Cassini mission revisited in 2006 and captured spectacular images. Each side of the hexagon measures about 13,800 km, which is more than the diameter of Earth. The hexagon rotates with the same period as radio emissions from Saturn's interior. According to physicist Ana Claudia Barbosa Aguiar and colleagues at Oxford University, the hexagon results from a steep latitudinal gradient in the speed of winds in the gas giant's atmosphere. The hexagon forms from the interactions of two different rotating fluid bodies with dissimilar speeds. Turbulence results from the steep gradient of a faster inner spin over a slower outer spin, which creates eddies and whirlpools around the edges that resolve into a self-ordering hexagonal shape. A giant jet stream with a stable polar cyclone (a set of vortices, spinning in opposite directions) exists at the centre of the hexagon. Aguiar recreated the hexagon in her lab using a cylinder of water on a slowly spinning table and a small rotating ring to represent the "jet stream."[46]

Photo 3.18: North polar hexagonal cloud storm formation on Saturn's north pole, taken by Cassini when?

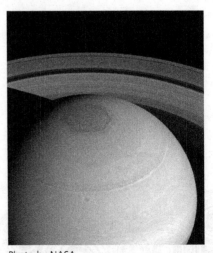

Photo by NASA

Holomovement & the Universal Flux

"Space is not empty. It is full, a plenum as opposed to a vacuum, and is the ground for the existence of everything, including ourselves. The Universe is not separate from this cosmic sea of energy."

—David Bohm.

According to theoretical physicist David Bohm, everything is in a state of process or becoming (which he calls the *universal flux*), a dynamic wholeness-in-motion in which everything moves together in an interconnected process: "undivided wholeness in flowing movement."[47]

Bohm posited that elementary particles were systems of complicated internal structure that acted as amplifiers of information contained in a quantum wave. His theory of "Implicate Order" embraces a holistic cosmic view of interconnectivity. One in which any individual element could reveal "detailed information about every other element in the universe," in an "unbroken wholeness of the totality of existence as an undivided flowing movement without borders." In his Holomovement theory of an enfolding–unfolding universe and consciousness, totalities continually form and dissolve out of the universal flux. Rather than explain the whole in terms of the parts, the parts are derived from the whole: "the whole in every part." This implies looking at reality, not just in terms of external interactions between things, but in terms of the internal (enfolded) relationships among things: "The relationships constituting the fundamental law are between the enfolded structures that interweave and inter-penetrate each other, through the whole of space, rather than between the abstracted and separated forms that are manifest to the senses (and to our instruments)."

Bohm was led to conceive his model of a holographic universe from the results of an experiment by Alain Aspect at the University of Paris in 1982.[48] Aspect and his team discovered that under certain circumstances subatomic particles can instantaneously communicate with each other from long distances—it didn't matter whether ten metres or ten

billion metres. Somehow, each particle knew what the other was doing. The discovery violated Einstein's long-held tenet that no communication could travel faster than the speed of light. Bohm believed that the reason subatomic particles can remain in contact with one another, regardless of distance separating them, is not because they are sending magical signals back and forth, but because their separateness is an illusion. Bohm argues that at a deeper level of reality these particles are not individual entities, but an extension of the same fundamental "something."

Water is You.

Motion is the demon and angel of change. Motion flows endlessly on a tangent with time, destroying and creating. Motion carves sinuous patterns of stable chaos. In its turbulent wake or gliding caress, motion heralds transcendence.

Motion is water.

References:

1. Schwenk, Theodor and Wolfram Schwenk. 1989. "Water: The Element of Life." Rudolf Steiner Press. 249 pp.
2. Ball, Philip. 2011. "Flow." *Oxford University Press*. 208 pp.
3. da Vinci, Leonardo. 1507–1510. Codex Leicester Folio 23V. Notebooks of handwritten notes and drawings. 72 pp.
4. Wilkens, Andreas, Michael Jacobi, and Wolfram Schwenk. 2005. "Understanding Water." *Floris Books*, Edinburgh. 107 pp.
5. Ball, Philip. 2006. "Van Gogh Painted Perfect Turbulence." *Nature News*. Online: http://www.nature.com/news/2006/060703/full/news060703-17.html
6. Main, Douglas. 2013. "How Cirrus Clouds Form—and Why It Matters." *Livescience*. May 9, 2013. Online Issue: http://www.live-science.com/29472-how-cirrus-clouds-form.html
7. Ienna, F., H. Yoo, and G.H. Pollack. 2012. "Spatially Resolved Evaporation Patterns from Water." *Soft Matter* 8 (47): 11850–11856.
8. Pollack, Gerald. 2013. "The Fourth Phase of Water: Beyond Solid, Liquid, and Vapor." *Ebner & Sons Publishers*, Seattle, WA. 357 pp.
9. Niagara Parks. 2015. "Niagara Falls Geology Facts & Figures." Online website: http://www.niagaraparks.com/about-niagara-falls/geology-facts-figures.html.
10. Wetzel, Robert G. 2001. "Limnology: Lake and River Ecosystems." 3rd edition. *Academic Press*, New York. 1006 pp.
11. Ball, Philip. 2000. "H2O: A Biography of Water." *Phoenix*, London, UK. 387 pp.
12. Pangman, M.J. and Melanie Evans. 2011."Dancing with Water: The New Science of Water." *Uplifting Press*. 255 pp.
13. Munteanu, N. and G.P. Thomas. 1997. "Benthic Community Populations Near Two Adjacent Northern Pulp Mill Discharges." *Water Sciences & Technology* 35 (2/3): 381.
14. Thomas, G.P. and N. Munteanu. 2000. "Biological Community

Assessment Program; Benthic Invertebrate and Periphyton Communities of the Columbia River." Prepared for Cominco Canada Ltd. by G3 Consulting Ltd., Richmond, BC.

15. Munteanu, N. 2006. "Fitness Indicators and Morphological Deformities of Benthic Invertebrates as an Assessment Tool in Ecosystem Health." In: *Benthic Biomonitoring* July 25–26, 2006. British Columbia Ministry of Environment and the University of British Columbia, B.C.

16. Cummins, K.W. and M.J. Klug. 1979. "Feeding Ecology of Stream Invertebrates." *Ann.Rev. Ecol. Syst.* 10: 147–172.

17. Allan, D.J. 2007. "Stream Ecology: Structure and Function of Running Waters." 2nd edition. *Springer*. 436 pp.

18. Merritt, Richard W. and Kenneth W. Cummings. 1996. "An Introduction to the Aquatic Insects of North America." *Kendall/Hunt Publishing*, Dubuque. 862 pp.

19. Vannote, R.L., G.W. Minshall, K.W. Cummins, J. R. Sedell, C.E. Cushing. 1980. "The River Continuum Concept." *Can. J. Fish. Aquat. Sci.* 37: 130–137.

20. Odum, E.P. 1969. "The strategy of ecosystem development." *Science* 164: 262–270.

21. Kolkwitz, R. and M. Marsson. 1909. "Okolgie der tierischen Saprobien." *Int. Rev. Hydrobiol.*2: 126–152.

22. Sladecek, V. 1973. "System of Water Quality from the Biological Point of View." *Arch. Hydrobiol. Beih.* 7: 1–218.

23. Metcalf-Smith, J.L. 1991. "Biological Water Quality Assessment of Rivers Based on Macroinvertebrate Communities." Section 3.3: NWRI Contribution No. 91–71 in "Rivers Handbook." Vol. 2, chapter 3 ("Monitoring Programmes"). *Nat. Water Res. Inst.*, Burlington, ON.

24. Winner, R.W., B.W. Boesel, and M.P. Farrell. 1980. "Insect Community Structure as an Index of Heavy Metal Pollution in Lotic Ecosystems." *Can. J. Fish. Aquat. Sci.* 37: 647–655.

25. Foekema, E.M., N.H.B.M. Kang, D.M. van Hussel, R.G. Jak, M.C.

Scholten, and C. van der Guchte. 1997. "Mesocosm Observations on the Ecological Response of an Aquatic Community to Sediment Contamination." *Wat. Sci. Tech*. 36: 249–256.

26. Credit Valley Conservation Authority. 2009. "A Handbook for Understanding and Protecting the Credit River Watershed." 1st edition. CVC Publication. 55 pp. Online: http://www.creditvalleyca.ca/wp-content/uploads/2011/02/RisingtotheChallenge.pdf

27. Clark, Gene. 2005. "Coastal Natural Hazards: Seiches and Storm Surges." University of Wisconsin Sea Grant. Online Website: http://www.seagrant.wisc.edu/coastalhazards/default.aspx?tabid=426

28. Michigan State University. 2015. "Seiches on the Great Lakes." Department of Geography. Online Website: http://geo.msu.edu/extra/geogmich/seiches.htm.

29. Munteanu, N. and E. Maly. 1981. "The Effect of Current on the Distribution of Diatoms Settling on Submerged Glass Slides." *Hydrobiologia* 78: 273–282.

30. Lauterwasser, Alexander. 2006. "Water Sound Images: The Creative Music of the Universe." *Macromedia Publishing*. 172 pp.

31. Schwenk, T. 1996. "Sensitive Chaos." Revised 2nd Edition. Rudolf Steiner Press. 232 pp.

32. Emoto, Masaru. 2005. "The Secret Life of Water." Atria Books. 178 pp.

33. Dmitriev, Alexey. 1997 (1998). "Planetophysical State of the Earth and Life". Translated into English by A.N. Dmitriev, Andrew Tetenov and Earl L. Crockett. IICA Transactions, Volume 4.

34. Cain, Fraser. 2014. "How Fast Do Black Holes Spin?" *Universe Today*, February 13. Online: http://www.universetoday.com/109308/how-fast-do-black-holes-spin/

35. NASA. 2006. "Glossary: O and P (Parker Spiral)". NASA Cosmicopia. Online: http://helios.gsfc.nasa.gov/gloss_op.html

36. Da Vinci, Leonardo. 1478–1519. *Codex Atlanticus*, 185v. Notebooks of handwritten notes and drawings.

37. Alexandersson, O. 1990. "Living Water: Viktor Schauberger and the Secrets of Natural Energy." *Gateway Books*. 161 pp.

38. Marks, William. 2001. "The Holy Order of Water." *Bell Pond Books*. 256 pp.

39. Ho, Mae-Wan et al. 1998. "Liquid Crystalline Meridians." *Am J. Chinese Med*. 26: 251–63.

40. Pischinger, A. 2007. "The Extracellular Matrix and Ground Regulation." *North Atlantic Books*. 232 pp.

41. Pal, S. et al. 2003. "Water at DNA surfaces: Ultrafast Dynamics in Minor Groove Recognition." *Proc. Natl. Acad. Sci. USA* 100 (14): 8113–8118.

42. Jhon, M.S. 2004. "The Water Puzzle and the Hexagonal Key." *Uplifting Press*. 147 pp.

43. Bai, Jaeil, Jun Wang and X.C. Zeng. 2006. "Multiwalled Ice Helixes and Ice Nanotubes." *Proc. Natl. Acad. Sci. USA* 103 (52): 19664–19667.

44. Mandelbrot, Benoit. 1982. "The Fractal Geometry of Nature." *W.H. Freeman and Company*. 480 pp.

45. Keplar, Johannes. 1619. *"Hamonices Mundi"* ["The Harmony of the World"]. Linz, Austria.

46. Aquiar, Ana, C. Barbosa, Peter.L. Read, Robin D. Wordsworth, Tara Salter, and Y. Hiro Yamazaki. 2010. "A Laboratory Model of Saturn's North Polar Hexagon." *Icarus* 206 (2): 755–763.

47. Bohm, David. 1980. "Wholeness and the Implicate Order." *Routledge*, London. 284 pp.

48. Aspect, Alain, Philippe Grangier, Gérard Roger. 1982. "Experimental Realization of Einstein-Podalsky-Rosen-Bohm Gedankenexperiment: A New Violation of Bell's Inequalities". *Phys. Rev. Lett.* 49 (2): 91-4.

4.
Water
is
Communication

Photo 4.1: Patterns of turbulence in flowing water, Credit River, Ontario, Canada.

Photo by Nina Munteanu

"Water connects what was once separate, urging it into a conscious being, melding into all an element of liquid heaven."

—Rainer Maria Rilke

During my first year biology course at Concordia University in Montreal, I experienced the thrill of watching the dance of chloroplasts in a cell. The simple experiment involved placing a leaf of the aquatic plant *Elodea* on a microscope and shining a light on it. Within a short time, a string of bright green chloroplasts began to flow along the edge of the cell around its central vacuole. The motion is called cytoplasmic streaming: the organelles are attached to actin filaments using myosin motors, which transform the chemical energy in ATP during photosynthesis into mechanical energy. The streaming helps transport materials within and between cells. And it couldn't happen without water.

In Chapter 3, I talk about how water creates opportunity through turbulence and chaos. Much of this arises from the shear forces generated where two different structures or patterns meet, interact and communicate. *Communication* is movement that causes more movement. It is a collision of sorts, where two "somethings" meet and interact. "Water's flow constantly links life and death," write Theodor and Wolfram Schwenk in *Water: the Element of Life*. "It is the mediator between the two, and its surface provides a common frontier in nature where they meet. Death is continuously being overcome there."[1]

Water is a song.

It sings in the interlaced notes of Mozart's *Serenade No. 10*, whose opening movement is a syncopated rhythmic flow of clarinet and oboe. When beautifully played, this piece makes me cry. Its complex rhythms caress my soul and touch my heart like the hand of God. In the movie *Amadeus*, the composer Salieri describes his rapturous experience at encountering this music: "On the page it looked nothing. The beginning simple, almost comic. Just a pulse, bassoons, basset horns. Like a rusty squeezebox. And then, suddenly—high above it—an oboe. A single note, hanging there, unwavering, until a clarinet took it over and sweetened it into a phrase of such delight! … This was a music I'd never heard … It seemed to me that I was hearing a voice of God."

Water warbles and bubbles with joyful notes. It rushes in an open-throated roar, scouring and grinding. Then drops its load in raspy jazz notes. It booms, coughs and drums in counterpoint. It is a playful orchestra of pulses and scalar glides. Not to be trifled with.

Water is a powerful communicator: from violent tsunami to gentle trickle.

Illustration 4.1: Cytoplasmic streaming (cyclosis) of chloroplasts with actin filaments and myosin motors of an Elodea leaf. A) cell wall; B) chloroplast; C) cytoplasmic streaming flow.

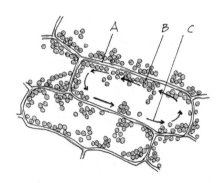

Illustration by Nina MUnteanu

Nature's Ecotones & Interfacial Water

In Chapter 3, I use the ecological term *ecotone* to describe that place where two opposites or polars—such as fluids flowing in different directions—meet and are changed by that meeting. An ecotone is the transition zone between two overlapping systems. It is essentially where two communities exchange information and integrate. In 1905, Clements described ecotones as "tension zones" with increased productivity between plant communities.[2] According to limnologist George K. Reid, an ecotone "constitutes a 'buffer' zone between two communities."[3] An example would be an *estuary*, which exists between the freshwater ecosystem of a river and the saltwater ecosystem of the open ocean. Estuaries are dynamic transition zones that provide opportunities for greater diversity and interaction. Ecotones typically support varied and rich communities, representing a boiling pot of two colliding worlds.

For me, this is a fitting metaphor for life, given that the big choices we must face usually involve a collision of ideas, beliefs, lifestyles or worldviews: these often prove to enrich our lives the most for having gone through them. *Evolution* (any significant change) doesn't happen within a stable system; adaptation and growth occurs only when stable systems come together, disturb the equilibrium, and create opportunity. Good social examples include a close friendship or a marriage in which the process of "I" and "you" becomes a dynamic "we" (the ecotone) through exchange and reciprocation. Another version of Bernard Shaw's quote, above, by the Missouri Pacific Agriculture Development Bulletin reads: "You have an idea. I have an idea. We swap. Now, you have two ideas and so do I. Both are richer. What you gave you have. What you got I did not lose. This is cooperation."

"If you have an apple and I have an apple and we exchange apples then you and I will still each have one apple. But if you have an idea and I have an idea and we exchange these ideas, then each of us will have two ideas."
—George Bernard Shaw

Water has ideas.

Ideas, like love—like water—are never lost when given away. They just transform; then they return to you in another form.

All ecotones provide opportunity for sharing of information, discovery and change. Ecotones are the synergistic blending of two ideas in the evolution of science. They are the vortex energy of a stream's eddy currents generated by the meeting of interfaces and boundaries. They are the stable, coherent domains—the *glassiness*—of polarized interfacial and intracellular water in cells and tissues.

Interfacial water is ecotone water. It was described in the late 1940s.[4,5] Four years after the end of the second world war, J.C. Henniker published an important review paper about the long-range effect of varied surfaces on many liquids, including water.[6] Henniker had cited evidence for long range impacts extending over thousands or even millions of molecular layers, surpassing the ordering of tens of molecular layers described by cell biologist Gerald Pollack in his 2001 book *Cells, Gels and the Engines of Life*.[7]

Photo 4.2: Saltwater marsh near Mahone Bay, NS, Canada; an ecotone where land, freshwater and saltwater meet and interact.

Photo by Nina Munteanu

According to water scientist Martin Chaplin, most if not all water in living organisms is interfacial water, given that it is almost never further away from surfaces, such as membranes or macromolecules, for more than a fraction of a micron. "Interfacial water molecules at the gas–liquid surface have a strong attraction towards the bulk liquid causing a high surface tension," writes Chaplin. "Liquid water at liquid–solid and liquid–gas interfaces behaves as a separate thermodynamic system from bulk water."[8]

In the 1960s, physiologist and Nobel Laureate Albert Szent-Gyorgyi proposed that water in living organisms exists in two states: the ground state and the excited state. Water at interfaces such as cell membranes exists in the excited state, which requires considerably lower energy to split.[9] This property of water enables energy transfer to take place in living organisms, ensuring long-lasting electronic excitations. Szent-Gyorgyi's ideas were largely ignored by the scientific mainstream at the time.

Gerald Pollack and his research team at the University of Washington demonstrated the existence and properties of interfacial water using a hydrophilic gel and a suspension of microspheres just visible to the eye. Pollack showed that interfacial water that forms on the surface of the gel excludes the microspheres and other solutes, such as proteins and dyes. Pollack named this region an *exclusion zone* (EZ) and noted that its formation depended on fixed charges on the gel, aligning with Szent-Gyorgyi's prediction. Pollack found EZ water to be about ten times more viscous as bulk water; and, it shows a peak light absorption at 270 nanometres and emits fluorescence when excited by light at the same wavelength.[10,11]

Del Guidice and his colleagues suggest that EZ water is a giant coherence domain (CD) stabilized on the surface of the attractive gel.[5] As Szent-Gyorgyi predicted, EZ water forms inside the cell on membrane and macromolecule surfaces. The "excited" coherent water easily transfers electrons to molecules on the cell's surface. The interface between coherent interfacial water and normal bulk water acts like a battery, recharged by incident radiant energy and resembling photosynthesis.[10,11]

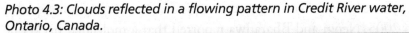

Photo 4.3: Clouds reflected in a flowing pattern in Credit River water, Ontario, Canada.

Photo by Nina Munteanu

Epitaxy

"In rivers, the water that you touch is the last of what has passed and the first of that which comes."

—Leonardo da Vinci

Epitaxy describes the transmission of structural atomic information from the surface of one material (usually a crystalline solid) to another (usually, but not always, a liquid)—*without transferring any of the material.* Information, not material, is transferred. While this may seem bizarre, examples of epitaxy are well known and used in everyday technologies in materials science. Materials scientist Rustum Roy provides the example of cloud seeding to make rain. "The seeding of clouds is epitaxial growth of crystalline-ice on a substrate of silver iodide (AgI), which has the same crystal structure. Information and "memory" are transmitted from the seed or substrate to adjacent layers of the liquid phase, which can completely control the structure of what is formed from it. No chemical transfer whatsoever occurs."[12,13]

"By providing a specific structure as a template (usually solid but sometimes liquid), one can induce an entire body of liquid (or even solid) to precipitate or crystallize in a pre-selected structure or morphology,"[13] says Roy, who suggests an epitaxial basis with homeopathy.

In 2005, Neogi and Bharadwa reported that a molecular backbone can cause water molecules to form a "thread" that can snake its way through the more open space of the larger molecules.[14] Water can exhibit a highly organized local structure when it interacts with molecules capable of imposing these structures on it. According to Roy, structure is transferred by epitaxy, with no presence of the controlling phase. This explains the success of homeopathy—which uses zero concentration of solute through successive dilution—given that it is the structure not the composition that exerts the effect.

Homeopathy, Roy tells us, relies on "active agents" changing, affecting or "imprinting" the liquid structure. The homeopathic solution is prepared through multiple serial dilution steps, each followed by multi-

ple *succussions* (vigorous shaking or turbulence) to generate pressure and nano-bubbles that catalyze a system-wide, hierarchical and self-organized form.[12]

Some homeopathic researchers have proposed structural models analogous to the Roy model. These involve aggregations or clusterings of water molecules, possibly seeded by the presence of molecules such as clathrates or zwitterions from the original source substance.[15,16,17] *Clathrates* are lattice-like substances that trap molecules. The International Union of Pure and Applied Chemistry (IUPAC) describe them as "inclusion compounds in which the guest molecule is in a cage formed by the host molecules or by a lattice of host molecules."[17] *Zwitterions* are hybrid molecules with a positive and negative charge, making them neutral. Amino acids are the best-known example. The Roy model of water structure combines epitaxy, nano-bubbles and pressure effects. Other researchers have also proposed the involvement of a coherent electromagnetic radiation field within the solvent that contributes order to molecular motion.[18,19] Del Giudice's concept of "super-radiance" or "coherence" in an electromagnetic field of molecular structural elements also reflects the Roy model, which includes epitaxy, for water structure.

Quartz crystals share a similar molecular geometry to water and can apparently convey structural information to water through *epitaxy*.[19] Quartz is the most abundant mineral on Earth. Used for centuries to improve water quality, it is still used today in many filtration systems. Marcel Vogel, the IBM scientist who developed liquid crystal technology, discovered that many of the unique qualities of crystals resulted from their ability to organize and direct energy. He found that quartz crystals act as resonators, transducers, and amplifiers of vibrational energy.[20] Quartz crystals also emit piezoelectric current in water, which helps generate water's basic structure.

According to Roy, water molecules aggregate or cluster in a self-organized way. "We must know how it is arranged," says Roy. "It is like the alphabet. If I give you the alphabet, you don't know a word, you don't know a letter or a sentence ... The molecular structure is the alphabet of water ... You must make a sentence out of [water's alphabet] and you can change the sentence."[21] In this way, water stores information and communicates it. "If you consider a cluster as a group of specific molecules, then it can survive only a short amount of time. But if you consider it as a structure whereby molecules can leave and other molecules come in, the cluster can last effectively for a very long time. The stability of the cluster structures confirms the hypothesis that water is capable of recording and storing information."

Dr. Vladimir Voeikov, professor of the Biology Faculty of the Moscow State University, Russia, tells us that, "Every seed, every embryo begins its life exclusively in water. Amniotic fluid plays a role in an embryo's development in preservation ... it is the surrounding water, like a universal computer, that reveals any biological program and thus water is also the only thing that can change it."[22]

Photo 4.4: Leaping boulders of Crater Lake, California, USA.

Photo by Nina Munteanu

Dowsing & Remote Communication

My good friend Margaret from New Westminster, British Columbia, is an avid traveller, like me. She enjoys driving, and she and I have journeyed on many trips together, both local and afar. In the thirty-odd years that I've travelled with her, one thing has stood out: she always finds a parking place exactly where she needs one. When I inquire, she shrugs with an arcane self-knowing smile. I also travel a lot in Europe and abroad with my friend Karen, from Chicago. We both enjoy spontaneous adventure and try not to second-guess where we'll end up. I usually drive and Karen navigates us through unknown country; she barely uses a map, glancing down just to make me feel better, and directs us to astounding places even locals don't know about. When I inquire, she shrugs with an arcane self-knowing smile. The universe provides. Both women are extremely intuitive and move with the flow.

I'm told that dowsing works in the same way. In a nutshell, *dowsing* is a kind of divination used to locate ground water, buried metals or ores, gemstones, and oil. While there is no scientific evidence to suggest that it is more effective than random chance, some dowsers practise it very effectively. The dowser uses a Y- or L-shaped twig or rod, or sometimes a crystal pendulum. The dowsing device moves to indicate a positive or negative response. When the dowser is near the object they are searching for, they will feel a "tug" by the device. According to dowser Helen Leathers, it is more likely the dowser who is making the device move. She believes that the successful dowser uses her intuition to tap into the "universal knowledge" available to all of us but only accessible by highly intuitive people. Some experienced dowsers don't use a dowsing tool, favouring their own body. Australian Aborigines dowse through the soles of their feet. Using their bodies as self-organized communities of water (we are composed of over 70% water), they "communicate" with the water below ground.

"Dowsers often find what are called 'blind springs',"[23] Alick Bartholomew writes in his book *The Spiritual Life of Water*. This is where a column of water rises up underground but doesn't reach the surface; instead, it pushes horizontally along rock fractures as an underground stream. Blind springs are often associated with places of power, Bartholomew writes. Many European traditional sacred sites are blind spring locations. I talk more about these in Chapter 10, *Water Is Prayer*.

Applied kinesiology, an alternative medical technique used by chiropractors—which tests a body's affinity with specific substances through the testing of muscles—is a form of dowsing that illustrates the principle of resonance. I recall being tested by a First Nations elder in Northern British Columbia, with some success.

Cleve Backster, who developed the lie detector in 1966, detected what he called *biocommunication* in plants, which he termed "primary perception."[24] His experiments were later documented in the Tomkins and Bird 1973 bestseller *The Secret Life of Plants*, which was largely condemned by the scientific community for making pseudoscientific claims. However, Backster's observations were not unique. They followed on those made by other scientific researchers, including the German experimental psychologist Gustav Theodor Fechner in the mid-1800s and the Bengali scientist Jagadish Chandra Bose, who documented in 1900 how plants responded to music, sound and intention.

Backster was criticized for not conducting his experiments in a fashion that aligned with the scientific method; he didn't use appropriate controls or other elements within the dogma of scientific methodology. As a result, his work—and others' like his—was largely ignored and condemned by the scientific community. This brings to mind what I mentioned about the pursuit of science in the preface of this book. I bring up the importance of curiosity, imagination and the willingness to

Photo 4.5: Rain falling on maple trees in Mississauga, Ontario, Canada.

Photo by Nina Munteanu

challenge and be challenged. I discuss how many great scientific discoveries arose not by following the current hegemony; instead, discoveries often resulted from breaking the rules, when intuition led an intrepid scientist on a journey. More than epistemologists—ground-breaking scientists reflect artistry and a willingness to discover a new world with new eyes. The ground-breaking scientist is a hero on a journey, poised to challenge the status quo (*especially if it's his or hers*), choosing to recognize that science is a process rather than a set of fixed rules. Science is a work in progress, as Princeton Dean Emeritus Robert Jahn was fond of saying.

Sometimes it's the "law-breakers" who find the new land.

As postscript, much of Backster's crude polygraph work to register the effect of thoughts has been verified and corroborated forty years later by various scientists including the physicist Konstantin Korotkov and his state-of-the-art equipment. Korotkov hooked up a potted plant to his Gas Discharge Visualization (GDV) machine and demonstrated how a plant's energy field diminished when it was threatened.[25]

Fractals & Information Flow

Science is beginning to understand that coherence, which exists on all levels—cellular, molecular, atomic and organic—governs all life processes. Life and all that informs it is a gestalt process. The flow of information is fractal and multidirectional, forming a complex network of paths created by resonance interactions in a self-organizing framework. It's stable chaos. And water drives the process.

The unifying interconnections proposed in quantum physics suggest that our DNA is controlled by signals outside our cells, "including our personal scripts—messages from positive and negative thoughts, from the environment,"[26] writes developmental biologist Bruce Lipton, author of *Biology of Belief*. Lipton argues that "biomedicine doesn't recognize the massive complexity of inter-communication between physical parts and the energy field that make up the whole. Cellular constituents are woven into a complex web of crosstalk, feedback, and feed-forward communication loops. A biological dysfunction may arise from a miscommunication along any of the routes of information flow."[26]

Water is information. Water is gestalt.

We are a fractal community. "When you look at yourself you see an individual person," says Lipton, "but if you understand the nature of who you are, you realize that you are actually a community of about 50 trillion living cells." Lipton goes on to say that, "each cell is a living individual, a sentient being that has its own life and functions but interacts with other cells in the nature of a community ... *Health* is when there is harmony in the community, and *disease* (dis-ease) is when there is disharmony that tends to fracture the community relationships."[27]

The fractal nature of our bodies is demonstrated in the relationships of our cells and tissues to our overall body function, says Lipton. For instance, each of our myriad systems (e.g., digestive, respiratory, excretory, endocrine, reproductive, musculoskeletal, nervous, and immune) exists in each cell. "In fact, we are made in the image of a cell," Lipton suggests. He compares the cell to a computer. It has programs built into it, with the nucleus as hard drive and with programs that are the genes; but what the computer expresses is not determined by the programs; expression is determined by the information that the user—as the environment—types onto the interface (the keyboard or screen). According to Lipton, the cell membrane acts as the interface, processing information, and the genes are the hard drive potentials. "That is why every cell in your body can form any kind of cell because every nucleus has all the genes that make up a human,"[27] says Lipton. The nature of the cell, however, relies on feedback of information from the environment, such as the unique identifying protein keys (receptors) that act on interfacing cell surfaces. The upshot of this is that we program our cells, and the consequence is that—if life isn't going well—what we have to do is not change our genes but change our perceptions.[27] I talk more about soft inheritance and epigenetics below.

Lipton suggests that much of North America's conventional biomedical knowledge remains based in Newtonian physics and Cartesian reductionism aimed at dominating and controlling Nature. Quantum theory—which came to us only when we were ready for it (see Chapter 11, *Water Is Story*)—embraces an emerging worldview that is holistic and integral. Quantum theory gives us the basis for seeing a universe that is not so much material, but rather form and pattern; not so much parts of a system, but rather a moving fractal whole within a worldview of evolution. And that view of evolution is based not so much on competition and "survival of the fittest in a struggle for existence" as it is on creative cooperation and integrated Nature.

Water is a universe of vibrating energy in constant communication.

Photo 4.6: Swiss cows on the steep meadows of Lake Lucerne, near Seelisberg, Switzerland.

Photo by Nina Munteanu

Nature, Nurture & Evolution

Is evolution the language of destiny? What is destiny, if not self-actualization and synchronicity in an interactive dance of nature and nurture? If evolution is the language of destiny, then choice and selection are the words of evolution, and "fractal ecology" is its plot.

How do we define today a concept that Darwin originated 200 years ago in a time without bio-engineering, nano-technology, chaos theory, quantum mechanics and the Internet? We live in an exciting era of complicated change, where science based on the limitation of traditional biology is being challenged and stretched by pioneers into areas some scientists might call heretical. Endosymbiosis, synchronicity, autopoiesis and self-organization, morphic resonance, the Gaia hypothesis and planetary intelligence: some of these might more aptly be described through the language of metaphysics. But should they be so confined? It comes down to language and how we communicate.

Is it possible for an individual to evolve in one's own lifetime? To become more than oneself? And then pass on one's personal experience irrevocably to others—vertically and laterally?

On the *vertical* argument, the French naturalist Jean-Baptiste Lamarck developed a theory of biological evolution in the early 19th century considered so ridiculous that it spawned a name: Lamarkism. His notion—that acquired traits could be passed along to offspring—was ridiculed for over two hundred years. Until he was proven right.

In 2008, evolutionary biologists at Tel Aviv University in Israel showed that all sorts of cellular machinery—an intelligence of sorts—played a vital role in how DNA sequences were inherited.[28] When re-

searchers inserted foreign genes into the DNA of laboratory animals and plants, something strange happened. The genes worked at first; then they were "silenced." Generation after generation. The host cells tagged the foreign genes with an "off switch" that made the genes inoperable. And, although the new genes were passed onto offspring, so was the off switch. It was Larmarkism in action: the parents' experience had influenced the offsprings' inheritance. Evolutionists gave it a new name. They called it *soft inheritance.*

"Life experiences alter DNA," writes Lizzie Buchen in *Nature*. "Not necessarily its sequence, but rather its form and structure, including the chemicals that decorate it and how tightly it winds and packs around proteins inside the cell. These changes [are] often referred to as epigenetic modifications."[29] In a 2014 article in *Nature*, Virginia Hughes discusses the work of Dias and Ressler on the phenomenon of *epigenetics* (chemical changes to the genome that affect how DNA is packaged and expressed, without altering its sequence).[30,31] Biologists first noticed transgenerational epigenetic inheritance (or soft inheritance) in plants. Tomatoes, for example, pass along chemical markings that control an important ripening gene, writes Hughes.

Photo 4.7: A lobster trap in the foreground of a typical maritime scene in Peggy's Cove, Nova Scotia, Canada.

"We are the product of nature via nurture,"[32,33] writes researcher Jeffrey Craig at the Murdoch Childrens Research Institute. "Our genes and environments interact. And 'environment' can be what we are experiencing now or at any time during our life." Conrad Waddington defined epigenetics over 70 years ago as "the interactions of genes with their environment, which bring the phenotype into being." According to Craig, epigenetic changes may occur via small molecules jumping onto our genes. "They would stay there, hanging on even through cell division (mitosis), providing a long-term epigenetic legacy ... [and] could persist from one generation to the next." Scientists have identified several epigenetic biomarkers of environment that may be passed down generations, including stress and smoking.[29,30,33,34]

Photo by Nina Munteanu

As for passing on one's experience and acquisitions to others *later-ally*, education in all its facets surely provides a mechanism. This may run the gamut from wise mentors, spiritual leaders, storytellers, courageous heroes, to our kindergarten teachers. Who's to say that these, too, are not irrevocable? Education relies, after all, on how we learn, and how we "remember." The still-controversial article in *Nature* by Lizzie Buchen, called "In Their Nurture," on the work of behavioural scientists in epigenetics brings the question of nurture vs. nature into colourful debate.[34] In the article, Buchen describes observations made by scientist Frances Champagne of Columbia University in New York on the sexual behaviour of female rats who were doted on or neglected in their first week of life. "The idea that epigenetics could explain the lasting effects of something as short-lived but profound as a mother's affection … [suggests that] epigenetic changes could be the conduit through which environment elicits life-long biological change."[29]

Evolution is choice. It is a choice made on many levels, from the intuitive mind to the intelligent cell. The British botanist Rupert Sheldrake proposed that the physical forms we take on are not necessarily contained inside our genes (which, he suggested, may be analogous to transistors tuned in to the proper frequencies for translating invisible information into visible form).[35] This notion is conveyed through other phenomena, which truly lie in the realm of metaphysics and lateral evolution; concepts like bilocation, psychic telegraphing, telekinesis and manifestation. Critics condemn these as crazy notions. Or is it just limited vision again? Our future cannot be foretold in our present language; that has yet to be written.

Non-Local Phenomena & Morphic Fields

British botanist Rupert Sheldrake drew on the work of French philosopher Henri Bergson to develop the theory of morphic resonance, which makes use of the older notion of morphogenic fields, in his 1981 controversial book *A New Science of Life*. For Sheldrake, the laws of the universe appear not to be laws at all, but rather deeply ingrained habits of action, built up over the eons … like ancient riverbeds on the surface of Mars. Sheldrake calls the habitual tendency of nature *morphic resonance*, in which present forms are influenced by past forms. According to Sheldrake, morphic resonance is transmitted through *morphogenic fields*, which are analogous to electromagnetic fields in that they transmit information, but differ in that they do so without using energy and are therefore not diminished by transmission through time or space.[35]

Take our physical forms, for instance. I mentioned above that Sheldrake suggested that any form looks the way it does because it "remembers" its form through repetition and that any new form having similar characteristics will use the pattern of already existing forms as a guide for its appearance. According to Sheldrake, morphogenic fields are located invisibly in and around organisms and may account for the regeneration of severed limbs in worms and salamanders, the holographic properties of memory, telepathy, and the increasing ease with which new skills are learned as greater quantities of a population acquire them. In his subsequent books, *The Presence of the Past* and *The Rebirth of Nature*, Sheldrake traced the evolution of the materialistic worldview, which is currently under siege by revolutionary concepts and

"Water is the means, medium and message of life, the rainbow within that mirrors the one in the sky."

—Mae-Wan Ho

paradigms, such as quantum theory and its cousin chaos theory, the Gaia Hypothesis, cellular symbiosis, and morphic resonance.

Sheldrake describes the mind as a field. Following on Jungian archetypal gestalt synchronicity, Sheldrake suggests that "our minds are extended in both space and time with other people's minds, and with the group mind or cultural mind by way of their connection to the collective unconscious."[36] Sheldrake posits that we tune into archetypal fields or patterns and "our minds are much broader than the 'things' inside our brains. They extend out into the past and into social groupings to which we are linked."[36]

An example of this social field phenomenon is the self-organized movement of birds in flight, fish in schools and wolves, dolphins and many other social animals.

Water is gestalt.

Sheldrake's morphic resonance aligns with the notion of consciousness as a global phenomenon that occurs everywhere in the body, not just our brains. "Consciousness, at its most basic, [is] coherent light,"[37] writes science journalist Lynne McTaggart in her book *The Field*. She discusses the contributions of scientists, such as Harold E. Puthoff, Fritz-Albert Popp, Jacques Benveniste and Karl Pribram, to the argument that the act of perception occurs at the quantum level.

"We don't see objects *per se*, but only their quantum information and out of that you construct your image of the world," McTaggart writes. "Perceiving the world [is] a matter of tuning into the Zero Point Field."[37] According to McTaggart, it took NASA astronaut Edgar Mitchel, founder of the Institute of Noetic Sciences to bring together these seminal works that harmonized with David Bohm's vision of a world of flowing "unbroken wholeness." Mitchel recognized that "as a totality, their work presented itself as a unified theory of mind and matter." The Universe is a vast dynamic cobweb of energy exchange, McTaggart concludes. And nature is open-ended, intelligent and purposeful, making use of a cohesive learning feedback process of infor-

mation flow. Its unifying mechanism is not a "fortunate mistake" but information which has been encoded and transmitted everywhere at once.[37,38]

Photo 4.8: Marshy pond in Credit River watershed, Ontario, Canada.

Photo by Nina Munteanu

Entangled Minds

"All things by immortal power, Near and Far Hiddenly To each other linked are, That thou canst not stir a flower Without troubling of a star."
—Francis Thompson

Shortly after high school, when I started travelling the world on my own, I took the fast overnight train from Venice to Nice. I didn't realize that this was a notorious line, stalked by train robbers known to the police in Nice.

In the deep of night, as I slept, I fell victim to a gang of robbers. I woke up just as they slipped out of my car with their booty. Overtaken by unruly rage—they'd taken my camera, after all—I foolishly chased them like a mad banshee. They jumped off the moving train, terrified of my incoherent wrath. When I returned to my home in Canada, my mother quizzed me and finally suggested that I'd experienced some kind of incident that very night. I shrugged and told her the truth; she always seemed to know when I was in trouble. Years later, working as a consultant and university instructor, I formed a close friendship with someone I would later call a soulmate. It felt as though we had known each other before, even though we'd never before met. Our friendship has endured for years despite living close to three thousand miles from each other, with sporadic and infrequent communication. To this day, *I know* when she will call or message me. I know just before she calls, which is random and irregular. Some would describe—and dismiss—this "distant knowing" or "premonition" as a coincidence. I just know that *I know*. Other descriptions and related phenomena include: "unmediated knowledge acquisition at a distance", telepathy, clairvoyance, pre-cognition, creative insight, and déjà vu. All these are non-local observations.

Is it all simply quantum entanglement? If in Bohm's universe, where all parts of a whole are connected in a flowing Holomovement, then is reincarnation simply a physical iteration of that continual matter forming and dissolving in physical reality? Are we all part of a single "something"—a singularity—and winking in and out of various states of awareness? Then intuition would simply be opening a door into an altered state (or dimension) of self and whole ...

The fabric of reality suggested by quantum theory and observations associated with psychic phenomena bear a striking resemblance, science author Dean Radin writes in his controversial book *Entangled Minds*. "They are eerily weird in precisely the right way to suggest a meaningful relationship."[39] Taking his cue from the recent discoveries of macroscopic entanglement (see my *Preface*), Radin asks the question: could "we occasionally have numinous feelings of connectedness with loved ones at a distance? ... Could 'entangled minds' result in the experience of you hearing the telephone ring and somehow knowing—instantly—who's calling?"[39] Some scientists posit that the high degree of coherence displayed by living systems may depend on entanglement (*bioentanglement*, specifically); while others suggest that conscious awareness is caused or related to entangled particles in the brain. Some propose that the entire Universe is a single, self-entangled object. This brings to mind David Bohm's concept of "Implicate Order" and the Universe as an interconnected whole.[40] It brings to mind the "Butterfly Effect" (a sensitivity of initial conditions) of Edward Lorenz's strange attractors in a fractal universe.[41] It brings to mind, also, the individuality of the whole in Harold Joachim's "coherentism."[42]

Radin uses water to explain the interconnected medium of multiple phases, with consciousness phase emerging like an iceberg: emerging structures (i.e., internal development and relationship between parts: the tip) from forms (i.e., expressed overall shape: the whole). In an entangled universe, Radin suggests that we might occasionally feel connected to others at a distance; we might know things without the use of the ordinary senses; and our intentions might reverberate throughout the entangled medium—like water.

Photo 4.9: A Monarch butterfly in a field.

Photo by Merridy Cox

One Person's Chaos Is Another's Order

When the Greek poet Hesiod wrote *Theogony* in the 8th century, he stated that "first of all, Chaos came to be,"[43] and then the Earth and everything stable followed. The ancient Greeks seemed to have accepted that chaos precedes order; that order comes from disorder—the opposite of what current science postulates. The dragon in Chinese myth represents the principal of order, yang, which emerges from chaos. Yin and yang, the female and male principals, create the universe and retain the qualities of chaos; too much of either one brings back chaos.

Chaos theory emerged in the 20th century as a new and exciting field of scientific inquiry during a flagging scientific discipline suffering the crisis of increasing specialization. Chaos breaks the lines that separate scientific discipline, bringing to the world a science of the global nature of systems. Here's how James Gleick describes it:

> *Where chaos begins, classical science stops. For as long as the world has had physicists inquiring into the laws of nature, it has suffered a special ignorance about disorder in the atmosphere, in the turbulent sea, in the fluctuations of wildlife populations, in the oscillations of the heart and the brain. The irregular side of nature, the discontinuous and erratic side—these have been puzzles to science, or worse, monstrosities.*[44]

In the 1970s, mathematicians, physicists, biologists, and chemists began to seek connections between different kinds of irregularity. From Gleick:

> *Physiologists found a surprising order in the chaos that develops in the human heart, the prime cause of sudden unexplained death. Ecologists explored the rise and fall of gypsy moth popula-*

tions. Economists dug out old stock price data and tried a new kind of analysis. The insights that emerged led directly into the natural world—the shapes of clouds, the paths of lightening, the microscopic intertwining of blood vessels, the galactic clustering of stars.[44]

Chaos theory presents "a universe that is at once deterministic and obeys the fundamental physical laws, but is capable of disorder, complexity and unpredictability,"[45] write Sardar and Abrams in their book *Introducing Chaos*. "Chaos describes aperiodic, apparently random events in a deterministic system. In chaos there is order and in order there is chaos. And "now that science is looking," says Gleick, "chaos seems everywhere. A rising column of cigarette smoke breaks into wild swirls. A flag snaps back and forth in the wind. A dripping faucet goes from a steady pattern to a random one."[44]

We can witness chaos in the random changes in weather, the spread of epidemics, the metabolism of the cells, the changing populations of insects and birds, the rise and fall of civilizations, and the propagation of impulses along our nerves. Gleick notes that "the most passionate advocates of the new science go so far as to say that twentieth-century science will be remembered for just three things: relativity, quantum mechanics and chaos."[44]

Photo 4.10: Sunset over Steveston Harbour, British Columbia, Canada.

Photo by Nina Munteanu

When Ocean Meets "Ocean"

The first time I visited the ocean—the Atlantic Ocean in Bar Harbor, Maine—I was five years old. I still remember the frisson of excitement I felt. What I didn't expect was the incredible thrill of peace that accompanied it. You might think that is an oxymoron; but the ocean felt primordial, powerful and restful at the same time. It was vast, scary and comforting. And I couldn't help being drawn to it. The rhythmic surge of oceanic waves and their dancing play with the light of the sun held my child-gaze for hours. It was the unknown, known. The unfamiliar, familiar. I was born in an "ocean", after all.

In the late 1800s and early 1900s, French scientist René Quinton revealed the striking similarity between the ocean and our own internal fluids, such as amniotic fluid.[46] He proved that organisms had to maintain their "internal ocean" to survive, confirming a tautology: *the need for an evolving organism to take the ocean with it*. Quinton used marine plasma, harvested from a specific plankton bloom within an oceanic vortex, to help many of his patients overcome a variety of illnesses. Known as QMP, it is a living matrix rich in DNA, RNA, vitamins, enzymes, proteins, fatty acids, organic acids, and other biochemicals that scientists have yet to define.[47]

Acting like an *internal ocean*, extracellular fluid bathes each cell of our body in a medium that allows organelles, nuclei and cell membranes to communicate and do commerce.

As I discuss above, cell biologist Bruce Lipton demonstrated that genes don't exert control over our health and physical expression, as we initially thought. He revealed that a cell's predisposition to genetic programming responds to signals in the environment.[26,27] When the extra-

cellular fluid deviates from its original oceanic composition, deficient genes may be activated followed by disease. If deficient genes are not activated, we have the chance to live long and vibrant lives. Nobel Prize laureate Dr. Alexis Carrel demonstrated that cells can live almost indefinitely when kept in an optimum environment. "The cell is immortal," said Carrel. "It is merely the fluid in which it floats that degenerates."[48]

"The Earth's oceans contain the blueprint for life,"[49] write Pangman and Evans, authors of *Dancing with Water*. The ocean is "a storehouse of genetic information we are just beginning to comprehend … [It is] literally the amniotic fluid of the Earth."

Photo 4.11: The ocean surf of Cozumel, Mexico.

Photo by Nina Munteanu

Salmon, Trees & Infrasound

In the fall of 1979, I moved to Vancouver Island, British Columbia, to teach ecology and limnology at the University of Victoria. Soon after I arrived, I hiked Goldstream Creek and witnessed my first annual salmon run. It was humbling to watch the heroic journey of these salmon as they shivered upstream against the current to spawn.

Along the Pacific Northwest, millions of Chum, Pink, Chinook, Sockeye, and Coho salmon return from the Pacific Ocean to their stream birthplace to create a new generation of salmon. The salmon must find the stream of their origin and battle upstream, sometimes against raging currents and dodging hungry bears, to the pebble-bed (called a *redd*) where they lay and fertilize their eggs. Task complete, the exhausted salmon then die—completing their cycle of life at almost the same place where they were born several years before—their carcasses providing a nutrient-rich fertilizer for the aquatic and terrestrial ecosystems.

Photo 4.12: Coastal rainsforest stream on Vancouver Island, British Columbia, Canada.

Photo by Kevin Klassen

Around the same time that I started teaching at the University of Victoria, Dr. Tom Reimchen and his team of students had already begun ground-breaking investigations of the Pacific Northwest salmon run that eventually involved bears, trees and salmon.

Two decades after, in 2001, Dr. Reimchen reported that his and others' investigations had yielded previously unrecognized linkages between the open ocean and forests. These linkages extend from the estuaries and small streams that fringe the coastlines, through to the headwaters of major rivers that penetrate far into the continents.[50,51] Reimchen's team and other researchers in Washington, British Columbia and Alaska observed that when bears catch salmon, they typically haul them into the nearby line of trees to feast. Bears focus on the protein-rich eggs and brain matter of the fish, in their need to fatten up for the long winter hibernation, leaving the rest of the carcass to rot in the forest. Using a marker protein called ^{15}N, Reimchen and other researchers showed that the fish carcasses provide fertilizer for nearby trees and plants.[50,51] This occurs through mutualistic cooperation with a microbe that breaks down decaying fish carcasses into a form digestible by the trees—in exchange for tree sugar.

The research revealed an intriguing relationship among the bears, rivers, trees, microbes and salmon: the bears depend on the salmon as a source of food, on the river to deliver the salmon, and the trees to provide cover; the salmon rely on the river to transport them to where they need to spawn, on a good tree canopy to keep the river cool for healthy egg production, and a predator (the bear) to cull the weaker fish to ensure a healthy future stock; the trees—and their associated microbes—benefit from the bears and the salmon for delivering the fertilizer for their healthy growth and, in turn, provide a supportive environment for the bear, the river and the salmon. Unsurprisingly, tree sugars ebbed and flowed with the salmon run.

Some suggest that there is evidence—though unsubstantiated—that the trees along the river increase their sugar levels *in anticipation* of the size and time of the salmon run—while the salmon are still hundreds of miles away in the ocean. This suggests a kind of interspecies communication.

In her book *The Global Forest*, botanist and medical biochemist Diana Beresford-Kroeger suggests that trees communicate by *infrasound* (what she calls "silent sound").[52] Infrasound propagates as long sound waves at a frequency below 20 Hz, too low in pitch to be heard by the human ear (as opposed to *ultrasounds*, which are inaudible frequencies over 16,000 Hz, like that emitted by bats). Known natural sources of infrasound include waterfalls, ocean waves, earthquakes, and atmospheric phenomena such as thunder, lightning and the northern lights.[53] Elephants use infrasound to communicate over long distances.[54] Whales use infrasound—and dolphins, ultrasound—to navigate the oceans. The roar of a tiger apparently incorporates infrasonic frequencies. Honeybees in a hive act as a self-organized aggregate when triggered by a storm, by generating an infrasonic alarm signal.[53] Because of their great size and tensile movement in air, forests produce infrasound. According to Beresford-Kroeger, they may communicate with one another and with other species by this means. She posits that each tree produces a sound as individual as the iris of an eye or fingerprint of a hand.[52]

Can we hear or feel them?   Are water and epitaxy involved? Beresford-Kroeger and others suggest that some of us do hear and feel the trees. She suggests that the low frequency affects the sympathetic nervous system and the emotional centres of the brain. "The acoustical experience of people who can register silent sound as a form of cross-species communication testifies to its being felt primarily in the chest as a reaction of immense intensity, together with a tightness that can bring one close to tears," says Beresford-Kroeger. "These kinds of feelings are commonly felt listening to music."[52]

Infrasound travels across vast distances. "Even the planet Earth rings a bell of life as the planet moves ahead in its orbital path,"[52] says Beresford-Kroeger. "The matter of space is forced into a giant wave pattern that travels outward into the galaxy in a registration of silent sound."

Telluric currents or Earth currents may carry infrasounds that move underground or through the sea. These electric currents are induced by changes in the outer part of the Earth's magnetic field caused by interactions between the solar wind and the magnetosphere or solar radiation effects on the ionosphere.

Photo 4.13: Bridge over the Credit River, Meadowvale, Ontario, Canada.

Photo by Nina Munteanu

When Planets Sing

Each planet sings a unique "song", given that it possesses unique frequencies from different amounts of charged particles flying around and the various strengths of magnetic fields surrounding it, including telluric currents mentioned above.

The Kepler space telescope "listens" to the sounds that stars make. This pursuit even has a name; it's called *astroseismology*. The technique measures tiny variations in a star's brightness as sound waves bounce within it. Using resonances, astroseismologists literally build up a picture of what the inside of a star looks like.[55]

Radio emissions—complex vibrations of charged electromagnetic particles from solar wind, ionosphere, planetary magnetosphere, and charged particle interactions within the magnetosphere of each planet's moons or rings—were captured by instruments on NASA's *Voyager, INJUN 1, ISEE, HAWKEYE* space probes and *Cassini* flights in our solar system and then converted to sound waves. The sounds generated by Earth and the other planets of our solar system ripple with existential paradox. Ranging from eerily other-worldly to gestalt familiarity, they reveal a drama both vast and deeply intimate. At once disturbing and calming, the sounds entangle déjà vu with the promise of a vast unknowable. To hear these sounds is like coming face to face with infinity.

Created by lightning, "whistlers" travel along Earth's magnetic field lines in a cacophony that resembles an alien jungle of birds. Chorus waves from electrons spiralling down from Earth's Van Allen radiation belts create a discordant symphony of a jungle night. Jupiter's charged particles "sing" across its hemisphere like a pulsing night chorus. Radio emissions from Jupiter send a haunting rhythmic chorus. Ganymede, Jupiter's largest moon, sounds suspiciously like the spooky blips, clicks and pows of an old science fiction movie. The sounds of Uranus, its moon Miranda, and its rings undulate with ominous anticipation, including "rockets" zooming; while Saturn's rings whistle and howl like a lost wind.[56]

On November 1, 2013, Don Gurnett, the James Van Allen professor of physics at the University of Iowa and the principal investigator for the Plasma Wave Science instrument on *Voyager 1*, announced that *Voyager 1* had finally surpassed the heliosphere and had sent back the first "sounds of interstellar space." As with infrasound, this kind of "sound" was not auditory sound, but waves of electrons in the plasma (or ionized gas) of space. Because plasma waves occur at audio frequencies between a few hundred and a few thousand hertz, "we can play the data through a loudspeaker and listen," says Gurnett. "The pitch and frequency tell us about the density of gas surrounding the spacecraft."[57]

Given the prevalence of water in space and its incredible mobility, I'll be interested to know when scientists determine water's role in interstellar communication.

Figure 4.1: Micrograph of a dried water drop from Lake Constance (Bodenseewaser), from Welt im Tropfen ("World in a Drop"), page 49.

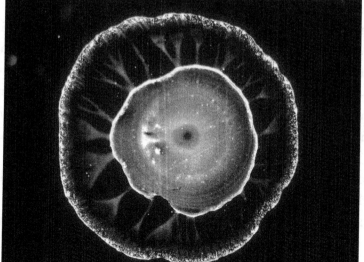

Berndt Kroplin, Institute for Static and Dynamics of Aerospace Structures, University of Stuttgart

Magnetic Fields & Intention

Biological researcher and geriatrician Bernard Grad of McGill University, Montreal, discovered in the 1970s that if water was subjected to a small magnetic field or to light, the atomic bonding in the water altered and surface tension was reduced. He went on to show that a person can emit enough of a magnetic field to alter the atomic bonds of water.[39] When someone focused positive intent into water that was used on plants, strong growth resulted. When someone who was upset or disturbed focused on the water, little or no additional plant growth resulted. Several other scientists confirmed Grad's findings.[39]

Dr. Bernd Kröplin at the University of Stuttgart looked at the mechanisms by which water collects, stores and disseminates information.[58] He showed that even the temporary influence of weak energy fields can cause changes in water structure. Kröplin showed that the effect on water was influenced by the experimenter, so the phenomenon cannot be reproduced independently of the observer. In effect, any work on water structure cannot be objective. The observer is part of the environment, says Kröplin, and his or her mood affects the properties expressed by water. Similarly, if you're looking at a quantum system it behaves like a particle; if you're not looking at it, it behaves like a wave.

Water is a quantum shape-shifter.

In his over thirteen-year-long research with consciousness and remote influences, William Braud reported on a series of laboratory experiments demonstrating that people can exert direct mental influences on a variety of biological systems at a distance without conventional and energetic influences.[59] Braud explored the use of *ganzfeld* (German for "whole field"), a relaxation technique that helped alter conscious-

"I am That, thou art That, all this is That, That alone is."
—Maharishi Mahesh Yogi

Photo 4.14: Reflections of a world in a drop of water.

Photo by Nina Munteanu

ness very much like the desensitization tank I experienced in the Bodhi Tree Wellness Centre in Vancouver. There is good anecdotal evidence that the healing technique of *Reiki* (which means "universal life energy" in Japanese) successfully utilizes gentle touch and distance healing, based on channelling of life force energy.

Braud also found that people were more likely to succeed if, "instead of believing in a distinction between themselves and the world and seeing individual people and things as isolated and divisible, they viewed everything as a connected continuum of interrelations—and also if they understood that there were other ways to communicate than through the usual channels."[37] Similarly, the Moscow Brain Research Institute's Laboratory of Neurocybernetics demonstrated that meditation increased information perception in the cortex and increased functioning relationship of the left and right hemispheres of the brain.[37] Any state of altered consciousness—meditation, relaxation, the *ganzfeld*, dreams—relaxes constraint, writes Lynne McTaggart in her book *The Field*. According to systems theorist Ervin Laszlo, it is as though we are a radio and our bandwidth expands.[37] McTaggart adds that when two people "relax their bandwidths" toward establishing a deep connection, their brain patterns become highly synchronized and a kind of "coherent domain" establishes, just as with molecules of water. "The brain of each member of the pair becomes less highly tuned in to his own separate information and more receptive to that of the other."[37] Just like the ecotone I talked about above.

Our natural state of being is a relationship: "A tango," says McTaggart, "a constant state of one influencing the other. Just as the subatomic particles that compose us cannot be separated from space and particles surrounding them, so living beings cannot be isolated from each other ... The natural state of the living world [is the result of a] drive toward greater coherence." *Negentropy* (the opposite of entropy) is the dominant force and by the act of observation and intention, we can extend a kind of super-radiance to the world.[37] Many of humanity's

greatest achievements arise from moments of inspiration that may in fact result from an individual gaining access to a shared accumulation of information through what McTaggart calls the *Zero Point Field* (the lowest energy state of a particular field), but can be variously described as intuition, the collective unconscious, the Source. Genius may simply be a greater ability to access the Universal Zero Point Field.[37,38]

Photo 4.15: Cliff jumping into the Pacific Ocean at Desolation Sound, British Columbia, Canada.

Photo by Nina Munteanu

Communicating in a Holographic Universe

"You are the world."
—Krishnamurti

"The pioneers of quantum physics—Erwin Schrodinger, Werner Heisenberg, Niels Bohr, and Wolfgang Pauli—had an inkling of the metaphysical territory they had trespassed into,"[37] writes Lynne McTaggart in her book *The Field*. Pauli turned to psychoanalysis, Jungian archetypes and the Kabbalah; Bohr examined Tao and Chinese philosophy; Schrödinger studied Hindu philosophy; and Heisenberg turned to the Platonic theory of ancient Greece. Yet, "a coherent theory of the spiritual implications of quantum physics remained beyond their grasp,"[37] writes McTaggart. She then notes that Neils Bohr hung a sign on his door saying, "Philosophers keep out. Work in progress."

Physicists struggled for years to reconcile quantum physics with the Newtonian/Cartesian view embraced by classical physics. The differences appeared insurmountable. Quantum mechanics requires reality to be discontinuous, non-causal, and non-local; whereas relativity theory requires reality to be continuous, causal, and local.

Seeking a resolution, physicist David Bohm started with what these two contradictory theories had in common: undivided wholeness. When the University of Paris team led by Alain Aspect demonstrated *proof of entanglement* (e.g., that under certain circumstances subatomic particles are able to instantaneously communicate with each other regardless of the distance separating them), Bohm suggested that their separateness is in fact an illusion.[40]

In Chapter 3, I mention that Bohm postulated a physical reality that was not a collection of separate objects—as it appears to us—but

an undivided whole in perpetual dynamic flux. Bohm conceived a universe like a hologram in constant flow.[40] And, because every part of a hologram contains all the information possessed by the whole—like the cells of the body—the whole lies in each part.

"If the apparent separateness of subatomic particles is illusory, it means that at a deeper level of reality all things in the universe are infinitely interconnected,"[60] writes Michael Talbot author of *The Universe as a Hologram*. "The electrons in a carbon atom in the human brain are connected to subatomic particles that comprise every salmon that swims, every heart that beats, and every star that shimmers in the sky."[60]

Bohm collaborated with neuroscientist Karl Pribram on a model of human cognition that described the brain as operating like a hologram. The non-locality of information storage in the hologram means that, even if most parts are damaged, the entirety will be contained within even a single remaining part of sufficient size. This is why people may continue to perform well even after struck by major brain damage. The brain is a coherent network.[60]

Coherence establishes communication. "It's like a subatomic telephone network," says McTaggart. "These subatomic waves or particles … are like a multitude of tuning forks that all begin resonating together. As the waves get into phase or synch, they begin acting like one giant wave and one giant subatomic particle."[37]

Water is coherence.

The Faces of Water

When I was a child growing up in the Eastern Townships of Quebec, I thought I would be an artist when I grew up. I drew and sketched and painted every day. I told stories with my art. I created graphic novels, and populated them with superheroes travelling in the Universe on great adventures. I wasn't a very good swimmer and the power of the sea both frightened and thrilled me. I witnessed the mercurial nature of water, both as a child playing in freshwater lakes and rivers and later as an avid boater on the Pacific Ocean of the coast of British Columbia.

Fascinated with water in its many forms, I used to stare for long periods of time at the turbulent flow of a stream or river and the cursive lap of waves on the shore of a lake. While my older brother and sister were out swimming, I was staring and studying—and drawing. Apparently, I wasn't the only one. In Chapter 3, I discuss da Vinci's fascination with eddies and vortexes. Philip Ball writes in his book *Flow* that da Vinci sat and stared for hours—enthralled by the turbulent motion of water—not to see things more sharply, but to stop seeing, to transcend the limitations of his eyes.[61] A Neo-Platonist, da Vinci wished to understand flowing water by essentially "entering" into its rhythmic movements.

Da Vinci integrated art, science and design in an empirical systematic and visual approach to gain knowledge about the natural world—to see the world as an integrated whole, "making a perceptual shift from the parts to the whole, objects to relationships, quantities to qualities,"[62] writes physicist Fritjof Capra, author of *The Science of da Vinci*. Da Vinci's approach to scientific knowledge was the approach of a painter. "Painting," he said, "embraces within itself all the forms of nature." Da Vinci understood nature's fractal self-similar qualities; that the part reflected the whole and the microcosm was similar to the macrocosm.[63]

Photo 4.16: Flow patterns of water over the shallows in the Credit River, Ontario, Canada.

Photo by Nina Munteanu

Unlike Bacon and Descartes, who would later describe nature mechanistically and something to dominate, da Vinci wished only to study her; he was in awe of Nature's beauty and ingenious design. Da Vinci was, like Goethe, a *deep ecologist* (with an eco-centric view in which humanity is not separate from Nature).

He was the original student of *biomimicry* (the science that studies and mimics Nature's design): "The virtues of grasses, stones, and trees do not exist because humans know them ... Grasses are noble in themselves without the aid of human languages or letters." Nature as a model and mentor is being rediscovered in the practices of ecological design and biomimicry, Capra tells us. "Like Leonardo, eco-designers today study the patterns and flows in the natural world and try to incorporate the underlying principles into their design processes. This attitude of appreciation and respect for nature is based on a philosophical stance that does not view humans as standing apart from the rest of the living world, but rather as being fundamentally embedded in, and dependent upon, the entire community of life in the biosphere."[62]

I also mention in Chapter 3 how van Gogh's intuitive grasp of turbulence in nature (particularly during the most unstable period of his life when he had checked himself into an asylum) enabled him to paint eddies of motion with scientific accuracy.

Water, whether lake, river, marsh or sea, features prominently in many of our great artists' works. How it is portrayed speaks to the temperament, culture and beliefs of an artist and, ultimately, his relationship with water. Great artists share that relationship with us: *Becalmed off Halfway Rock*, the classical serene seascape of Fitz Hugh Lane; the fearful power of the sea in *The Ninth Wave* by Ivan Aivozovsky; the icy death of Frederic Edwin Church's *The Icebergs*; Claude Monet's cheerful *La Terrace de Sainte Adresse*; William Turner's audacious and avant-garde *The Fighting Temerarie*.

In 1830, the Japanese artist Hokusai painted *The Great Wave*. One of the most recognized works of art from Japan, it depicts a large rogue wave or *okinami* (wave of the open sea) off Kanagawa with Mount Fuji (considered sacred and a symbol for beauty) in the background. Edmond de Goncourt suggested that the giant wave was a deification of the sea by a man who lived with the terror of the overwhelming ocean that completely surrounded his country. Hokusai "is impressed by the sudden fury of the ocean's leap toward the sky, by the deep blue of the inner side of the curve, by the splash of its claw-like crest as it sprays forth droplets."[64] The writer Andreas Ramos writes of the painting: "The waves form a frame through which we see the mountain. The gigantic wave is a yin yang of empty space beneath the mountain. The inevitable breaking that we await creates a tension in the picture. In the foreground, a small wave forming a miniature Fuji is reflected by the distant mountain, itself shrunk in perspective. The little wave is larger than the mountain. The small fishermen cling to their fishing boats that slide on a sea-mount, looking to dodge the wave. The violent *Yang* of nature is overcome by the *yin* of the confidence of these experienced fishermen. Strangely, despite a storm, the sun shines high."[64] The image, while simple in design, was the result of a long process of methodical reflection. Every object was drawn using the relationship of the circle and the square.[65]

Figure 4.2: The Great Wave, *painted in 1832 by Hokusai.*

Private collection

When Water Speaks

Socrates travelled at least once from his home in Athens some 180 kilometres to Delphi, where he sought the wisdom of the oracle. There, he climbed the limestone steps of the Sacred Way toward the temple on the slope of Mount Parnassus. Upon passing the inscription *"know thyself"* carved in the cool stone of the temple entrance, he proceeded inside, where he met with the priestess, the Pythia, seated on a tall stool over a fissure in the earth that led to a sacred spring. The oracle inhaled the magical vapours that swirled up from beneath with divine messages from Apollo. She delivered her answers to Socrates in ambiguous verse, upon which he was tasked with interpreting. The Pythia was known to ritually bathe in a nearby stream and chew oleander before performing her duties as seer.

Water is a teacher.

The ancient Greeks believed in spirits that dwelt in freshwater, particularly where water springs from the ground naturally. Many springs in Europe were enclosed with stone and made into wells or fountains. I talk more about these in Chapter 10, *Water Is Prayer*. The Swiss physician Paracelsus called these spirits of elemental water *Undines*.

Japanese researcher and philosopher Masaru Emoto suggests that the first language of humankind arose through listening to the various vibrations and sounds created by Nature. The Japanese word for cosmos, *uchu*, supposedly came from the sounds the stars make, says Emoto. "Although there are many different words for the cosmos, there is only one cosmos," Emoto shares. "And all the different words are perhaps nothing more than different ways of hearing the same thing."[66]

Our languages evolved with Nature and reflect the unique, as well as universal, aspects of each region. The vibrations and sounds emitted by nature in each region are distinct, accounting for our many different

Figure 4.3: The symbol Mizu *in Japanese means water and represents the fluid, formless things in the world.*

languages and forms of communication. Emoto describes Japan as "a country blessed with bountiful nature, filling the air with a rich variety of sounds that would, over time, have become the source of an equally rich variety of words, including those used in distinctive forms of Japanese poetry, such as haiku and tanka."[66] By contrast, the Ainu—a minority living in northern Japan—have very few words in their vocabulary, although a hundred and sixty of these describe water. Northern Japan is known for its many streams and lakes and heavy precipitation.

Our dependence on water is reflected linguistically in Persian, Phillip Ball tells us in his book, *H₂O: A Biography of Water*.[67] The first word of the Persian dictionary is *ab*, which means water, and is the root of "abode," from the Persian, *abad*. It's derived from *abadan*, which means "civilized." In this context, water is literally the root and home of civilization.

"How water informs [our] language is hinted at by many of the ancient scripts, which employ flowing lines like water in their characters (for instance Hebrew),"[23] writes nature writer Alick Bartholomew. As I mentioned already, the Chinese character for water, *sui*, is composed of three rippled lines that indicate flowing water. Water in Chinese always refers to water flowing or moving. The letters of the Greek language "became more disciplined," adds Bartholomew, "but it was Latin with its upright, straight characters that forgot the memory of water." Bartholomew shares that the Phoenicians called water *mem*, the root for "memory," a reminder of the ancient belief in water's ability to record and transfer information. *Mem*, the thirteenth letter in the Hebrew alphabet, evolved into the letter em in ours, and the shape of the letter still reflects the shape of a wave.

The ancient Egyptian name for water, *isuat*, also means the colour green. In early mystical lore, water and green were considered synonymous because water was believed to typify the earliest form of soul or generative essence. For the Egyptians, the word *uat* also signified the hard green stone, the emerald, and the green feldspar. Emerald is as-

sociated with romantic love and the sensual side of Nature. It is sacred to the goddess Aphrodite/Venus, who was born from the sea. Because of its connection with the life-giving river Nile, the water-lily was also associated symbolically with water. It can also signify the female principle in life.

The sacred lotus, often featured in mythology, is the large, fragrant, night-flowering white water-lily (*Nymphaea lotus*). The plant is native to Africa. Another African species with blue flowers appears in ancient Egyptian representations. There, the blue lotus was a common votive offering associated with fertility and resurrection and was used in funeral rites.

The so-called Indian lotus, *Nelumbium speciosum*, has a large globular pink flower held well out of the water and considered a holy plant in India. The Hindu goddess Lakshmi and the god Brahma, as well as many others, sit on the lotus flower. The Buddha is often represented sitting on a lotus.

The Sumerian word *mar* meant "sea" as well as "womb" and correlates with their belief that all creation arose from the sea, after the storm god Huracan moved upon it.[68]

Photo 4.17: Pond lily (Nymphea odorata) in a small pond of the Credit River watershed, Ontario, Canada.

In his book *The Holy Order of Water*, science writer William Marks writes about Ea-Enki, the principal divinity of the liquid elements, who was featured in the *Epic of Gilgamesh* as part of an ancient and pre-biblical account of the great flood. Marks tells us that the name *Ea*, which means "House of Water," makes up the first two letters of "Earth," the present name of our watery home. "Ea's domain was the *Apsu*—all the waters that surrounded the planet and kept it afloat,"[68] writes Marks.

As an interesting aside, it is now widely accepted that the creation story of *Genesis* demonstrates a strong Mesopotamian influence with similarity to the early Sumerian epic *Gilgamesh*. What is interesting is that the term "Eden," used in the Bible to describe God's paradise for humanity before "the Fall," also means "flow" in Sumerian, representing an underground swell of water from below (as in a spring or oasis).

Photo by Merridy Cox

Marks concludes, "This [Bible] passage tells us that there was an underground spring that flowed to the surface in Eden to water the garden of life; giving us another example of water energy rising from below to create a holy place on the surface."[68]

Communication is the dance of singularity in a sea of Unity. It is the river of connection, uniting and expressing the fractal whole. Communication collides in a waterfall of notion and surprise. Informing. Transforming. Evolving. Communication floods the iconic dam, surging through conformity toward its own imaginings.

Communication is water.

Photo 4.18: Lifeguard house on Lake Ontario in The Beaches, Ontario, Canada.

Photo by Nina Munteanu

References:

1. Schwenk, Theodor and Wolfram Schwenk. 1989. "Water: The Element of Life." *Rudolf Steiner Press*. 249 pp.

2. Clements, F.E. 1905. "Research methods in Ecology." *University Publishing Company*, Lincoln, NE. 368 pp.

3. Reid, George K. 1961. "Ecology of Inland Water and Estuaries." *D Van Nostrand Company Inc.* 390 pp.

4. Clegg, J.S. 1984. "Properties and Metabolism of the Aqueous Cytoplasm and Its Boundaries." *The American Journal of Physiology* 246: 133–51.

5. Del Giudice, E., P.R. Spinetti, and A.Tedeschi. 2010. "Water Dynamics at the Root of Metamorphosis in Living Organisms." *Water* 2: 566–86.

6. Henniker, J.C. 1949. "The Depth of the Surface Zone of a Liquid." *Rev. Mod. Phys.* 21(2): 322–341.

7. Pollack, Gerald. 2001. "Cells, Gels and the Engines of Life: A New Unifying Approach to Cell Function." *Ebner and Sons*, Seattle. 305 pp.

8. Chaplin, Martin. 2015. "Interfacial Water and Water–Gas Interfaces." *Water Structure and Science*. Online: http://www1.lsbu.ac.uk/water/interfacial_water.html

9. Szent-Gyorgyi, A. 1960. "Introduction to a Supramolecular Biology." *Academic Press*, New York. 135 pp.

10. Pollack, Gerald. 2013. "The Fourth Phase of Water: Beyond Solid, Liquid, and Vapor." *Ebner & Sons.* 357 pp.

11. Pollack, G.H. and J. Clegg. 2008. "Unexpected Linkage between Unstirred Layers, Exclusion Zones, and Water." In *Phase Transitions in Cell Biology* (G.H. Pollack and W.C. Chin, eds.). *Springer Science & Business Media*, Berlin. p. 143–152.

12. Roy, Rustum, W.A. Tiller, Iris Bell, and M.R. Hoover. 2005. "The Structure of Liquid Water; Novel Insights from Materials Research; Potential Relevance to Homeopathy." *Materials Research Innovations Online* 9–4: 577–608.

13. Liu, C.S., S. Komarneni, and R. Roy. 1992. "Epitaxial Crystalization." *J Am Cer Soc* 75: 2665.

14. Neogi, Subhadip and Parimal K. Bharadwa. 2005. "An Infinite Water Chain Passes Through an Array of Zn(II) Metallocycles Built with a Pod and Bearing Terminal Carboxylates." *Org. Chem.* 44 (4): 816–818.

15. Chaplin, M.F. 2000. "A Proposal for the Structuring of Water." *Biophys. Chem.* 83: 211–221.

16. Wales, D.J. and M.P. Hodges. 1998. "Global Minima of Water Clusters $[H_2O]_n$, n=<21, Described by an Empirical Potential." *Chem. Phys. Lett.* 286: 65–72.

17. IUPAC. 2006 (1997). "Clathrates." In: Compendium of Chemical Terminology, 2nd ed. (the "Gold Book"). Compiled by A.D. McNaught and A. Wilkinson. *Blackwell Scientific Publications*, Oxford. International Union of Pure and Applied Chemistry. Online corrected version, 2006: http://goldbook.iupac.org/C01097.html

18. Smith, R.S. and B.D. Kay. 1999. "The Existence of Supercooled Liquid Water at 150 K." *Nature* 398: 788–791.

19. Martin, R.B. 1988. "Localized and Spectroscopic Orbitals: Squirrel Ears on Water." *J. Chem. Educ.* 65: 668–670.

20. Vogel, Marcel. 2003-2015. "The Crystal Wisdom of Marcel Vogel." Manuscript archives, ed. Curtis Lang. *Santya Center*. Online: http://www.satyacenter.com/marcel-vogel-crystal-book

21. Roy, Rustom. 2006. In: "Water: The Great Mystery." Julia Perkul and Anastasiya Popova, directors. *Intention Media*. 87 min.

22. Voeikov, Vladimir. 2006. In: "Water: The Great Mystery." Julia Perkul and Anastasiya Popova, directors. *Intention Media*. 87 min.

23. Bartholomew, Alick. 2010. "The Spiritual Life of Water." *Park Street Press*. 368 pp.

24. Backster, Cleve. 1968. "Evidence of a Primary Perception in Plant Life," *International Journal of Parapsychology* 10 (4): 329–348.

25. McTaggart, Lynne. 2008. "The Intention Experiment". Atria Books. 336 pp.

26. Lipton, Bruce. 2008. "The Biology of Belief." *Hay House*. 240 pp.

27. Lipton, Bruce. 2012. "The Wisdom of Your Cells." In: "How Your Beliefs Control Your Biology." *Sounds True Audio Listening Course, 2007*. Online: https://www.brucelipton.com/resource/article/the-wisdom-your-cells

28. Jablonka, Eva and Marion J. Lamb. 2008. "Soft Inheritance: Challenging the Modern Synthesis." *Genet. Mol. Biol.* 31 (2): 389–395.

29. Buchem, Lizzie. 2010. "In Their Nurture." *Nature* 467: 146–148.

30. Hughes, Virginia. 2014. "Epigenetics: The Sins of the Father." *Nature* 507: 22–24.

31. Dias, Brian and Kerry Ressler. 2013. "Parental Olfactory Experience Influences Behaviour and Neural Structure in Subsequent Generations." *Nature Neuroscience* 17: 89–96.

32. Ridley, Matt. 2004. "Nature Via Nurture: Genes, Experience and What Makes Us Human." *Harper Perennial*. 352 pp.

33. Craig, Jeffrey. 2015. "Epigenetics: Phenomenon or Quackery?" In: "The Conversation." July 23, 2015. Online: http://theconversation.com/epigenetics-phenomenon-or-quackery-44961

34. Simmons, Danielle. 2008. "Epigenetic Influences and Disease." *Nature Education* 1(1): 6.

35. Sheldrake, Rupert. 1982. "A New Science of Life: The Hypothesis of Formative Causation." *J.P.Tarcher, Inc.*, Los Angeles. 229 pp.

36. Sheldrake, Rupert. 1988. "Extended Mind, Power, and Prayer: Morphic Resonance and the Collective Unconscious—Part III." *Psychological Perspectives* 19(1): 64–78.

37. McTaggart, Lynne. 2003. "The Field." *Element*. 384 pp.

38. Laszlo, E. 1995. "The Interconnected Universe: Conceptual Foundations of Transdisciplinary Unified Theory." *World Scientific Pub Co Inc.* 166 pp.

39. Radin, Dean. 2006. "Entangled Minds." *Paraview Pocket Books*, New York. 368 pp.

40. Bohm, David. 1980. "Wholeness and the Implicate Order." *Routledge*. 284 pp.

41. Lorenz, Edward. 1979. "Predictability: Does the Flap of a Butterfly's Wings in Brazil Set off a Tornado in Texas?" Paper presented at the annual meeting of the American Association for the Advancement of Science, Washington. December 29, 1979.

42. Metivier, Chris. 2015. "Part 11: the Parts and the Whole." In: Introduction to Philosophy, *Philosophia*. Online: http://philosophia.uncg.edu/phi111-metivier/module-2/part-11-the-parts-and-the-whole/.

43. Hesiod. 700 BCE (1914). "Theogony". Hugh G. Evelyn-White (trans). Sacred Texts. Online: http://www.sacred-texts.com/cla/hesiod/theogony.htm

44. Gleick, James. 1987. "Chaos: Making a New Science." *Penguin Books*, New York, N.Y. 352pp.

45. Sardar, Ziauddin and Iwona Abrams. 1999. "Introducing Chaos." *Totem Books*, New York, N.Y. 176pp.

46. Quinton, R. 1904. "L'eau de mer Milieu organique : Constance du milieu marin originel, comme milieu vital des cellules, a travers la série animale." Masson et cie, éditeurs. *Libraires de l'Académie de Médecine*. Paris. 503 pp.

47. Flament, P., S. Kennan, R. Knox, P. Niller, and R. Bernstein. 1996. "The Three-Dimensional Structure of an Upper Ocean Vortex in the Tropical Pacific Ocean." *Nature*, vol. 383: 610–613.

48. Carrell. A. 1912. Nobel lecture. Online: http://nobelprize.org/nobel_prizes/medicine/laureates/1912/carrel-lecture.html

49. Pangman, M.J. and Melanie Evans. 2011. "Dancing with Water: The New Science of Water." *Uplifting Press*. 255 pp.

50. Reimchen, T.E. 2001. "Salmon Nutrients, Nitrogen Isotopes and Coastal Forests." *Ecoforestry*. Victoria, British Columbia. Fall, 2001. Online: www.ecoforestry.ca

51. Reimchen, T.E., D. Mathewson, M.D. Hocking, and J. Moran. 2002. "Evidence for Enrichment of Salmon-derived Nutrients in Vegetation, Soil, and Insects in Riparian Zones in Coastal British Columbia." *American Fisheries Society Symposium XX*: 1–12 pp.

52. Beresford-Kroeger, Diana. 2010. "The Global Forest." *Viking*, New York, NY. 173 pp.

53. Ramsayer, Kate. 2004. "Infrasonic Symphony: The Greatest Sounds Never Heard." *Science News Online* 165 (2), January 10, 2004. Pearson Prentice Hall. Online: www.phschool.com/science/science_news/articles/infrasonic_symphony.html

54. O'Connel-Rodwell, Caitlin E. 2001. "Elephant Low-frequency Vocalizations Propagate in the Ground and Seismic Playbacks of These Vocalizations are Detectable by Wild African Elephants (*Loxodonta Africana*)." *Acoustical Society of America Journal* 115 (5): 2554–2554.

55. Palmer, Jason. 2011. "'Music of the Stars' Now Louder." *BBC News*, Washington, DC. Online: http://www.bbc.com/news/science-environment-12507032

56. Space.com. 2013. "Earth and Planets Make Strange Noises—Video Compilation." *University of Iowa/AGU/NASA/JPL*. Online: http://www.space.com/26605-earth-and-planets-make-strange-exquisite-noises-video-compilation.html

57. Gurnett, Don. 2013. In: "The Sounds of Interstellar Space." *Nasa Science News*. Online: http://science.nasa.gov/science-news/science-at-nasa/2013/01nov_ismsounds/

58. Kröplin, Bernd. 2005. "Welt im Tropfen ṣWorld in a Dropṭ." *Institutfür Statik und Dynamik der Luft- und Raumfahrtkonstruktionen.* Germany. 83 pp.

59. Braud, William G. 1991. "Consciousness Interactions with Remote Biological Systems: Anomalous Intentionality Effects." *Subtle Energies* 2 (1): 1–46.

60. Talbot, Michael. 2011. "The Universe as a Hologram." *Harper Perennial*. 338 pp.

61. Ball, Philip. 2011. "Flow." *Oxford University Press*. 208 pp.

62. Capra, Fritjof. 2010. "What We Can Learn from Leonardo." *Centre for Ecoliteracy*. Online: http://www.ecoliteracy.org/article/what-we-can-learn-leonardo

63. Capra, Fritjof. 2008. "The Science of Leonardo." *Anchor*. 352 pp.

64. Radio UNAM. 2014. "La Gran Ola de Kanagawa." Universidad Nacional Autonoma de Mexico. Online: http://www.radiounam.unam.mx/index.php?option=com_k2&view=item&id=301:la-gran-ola-de-kanagawa

66. Cartwright, H.E. and H.Nakamura. 2009. "What Kind of Wave is Hokusai's Great Wave off Kanagawa?" *Royal Society Publishing*, Notes and Records. Online: http://rsnr.royalsocietypublishing.org/content/63/2/119

67. Emoto, Masaru. 2011. "The Miracle of Water." *Atria Paperback*. 160 pp.

68. Ball, Philip. 2000. "H2O: A Biography of Water." *Phoenix*, London, UK. 387 pp.

69. Marks, William. 2001. "The Holy Order of Water." *Bell Pond Books*. 256 pp.

5. Water is Memory

Photo 5.1: Water patterns among weeds in the Upper Credit River, Ontario, Canada.

Photo by Nina Munteanu

"When you drink the water, remember the spring."
—***Chinese proverb***

"The story tells that water has a consciousness, that it carries in its memory everything that's ever happened in this world, from the time before humans until this moment, which draws itself in its memory even as it passes. Water understands the movements of the world; it knows when it is sought and where it is needed. Sometimes a spring or a well dries for no reason, without explanation. It's as if the water escapes of its own will, withdrawing into the cover of the earth to look for another channel. Tea masters believe there are times when water doesn't wish to be found because it knows it will be chained in ways that are against its nature."[1]

So says Noria's Tea Master father in a scene from Emmi Itäranta's 2014 post-climate change novel *Memory of Water*.

Of course, it's only fiction. Science fiction, in fact. Just as Margaret Atwood's *After the Flood* or *The Penelopiad* is just fiction. Or Barbara Kingsolver's *Flight Behavior* is just fiction. They are all just stories we read and share with one another.

But is that all they are?

Water's Story of Synchronicity

"'The water will tell you,' said the guide, when the travellers asked how deep was the water."
—Plato

I teach new writers at university how to tell stories. I teach how stories can tell us who we are. Where we've been. And sometimes, where we are going. The stories that stir our hearts come from deep inside, where the personal meets the universal, through symbols or *archetypes*. Depth psychologist Carl Jung described these shared symbols or archetypes as pre-existing forms of the psyche and drew parallels between synchronicity, relativity theory and quantum mechanics to describe life as an expression of a deeper order. He believed that we are both embedded in a framework of a whole and are the focus of that whole.[2] I talk more about this in Chapter 11, *Water Is Wisdom*.

Jung was describing a *fractal whole*, which reflects David Bohm's quantum vision of *Holomovement*.[3] Jung's concept of embedded whole and a universal collective unconscious was embraced by scholar and mythologist Joseph Campbell, who suggested that these mythic images lie at the depth of the unconscious where humans are no longer distinct individuals, where our minds widen and merge into the mind and memory of humankind—where we are all the same, in Unity.[4]

Carl Jung's thesis of the "collective unconscious" in fact linked with what Freud called *archaic remnants*: mental forms whose presence cannot be explained by anything in the individual's own life and which seem aboriginal, innate, and the inherited shapes of the human mind.[5]

Marie-Louise von Franz, in 1985, identified Jung's hypothesis of the collective unconscious with the ancient idea of an all-extensive world-soul.[6] D.A.G. Cook suggested that Jung "was attracted to the idea that the archetypes afford evidence of some communion with some divine or world mind."[7] Writer Sherry Healy explored these ideas further and

suggested that Jung viewed the human mind as linked to "a body of unconscious energy that lives forever."[8]

This is the idea of *monopsychism*, which unlike Cartesian Dualism, holds that all humans share the same eternal consciousness, soul, mind or intellect. It is part of a family of philosophies that includes the Jewish Kabbalah, Islamic Averroism, and Rastafarian beliefs that view consciousness, mind and soul as universal.

Panpsychism holds a holistic view that the whole Universe is an organism that possesses a mind or cosmic consciousness, a "universal consciousness." Panpsychism is one of the oldest philosophical theories—embraced by Thales, Plato, and Spinoza, in addition to the Vedanta and Mahayana Buddhism. According to Plato, all things participate in the form of Being and must have a psychic aspect of mind and soul.[9] He argued for a world soul or *anima mundi*. "This world is indeed a living being endowed with a soul and intelligence ... a single visible living entity containing all other living entities, which by their nature are all related."[10] This view was also promoted by philosopher Gustav Theodor Fechner, who called the Earth a living organism. Other beliefs and philosophies such as theosophy, pantheism, cosmotheism, non-dualism, and panentheism share aspects of Panpsychism. Tiantai Buddhism, for example, argues that inanimate objects such as lotus flowers, trees, rocks and mountains have *Buddha nature* (i.e., contain the essence or seed-embryo of Buddha and a soul). Tiantai Buddhism expresses Panpsychism this way: "when one attains it, all attain it."[11,12]

Water has "Buddha nature." And Buddha nature is connected to all that was, is and will be. It's synchronicity.

Photo 5.2: Water reflections in Toogood Pond, Unionville, Ontario, Canada.

Photo by Nina Munteanu

Synchronicity and Backwards Memory

Apparently one of Jung's favourite quotes on synchronicity was from *Alice Through the Looking-Glass* by Lewis Carroll, in a scene where Alice meets the White Queen:

"The rule is, jam to-morrow and jam yesterday—but never jam to-day."

"It MUST come sometimes to 'jam to-day'," Alice objected.

"No, it can't," said the Queen. "It's jam every OTHER day: to-day isn't any OTHER day, you know."

"I don't understand you," said Alice. "It's dreadfully confusing!"

"That's the effect of living backwards," the Queen said kindly: "it always makes one a little giddy at first—"

"Living backwards!" Alice repeated in great astonishment. "I never heard of such a thing!"

"—but there's one great advantage in it, that one's memory works both ways."

"I'm sure MINE only works one way," Alice remarked. "I can't remember things before they happen."

"It's a poor sort of memory that only works backwards," the Queen remarked.[13]

Figure 5.1: "You're mothing but a pack of cards", from "Alice's Adventures in Wonderland" by Louis Caroll, Macmillan and Co., 1865.

Illustration by John Tenniel (Wikimedia Commons)

Information Transfer in a Fractal World

According to biochemist and plant biologist Rupert Sheldrake, all living things have their own fields. Morphic fields create information clusters through their living memory bank, which regulate the networks of living systems. This drives evolution, says Sheldrake, who posited that nature conveys information from the macro- to the micro-world through the repeating geometric form of fractals.[14]

Science writer Alick Bartholomew writes that, "Fractals are generated by the quantum field working with water in the transfer of information."[15]

From atoms and orbiting electrons to galaxies, we see self-similarity in objects from small to large. They're everywhere: in the clouds above you, in a piece of coastline or a river network; in the shape of leaves and snowflakes. Scientists call these self-similar shapes *fractals*. Because they appear similar at all levels of magnification, fractals are often considered infinitely complex. Other examples of natural fractals include mountain ranges, lightning bolts, trees, river networks, lines in the palm of your hand and blood vessels. A branch of a tree or frond of a fern is said to be recursive because each is a replica of the whole, not identical but similar in nature. Repeating a process indefinitely and asking whether the result is infinite resembles feedback processes in the everyday world, according to James Gleick, author of *Chaos: Making a New Science*.[16]

The concept of fractal geometry, developed by Benoit Mandelbrot in 1975, originated in chaos theory, both of which show that natural order is not random, given that it generates its own order. It's self-organized.[17]

"What else, when chaos draws all forces inward to shape a single leaf."

—Conrad Aiken

"Water is a self-organizing system,"[18] writes Dr. Paolo Consigli, author of *Water, Pure and Simple*. Water's self-organizing generates spontaneous order and synchronicity from disorder through the local interactions of components within its disordered state. The system creates islands of predictability in a sea of chaotic unpredictability. It's self-creating; it's "autopoietic."

In 1974, Chilean scientists Francisco Varela, Humberto Maturana, and R. Uribe used the term *autopoiesis* to describe systems that produce themselves in a ceaseless way. Autopoiesis describes the dynamics of a non-equilibrium system in achieving an organized state that remains stable for long periods of time despite matter and energy continually flowing through it. It is, in fact, this flow that helps maintain the self-organizing aspect of an open autopoietic system. It is both producer and product.[19]

Decades ago, at university, I learned in my ecology and limnology courses that the environment of inanimate and animate things was interconnected and interdependent. Nature and her ecosystems flowed in a dynamic network of relationships, succession and sustainability. Systems generally operated through a closed loop of natural creative-destruction; from birth, growth and production to senescence, decay, and recycling to a redistribution, reclaiming and rebirth. The yin–yang closed circle of the Ouroboros. Unlike most reductionist mainstream sciences, the study of ecology elucidates Nature's "intent" (in defying the second law of thermodynamics) to not only conserve, but sometimes to create energy and promote evolution.

While mainstream science recognizes many of water's weird and anomalous qualities—such as being a powerful solvent, its need to move, spiral and pulsate, that it balances temperature and has unique density properties—mainstream scientists do not understand (or even accept) some of water's quantum properties—such as its ability to store or transmit information, self-organize, self-purify, and exhibit some of the properties of life.

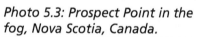
Photo 5.3: Prospect Point in the fog, Nova Scotia, Canada.

Photo by Nina Munteanu

Like communication and memory.

For instance, water can transfer vibrational information, through a phenomenon called *jump conduction* or proton tunnelling, delivering frequencies for long distances at the speed of light.[20] Jump conduction describes how water molecules continually switch polarities as protons pass rapidly through the matrix of fairly static, hydrogen-bonded water molecules.[21] This establishes a kind of coded history or "memory" not unlike what a computer does.

As early as 1806, Theodor Grotthuss proposed a theory of liquid "decomposition" mediated by electrical currents. He envisioned the electrolytic reaction as a kind of "bucket line," in which each oxygen atom passes and receives a single hydrogen atom. His description of proton-hopping through the cooperation of neighbouring water molecules was later known as the *Grotthus mechanism*. The mechanism, also called proton jumping describes how an "excess" proton travels along the hydrogen bond network of water molecules as covalent bonds form and cleave.

Photo 5.4: Icy water of LaHave River near Bridgewater, NS, Canada.

Photo by Nina Munteanu

Water Formatics

Researchers at the School of Physics and Astronomy at Tel Aviv University are exploring the question of whether water can tell if it is subjected to weak electromagnetic radiation. In 2007, Eshel Ben-Jacob and his team published a paper in the *American Journal of the Electrochemical Society* on how water organized itself when subjected to certain radio frequencies. A hierarchical organization arose from the formation of a pliable network of gas nanobubbles, reported the scientists. "The emerged nanobubble network is the outcome of a self-organization process due to the collective effect of bubble–bubble exchange interactions."[22] The interactions were mediated by the ordering of the water molecules surrounding each nanobubble, through a combination of radio frequency and acoustic treatment.

Ben-Jacob and his co-workers found an increase in growth rate of bacteria grown in water treated by radio frequency signals.[23,24] These findings reflect conclusions made by materials scientist Rustum Roy and his colleagues, regarding water's ability to collect, store and transmit information (see Chapter 4).[25,26]

Photo 5.5: Ice-covered winter path in Guildwood Forest, Scarborough, Ontario, Canada.

Photo by Nina Munteanu

Memory, Morphic Resonance & Synchronicity

In 1997, Walter Schempp proposed a quantum memory model suggesting that short- and long-term memory doesn't reside in our brain, but is instead stored in the *Zero Point Field* (also called "Implicate Order" by David Bohm[3]).[27] This notion, that the brain is a macroscopic quantum system, harmonizes with the findings of neuroscientist Karl Pribram[28] and later physicist David Bohm, who, with Pribram, demonstrated that the brain acts like a hologram.[29]

Scientists eventually argued that the brain is simply a retrieval and storehouse of coherent signal emissions from the Zero Point Field to create what we know as memory. Long-term memories are structured groupings of this wave information, they suggest. Perhaps this is why a tiny association often triggers a burst of sights, sounds and smells. It would also explain why recall is instantaneous without need for a scanning mechanism to search through years of memory, suggests Lynne McTaggart in her book *The Field*.[30] This also resonates with Rupert Sheldrake's "morphic resonance" concept, in which memory is inherent in Nature,[14] as I discuss briefly in Chapter 4. Sheldrake's theory proposes that the templates for our physical forms are not necessarily contained inside our genes. He suggests that genes act more like transistors tuned in to the proper frequencies for translating invisible information into visible form. Form then arises from a "collective instinctive memory," and any new form uses the pattern of already existing forms as a guide for its appearance. According to Sheldrake, morphogenesis depends on organizing fields. Morphogenetic fields impose patterns on otherwise

"Memory is a complicated thing, a relative to truth, but not its twin."

—Barbara Kingsolver

random and indeterminate patterns of activity, says Sheldrake. He gives the example of microtubules crystalizing in one part of the cell rather than another, even though the subunits from which they are made are present throughout the cell. Sheldrake then gives the following example: "if rats of a particular breed learn a new trick in Harvard, then rats of that breed should be able to learn the same trick faster all over the world. There is already evidence from laboratory experiments that this actually happens."[14] This makes perfect sense in Bohm's Implicate Order within a Holomovement Universe.[3]

This may also help explain the phenomenon of "multiple independent discoveries", which I discuss in Chapter 7, *Water is Vibration*.

Photo 5.6: Sunset in Steveston Harbour, Richmond, BC, Canada.

Photo by Nina Munteanu

水 **Homeopathy**

In 1985, French scientist and immunologist, Jacques Benveniste obtained evidence that water could retain information from the molecules with which it interacted. His experiments involved the successive dilutions of biologically active substances in water until there was, effectively, no substance left except water. Benveniste's group determined that the "pure" water, previously exposed to an active biological solution, retained the same characteristics. Pouring either the concentrated substance or the serially diluted substance onto cells triggered the same effect. This suggested that the diluted water retained a "memory" of the molecules with which it had been in contact, for only those molecules were specific enough to initiate the effect.[31] Although the work was objectively replicated by other French scientists and initially published by *Nature*, subsequent external quality assurance failed to replicate the results and *Nature* removed the paper; the idea of water memory was … well … forgotten. For a while.

Benveniste's work is, of course, the basis for the practice of homeopathy and it has serious ramifications by providing evidence for water's ability to store and share information. The subject drew and continues to draw controversy among scientists who reject it outright without studying the evidence, London University scientist Martin Chaplin writes.[32]

Thirty years after Benveniste's article in *Nature*, scientists are confirming his work. Materials scientist Rustum Roy and others suggest that information transfers through epitaxy, and therefore, the chemical nature (i.e., no more solute) is not as important as the changed structure of the water.[24,25] Nobel laureate Luc Montagnier's research showed that microwave irradiation gives rise to a memory effect on the surface tension of water that lasts for minutes. He and his colleagues concluded that water stores information.[33]

Montagnier's team also described memory effects in aqueous DNA solutions, which they proposed depend on interactions with the background electromagnetic field. These memory effects, if real, require prior processing and dilution of the solutions, and Montagnier explains them as resonance phenomena with nanostructures derived from the DNA and water.[33]

Benveniste later asserted that this "memory" could be digitized, transmitted, and reinserted into another sample of water, which would then contain the same active qualities as the first sample.[34] Materials scientist Rustum Roy supports this claim: "Water has photographic memory, and you can imprint it with very subtle energies even from ten thousand kilometers."[35] As with Benveniste and Roy, others have documented how "intention"—supposedly at the vibrational level—affected water's structure and quality. This phenomenon is similar to the *Maharishi Effect*, which I talk about in Chapter 7 and 10. Japanese researcher Masaru Emoto has led many prayer groups over various lakes and watercourses throughout the world.[54]

Figure 5.2: Micrograph of a dried water drop from the Alps (Alpenwasser), 2015; Welt im Tropfen *("World in a Drop").*

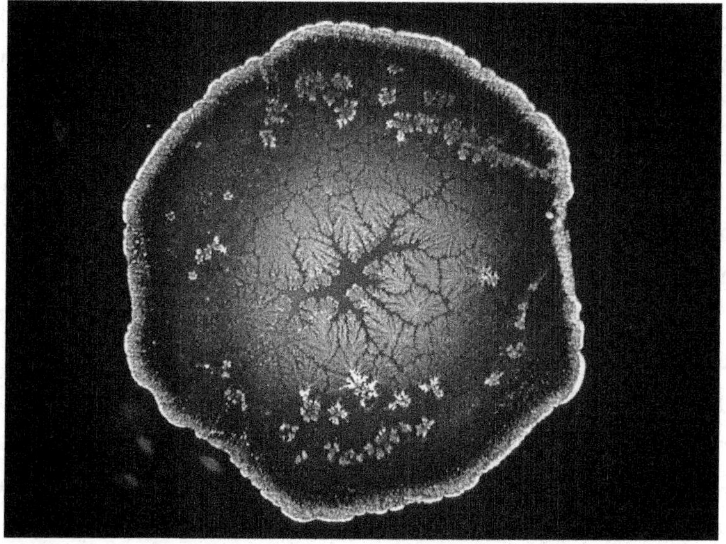

Berndt Kröplin, Institute for Static and Dynamics of Aerospace Structures, University of Stuttgart

Water as a Computer

In Chapter 4, I talk about the work of the late materials scientist Rustum Roy with epitaxy, nano-bubbles and pressure to create water structure. Roy stated that water's structure was more important than its chemistry in certain interactions. He likened it to the arrangement of an alphabet and called water a "single-most malleable computer." Roy suggested that water's "memory" was based on the structure it takes on, as a result of electromagnetic fields and various frequencies to which it is exposed.[35]

London University scientist Martin Chaplin tells us that, "If you consider a cluster of specific molecules, then it can survive only a short amount of time. But if you consider it as a structure whereby molecules can leave and other molecules can come in, the cluster can last for a very long time."[36] The stability of the cluster revealed that water is capable of recording and storing memory. "At a molecular level water creates the structure of DNA. We wouldn't have the DNA helix without water. It creates the structure of proteins, so our bodies wouldn't work without water."[36]

"If water had a memory, the glacier would know about the sea, the river about the spring, the flower about the root."
—Bernd Kröplin

"World in a Drop"

"A drop of water is a universe unto itself."

—Paolo Consigli

"Memory is a widely defined concept,"[37] writes Dr. Bernd Kröplin in his 2005 book, *Welt im Tropfen: Gedächtnis und Gedankenformenim Wasser* [*The World in a Drop: Memory and Forms of Thought in Water*]. Memory is a concept "not restricted to higher life forms only." In fact, he tells us, "it is not restricted to living beings at all."[37] Many inanimate things, not just computers, display properties of memory, adds Kröplin. Erosion, oxidation, aging and radiation are all phenomena that display *memory*: a change that provides information about the history of a substance. *Smart materials* are adaptive materials that carry memory. Metallic "shape–memory" alloys can remember shapes they have taken on earlier and reconfigure once activated by the same influence. This ability, Kröplin shares, results from the *austenite–martensite* (steel crystalline structures) conversion of the crystal structure of the metal.

Substances can also forget, Kröplin writes. *Forgetting* occurs through some form of reorientation of the structure; for instance through a strong increase in temperature, leading to the disappearance of residual "stresses" in the original structure of the material. Kröplin suggests that this concept can be applied to water, its crystalline form and its changing states.

While researching a bio-energetic medicine for use in outer space, Dr. Kröplin discovered one of water's many anomalies: low field strengths, which are not detectable with the usual techniques, show up in water and can be viewed under the microscope and photographed. At the Institute for Static and Dynamics in Aerospace Constructions, University of Stuttgart (ISD), Dr. Kröplin subjected water to ultrasound, music, and mobile radiation; then he observed dried water droplets under dark field microscopy. The drops indicated unique patterns according to each treatment. An intuitive researcher, Kröplin demon-

strated a connection between the subject and the object of an experiment, using different students in his drop tests. Using different water sources and different students, he showed that the variation in pattern was significantly less for the student over the source. When he placed a particular flower in water, the drops revealed its unique signature. A different flower revealed its own unique signature and distinctive pattern.[38] Kröplin's experiments and his observations reflect the findings of Roy, Chaplin, Benveniste and others about water's ability to record, store and transmit information.

Kröplin talks about the Rhine figuratively, likening its system to a quantum computer: the water picks up information as it flows downstream and has more information at its mouth than at its source, says Kröplin. In such a scenario, "The world's oceans would no longer separate us; but, instead be a giant storehouse of information, and the rain a data medium carrying information to the world."[38]

Figure 5.3: Micrograph of a dried water drop from Macao, 2015; Welt im Tropfen *("World in a Drop").*

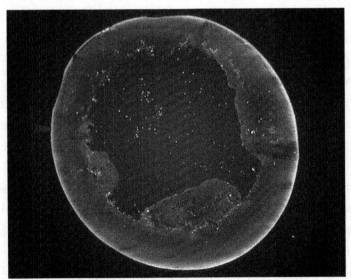

Berndt Kröplin, Institute for Static and Dynamics of Aerospace Structures, University of Stuttgart

The Faces of Memory

In 1939, Semyno Kirlian accidentally discovered that if an object on a photographic plate received a high-voltage charge, a radiating image was produced on the photographic plate. Essentially a captured "coronal discharge", the electrograph or bioelectrograph was later used by both mainstream science and frontier science to describe biofields and other phenomena of conducting objects.[39]

Photon energy can be seen under dark field photo-microscopy and is considered by some to indicate life force (as biophotons). Appearing as bright spots of light against a dark field, *biophotons* have demonstrated healthy versus unhealthy systems. Met with skepticism, the method has been successfully used by biophysicist Fritz-Albert Popp[40,41,42] and quantum physicist Konstantin Korotkov,[43,44,45,46] and many practitioners of energy medicine.

Energy medicine forms a large part of complementary and alternative medicine (CAM), writes Dr. Beverly Rubik, a medical doctor and practitioner of CAM in the USA. Energy medicine typically involves low-level energy field interactions and includes: human energy therapies, homeopathy, acupuncture, magnet therapy, bioelectromagnetic therapy, electrodermal therapy, and phototherapy, among others.[47] Rubik acknowledges that many of these CAMs challenge the dominant biomedical paradigm, given they cannot be explained by current biochemical methods. Rubik suggests that biofield phenomena may act directly on molecular structures, changing their conformation and functionality in significant ways. They may also transfer bioinformation within the energy field of life known as the *biofield*.[48]

"The concept of an organizing field in biology and medicine evokes

Photo 5.7: Kirlian photograph of a Coleus leaf using 35 mm colour film and a small tesla coil as power source, 1980.

Photo by Wikipedia user MrX, Wikimedia Commons

shades of *vitalism*, an old philosophical concept in the West from the 1600s that was overthrown in nineteenth-century science," says Rubik. "In this view, the essence of life is seen as a metaphysical, irreducible life force that cannot be measured. Indigenous systems of healing, such as Ayurvedic and Chinese medicine, and modern modalities, such as chiropractic, rest on concepts of a vital force or subtle life energy that is central to healing. Called by many names, including *prana* in Ayurvedic medicine and *qi* [or *chi*] in Chinese medicine, these indigenous terms go back thousands of years. They may actually refer to something similar to the present-day concept of the biofield, which is, at least in part, based on the electromagnetic field theory of modern physics but, in principle, might also include acoustic and possibly other subtler energy fields not yet known to science."[49] Biofield therapies, which incorporate notions of universal life energy, include Reiki (a form of spiritual healing from Japan), qigong therapy (from China) and many others.[51] Like dowsers, biofield therapists may also assess imbalances in the human biofield either with their hands or intuitively.

Rubik argues for a synergistic application of viewpoints on life and in therapeutic treatment. On the one hand, one could compare the organism to a crystalline structure of ordered biomolecules, says Rubik. "On the other hand, the essence of life is more similar to a flame," she adds, "burning matter into energy and dancing not only with organized vitality, but also with an element of unpredictability or chaos. Both views," she suggests, "may be necessary to describe life in the same way that, in quantum physics, both a particle view and a wave view are necessary to describe fully the nature of light, as well as matter at the smallest scales."[47]

Rubik argues that, as with the principle of complementarity that requires a description of both wave and particle properties; an energy field view may complement—rather than antagonize—the conventional biomolecular view. "The brain, for example, can be analyzed in terms of the receptors, neurotransmitters, ion channels, and so forth that help explain neuronal firing; or it can be viewed in terms of the oscillations of its neuronal circuits and the magnetic and electrical fields of its continual activity, with possible regulatory feedback from the fields themselves."[47]

Rubik describes two existing schools of interpretation of biophoton emissions, one reflecting a reductionist mechanism (e.g., chemiluminescence school) and the other vitalism (e.g., biophysical school). The biophysical approach maintains that the organism receives and relays a particular range of electromagnetic frequencies or biophotons that are coherent (in phase) and are used for communication, growth, and regulation in the living state. From results by Frohlick in 1968, we also expect long-range, coherent interactions in living systems,[51] which harmonizes with the work and findings of Rupert Sheldrake, Mae Wan Ho, David Bohm and many others.[3,14,21,25,27,29,47]

Russian physicist Konstantin Korotkov developed a Gas Discharge Visualization (GDV) camera, based on *Kirlian photography* (images of high-frequency electric discharge) to observe biophotons discharged by biofields. Any conductive object (such as living tissue) when placed on a plate made of insulating material (such as glass) and exposed to high-voltage/high frequency electricity, will emit a halo of coloured light. The greater the energy the object possesses, the brighter it shines.

Already known for his work with human bioenergy fields using high-voltage electrophotography, Korotkov used his GDV machine to measure the energetics of water. He travelled to the area of Mount Roraima in Venezuela, where some of the highest waterfalls in the world flow from the top of the mountain. Korotkov compared the *uber*-pristine Roraima headwaters to the drinking water in Saint Petersburg, Russia, and found significantly more energy in the Roraima water.[52]

In 1996, Dr. David Schweitzer developed a fluorescent microscope using a light temperature of 732 nm through which he observed small light bodies (e.g., biophotons or somatids, presumably found in all life-fluids) that could be directly influenced by positive and negative

emotions. He showed that the biophotons of cells responded with greater luminosity in the presence of positive thoughts. Schweitzer's work suggested that water acted as a liquid memory system that could store information. In an interview in *Shared Vision Magazine*, Schweitzer shared his observations of blood expressing different forms based on various scenarios. Schweitzer observed that blood cells expressed themselves with a language based on sacred geometry, colour and harmonious shapes. He hypothesized that water was the medium that helped transmit information from one area of the brain to another. Based on Einstein's concept of *somatids* (particulate light bodies), Schweitzer created the conditions necessary to make them visible and then to observe how they changed in response to thought and other environmental influences. Schweitzer observed that the somatids became more intense in the presence of positive thought, particularly faith.[53]

In the 1990s, Japanese researcher Dr. Masaru Emoto developed a method to freeze water samples and then photograph the resulting crystalline form using a microscope at x500 magnification. In 1999, he published a collection of photographs of water crystals in a book, *The Messages of Water*.[54] The water crystals are stunningly beautiful. Emoto's photographs showed how the crystals varied greatly according to water source and water quality.

Photo 5.8: Stellar-plate snowflake, photographed with a Canon Powershot A650 and 44M-5 Helios lens.

Photo by Alexey Kljatov

An intuitive researcher, Emoto one day whimsically exposed the water he was testing to music and found that the crystals differed according to musical form. Emoto also used intentions and words on paper—arguing that words, even on paper, carry a unique vibration, and that water incorporates these in its structure as a kind of "memory." Emoto contended that positive changes to the water crystals could be attained through prayer, music and words of gratitude, appreciation and love.[55,56] Emoto and his telling crystals have since become known worldwide for the story they tell about water's changing structure. Emoto's research techniques have been criticized for human error and for using insufficient controls. Emoto acknowledged that he was not a scientist; yet his work and observations appear to harmonize with emerging research by frontier scientists on water's ability to act as a liquid memory store: these include Russian researcher Leonod Izvekov, Canadian scientist Dr. David Schweitzer, German scientist Dr. Bernd Kröplin, Austrian researcher Alois Grüber, and others.

Effe Chow, member of the Executive Council on Alternative Medicine, USA, tells the story of attending an outdoor wedding in Ontario. The rain started to come half an hour before the wedding and, as it started to rain, all the umbrellas went up. Chow and three of her students decided to meditate for better weather: within a minute, the clouds opened up and the sun shone down in the immediate area like a spotlight.[57] While I cannot claim having participated successfully in such an endeavour, when I worked in rainy British Columbia as an independent environmental consultant, I acquired a reputation for "ordering up" sunny days for my field trips.

Memory streams in a braided and recursive path, meandering Ouroboros-like toward itself. Memory stirs up sediments that have lain for eons; re-suspending, re-examining, as if new. Then cascading toward the abyss of truth and paradox. The collective. The great ocean of thought.

Memory is water.

References

1. Itäranta, Emmi. 2014. "Memory of Water." *Harper Voyager*. 272 pp.

2. Jung, Carl. 1952 (1993). "Synchronicity—An Acausal Connecting Principle." *Bollingen Foundation*, Bollingen, Switzerland.

3. Bohm, David. 1980. "Wholeness and the Implicate Order." *Routledge*. 284 pp.

4. Campbell, Joseph. 2008. "A Hero with a Thousand Faces." 3rd edition. *New World Library*. 432 pp.

5. Jung, Carl. 1991. "The Archetypes and the Collective Unconscious." *Routledge*, London. 560 pp.

6. von Franz, Marie-Louise. 1985. "Projection and Re-Collection in Jungian Psychology". *Open Court Publishing Company*. 254 pp.

7. Cook D.A.G.. 1987. In: Gregory, Richard (ed.) "The Oxford Companion to the Mind." *Oxford University Press*. 856 pp.

8. Healy, Sherry. 2005. "Dare to Be Intuitive." *We Publish Books*. 152 pp.

9. Skrbina, David. 2007. "Panpsychism". *Internet Encyclopedia of Philosophy*. Online: http://www.iep.utm.edu/panpsych/

10. Plato. 360 BCE. "Timaeus." Translated by Benjamin Jowett (1817–1893). *MIT Classics*. Online: http://classics.mit.edu/Plato/timaeus.html

11. Skrbina, David. 2005. "Panpsychism in the West." *MIT Press*. 326 pp.

12. Parks, Graham. 2009. "The Awareness of Rocks." Chapter 17 in: David Skrbina "Mind that Abides." *John Benjamins Publishing Company*. 415 pp.

13. Caroll, Lewis. 1872 (1999)."Alice Through the Looking-Glass." *Dover Publications*. 128 pp.

14. Sheldrake, Rupert. 1982. "A New Science of Life: The Hypothesis of Formative Causation." *J.P. Tarcher, Inc.*, Los Angeles. 229 pp.

15. Bartholomew, Alick. 2010. "The Spiritual Life of Water: Its Power and Purpose." *Park Street Press*. 368 pp.

16. Gleick, James. 1987 (2008). "Chaos: Making a New Science." *Penguin Books*. 384 pp.

17. Mandelbrot, Benoit. 1982. "The Fractal Geometry of Nature." *W.H. Freeman and Company*. 480 pp.

18. Consigli, Paolo. 2012. "Water, Pure and Simple: The Infinite Wisdom

of an Extraordinary Molecule." *Watkins Publishing*. 244 pp.

19. Varela, Francisco, Humberto Maturana, and R. Uribe. 1980. "Autopoiesis and Cognition: The Organization of the Living." *Reidel*, Boston. 141 pp.

20. Riistama, S., G. Hummer, A. Puustinen, R.B. Dyer, W.H. Woodruff, and M. Sikatrom. 1997. "Bound Water in the Proton Translocation Mechanism of the Haem–Copper Oxidation." *FEBS Letters* 414: 275–289.

21. Ho, Mae-Wan. 2014. "Water Is the Means, Medium and Message of Life." Int. J. Design & Nature and Ecodynamics 9 (1): 1–12.

22. Katsir, L. Miller, Y. Aharonov, and E. Ben-Jacob. 2007. "The Effect of rf–Irradiation on Electrochemical Deposition and Its Stabilization by Nanoparticle Doping." *J. Electrochemical Society* 154 (4): D249–D259.

23. Raichman, N, T. Gabay, Y. Katsir, Y. Shapira, and E. Ben Jacob. 2004. Engineered self organization in natural and man-made systems". In: D. Bergman and E. Inan, (eds.) "Continuum Models and Discrete Systems." *Kluwer Academic Publishers*, Dordrecht, Netherlands. 425 pp.

24. Ben Jacob, E., Y. Aharonov, and Y. Shapira. 2004. "Bacteria Harnessing Complexity." *Biofilms*, 1, 239–263.

25. Roy, Rustum, W.A. Tiller, Iris Bell, and M.R. Hoover. 2005. "The Structure of Liquid Water; Novel Insights from Materials Research; Potential Relevance to Homeopathy." *Materials Research Innovations Online* 9–4: 577–608.

26. Liu, C.S., S. Komarneni, and R. Roy. 1992. "Epitaxial Crystalization." *J Am Cer Soc* 75: 2665.

27. Schempp, Walter. 1997. "Quantum Holography and Magnetic Resonance Tomography: An Ensemble Quantum Computing Approach." *Informatica* (Slovenia) 21(3).

28. Pribram, Karl. 1991. "Brain and Perception: Holonomy and Structure in Figural Processing." *John M. Maceachran Memorial Lecture Series*, Mahwah, NJ. 388 pp.

29. Talbot, Michael. 2011. "The Universe as a Hologram." *Harper Perennial*. 338 pp.

30. McTaggart, Lynne. 2003. "The Field." *Element*. 384 pp.

31. Davenas, E. F. Beauvais, J. Amara, J. Benvaniste, Jacques. 1988. "Human Basophil Degranulation Triggered by Very Dilute Antiserum Against IgE." *Nature* 333 (6176): 816–8.

32. Chaplin, Martin. 2015. "Anomalous Properties of Water." Online at "Water Structure and Science": http://www1.lsbu.ac.uk/water/water_anomalies.html

33. Montagnier, L, J. Aissa, E. Del Guidice, C. Lavallee, A. Tedeschi and G. Vitiello. 2011. "DNA, Waves and Water." *J. Phys. Conf. Series* 306: 1–10.

34. J. Benveniste, P. Jurgens, W. Hsueh, J. Aissa. 1997. "Transatlantic Transfer of Digitized Antigen Signal by Telephone Link." *Journal of Allergy and Clinical Immunology* 99 (1): S175.

35. Roy, Rustom. 2006. In: "Water: The Great Mystery." Julia Perkul and Anastasiya Popova (directors) *Intention Media*. 87 min.

36. Chaplin, Martin. 2006. In: "Water: The Great Mystery." Julia Perkul and Anastasiya Popova (directors) *Intention Media*. 87 min.

37. Kröplin, Bernd. 2005. "Welt im Tropfen [World in a Drop]." *Institut für Statik und Dynamik der Luft- und Raumfahrtkonstruktionen*. Germany. 83 pp.

38. Kröplin, Bernd. 2011. "Water Has Memory." *Love Nature* (YouTube video). 2.49 min. Online: https://www.youtube.com/watch?v=ILSyt_Hhbjg

39. McTaggart, Lynne. 2008. "The Intention Experiment: Using Your Thoughts to Change Your Life and the World." *Atria Books*. 336 pp.

40. Cohen S, Popp F A. 1997. "Biophoton Emission of the Human Body." *J Photochem Photobiol B, Biol* 40: 187.

41. Popp F A., G. Becker, H.L. Konig, W. Peschka (eds.) 1979. "Electromagnetic Bio-information." *Urban & Schwarzenberg, Munchen*. 123-149 pp.

42. Cohen S, Popp F A. 2003. "Biophoton Emission of the Human Body." *Indian J Exp Biol* 41(5): 440.

43. Korotkov, K. 1999. "Aura and Consciousness." *Russian Ministry of Culture, State Editing and Publishing Unit*, St Petersburg, Russia.

44. Bundzen, P.V., K.G. Korotkov, L.E. Unestahl. 2002. "Altered States of Consciousness: Review of Experimental Data Obtained with a Multiple Techniques Approach." *J Altern Complement Med* 8 (2): 153–165.

45. Korotkov K. 2002. "Human Energy Field: Study with GDV Bioelectrography." *Backbone Publishing*, Fair Lawn, NJ.

46. Korotkov K, B. Williams, and L.A. Wisneski. 2004. "Assessing Biophysical Energy Transfer Mechanisms in Living Systems: The Basis of Life Processes." *J Altern Complement Med* 10 (1): 49.

47. Rubik, Beverly. 2008 "Measurement of the Human Biofield and Other Energetic Instruments." In: Lyn Freeman (ed.) "Mosby's Complimentary & Alternative Medicine." Chapter 20, "Energetics and Spirituality". 640 pp.

48. Rubik B. 1994."Manual Healing Methods. Alternative Medicine: Expanding Medical Horizons." US Government Printing Office, Washington, DC. NIH Publication No. 94–066.

49. Rubik B. 2002. "The Biofield Hypothesis: Its Biophysical Basis and Role in Medicine." J Altern Complement Med 8 (6): 703.

50. Rubik B. 1997. "The Unifying Concept of Information in Acupuncture and Other Energy Medicine Modalities." *J Altern Complement Med* 3 (suppl. 1): S67.

50. Rubik B., A.J. Brooks and G.E. Schwartz. 2006. "In Vitro Effect of Reiki Treatment on Bacterial Cultures: Role of Experimental Context and Practitioner Well-being". *J Altern Complement Med* 12: 7.

51. Fröhlich H. 1968. "Long-range Coherence and Energy Storage in Biological Systems." *Int. J. Quantum Chemistry* 2: 641–649.

52. Korotkov, Konstantin. 2006. In: "Water: The Great Mystery." Julia Perkul and Anastasiya Popova (directors) *Intention Media*. 87 min.

53. Schweitzer, David. 1997. Interview in: *Shared Vision Magazine*, Vancouver, BC. September issue.

54. Emoto, Masaru. 2001. "The Hidden Messages in Water." *Atria Books*, NY. 159 pp.

55. Emoto, Masaru. 2005. "The Secret Life of Water." *Atria Books*, NY. 178 pp.

56. Emoto, Masaru. 2006. In: "Water: The Great Mystery." Julia Perkul and Anastasiya Popova (directors) *Intention Media*. 87 min.

57. Chow, Effe. 2006. In: "Water: The Great Mystery." Julia Perkul and Anastasiya Popova (directors) *Intention Media*. 87 min.

6.
Water is
Rhythm

Photo 6.1: Patterns in flowing water of the Upper Credit River, Ontario, Canada.

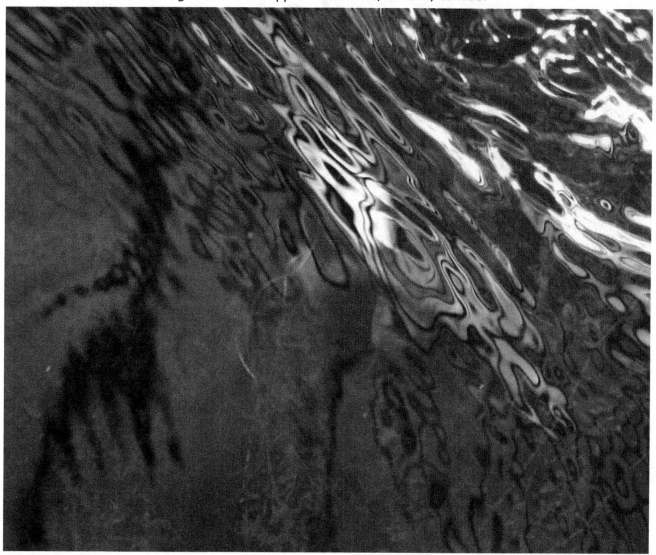

"Music is a holy place, a cathedral so majestic that we can sense the magnificence of the universe, and also a hovel so simple and private that none of us can plumb its deepest secrets."

—Don Campbell

I remember a brief but memorable discussion I had with a bright student during my fourth year in university. He'd asked me what I meant to pursue for my master's degree and after relating that I intended to study attached algal populations in clean versus polluted streams, I asked him what he wanted to study. He first admitted that he was really just dabbling in science, being an art student, then blithely shared that he was thinking of studying "how to make algae sing." I laughed, rather uneasily, as an arcane smile slid across his face. I will never know if he was teasing me or was in some way expressing some sincerity. No matter; it has resonated with me to this day.

The Merriam–Webster Dictionary defines *rhythm* as a regular, repeated pattern of sounds or movements, events, changes or activities and as the movement, fluctuation, or variation marked by the regular recurrence of natural flow of related elements. The word *rhythm* comes from the Greek word "to flow."

Song is just one of the many rhythms expressed by Nature. In fact, one could say that rhythm through oscillation, frequency and pattern are Nature's way of communicating with itself. Rhythm gathers vibration, frequency, intent, action and motion in one continuous movement. Rhythm naturally exerts a fractal continuum from microscopic to cosmic proportions. Cell division aligns with the planet's circadian rhythms;[1] the flight activity of a community of bees synchronizes with the phase of the moon;[2] planets and stars exert gravity on each other in a rhythmic symphony of spheres.

Our world is in constant and dynamic flow—oscillating from high to low, particle to wave, dark to light, separating and uniting, creating and destroying, and back again.

"True observers of nature, although they may think differently, will still agree that everything that is, everything that is observable as a phenomenon, can only exhibit itself in one of two ways," writes Goethe. "It is either a primal polarity that is able to unify, or it is a primal unity that is able to divide. The operation of nature consists of splitting the united or uniting the divided; this is the eternal movement of systole and diastole of the heartbeat, the inhalation and exhalation of the world in which we live, act and exist."[3]

We are creatures of rhythm. Virtually all our routines arise from some internal rhythm-based motivation. Our bodies naturally respond to our Planet's circadian, diurnal, lunar, and seasonal rhythms to name just a few. Light affects our behaviour, psychologically, physiologically and socially. Mood-altering chemicals generated in the pineal gland in our brain, are partially affected by the light received from our retina. Music can heal the body, strengthen the mind and unlock the creative spirit. Music with a pulse of about sixty beats per minute (e.g., baroque music and Mozart's music) can shift consciousness from the beta wave (ordinary consciousness at 14–20 Hz) toward the alpha range (heightened awareness at 8–13 Hz), enhancing alertness and general well-being. According to some water scientists, the quality of water depends as much on its form and rhythm as upon its structure and chemistry.

German scientist Theodor Schwenk recognized water's rhythms from the rising and falling tides, the recursive wave surges on a beach, the meanders of a river, and water's planetary cycle of motion and phase from vapour to liquid to solid and back. He proposed that water acquired some of its regenerative properties through its movement across specific surfaces. Recognizing that water's vitality relied on its rhythmic movement, Schwenk developed sinuous flow-form structures (a series of deep water channels and pools to create vortex flow). These flow forms create cascades that re-oxygenate the water as nature does and promote aquatic life. [4,5]

Photo 6.2: Rainforest stream on Vancouver Island, BC, Canada.

Photo by Kevin Klassen

Water in Sync

"I should have known no less. It hath been taught us from the primal state, That he which is was wish'd until he were."
—Shakespeare (Octavius Caesar in Antony & Cleopatra)

"At the heart of the Universe is a steady, insistent beat: the sound of cycles in sync,"[6] says Steven Strogatz in the opening to his compelling book, *Sync: the Emerging Science of Spontaneous Order*. He describes how every night, along the tidal rivers of Malaysia, thousands of fireflies congregate in the mangroves and flash in unison, without any leader or cue from the environment. "Even our bodies are symphonies of rhythm, kept alive by the relentless, coordinated firing of thousands of pacemaker cells in our hearts … almost as if nature has an eerie yearning for order,"[6] adds Strogatz. Synchronicity defies the first and second laws of thermodynamics. The first law, for instance, expresses the universal law of conservation of energy and identifies heat transfer as a form of energy transfer. The second law expresses the universal law of increasing entropy (a classic example of increasing entropy is ice melting).

Temporary synchronicity, which usually occurs by accident, can be found everywhere (e.g., pigeons startled by a car backfiring will take off at the same time). Persistent sync, however, is entirely different. Persistent sync comes easily to human beings and gives us pleasure: we like to dance together, sing in a choir, or play in a band. Strogatz says, "We interpret persistent sync as a sign of intelligence, planning and choreography. So, when sync occurs among unconscious entities like electrons or cells [or even fireflies], it seems almost miraculous."[6]

A new science is emerging that is devoted to studying sync and centres on the investigation of *coupled oscillators*. Two or more oscillators are said to be coupled if some physical or chemical process lets them influence one another. The result is a conversation of synchronicity leading to a harmony of action—chaos leading to order: a direct contradiction of the second law of thermodynamics. The mass synchronicity of fireflies observed in Malaysia, Thailand and Africa not only flashed in

unison, but in rhythm. Scientists now explain that their flash rhythm is regulated by an internal, resettable oscillator: every firefly is continually sending and receiving signals, shifting the rhythms of others and being shifted by them in turn. "Out of the hubbub, sync somehow emerges spontaneously," says Strogatz. "Fireflies organize themselves … Sync occurs through mutual cuing, in the same way that an orchestra can keep perfect time without a conductor."[6] But the insects don't need to be intelligent. They just do it. Like birds flying in formation during migration. Or electrons synchronizing by the billions and passing through impenetrable barriers. But why do they do it? What's the advantage to synchronicity?

All we know is that the tendency to synchronize and the existence of spontaneous order pervade our fractal universe, from atoms to animals, and people to planets. Female friends or co-workers eventually find their menstrual cycles synchronizing; sperm swimming side by side toward the egg beat their tails in unison; the tides have locked the moon's spin to its orbit. Strogatz and others suggest that the defining commonality to these sync phenomena is *mathematics*: the mathematics of chaos theory and self-organization. This spontaneous emergence of order out of chaos is what Strogatz calls "synchronized chaos" and what I call *stable chaos*.

Rhythms of sync abound in humans: heart rhythms, brain waves, menstrual cycles, cell division cycles, waves in the gut, and circadian rhythms, to name a few. Circadian rhythms of sleep duration, alertness and rapid eye movement (REM) march in lockstep with the body temperature cycle. The rhythms of short-term memory, secretion of melatonin, and several other cognitive and physiological functions run in the same phase relationship. Even single-celled algae exhibit circadian rhythms. Theoretical biologist Art Winfree, having discovered an unexpected link between biology and physics, showed that mutual synchronization in biology is analogous to a phase transition (e.g. from liquid to solid).[7]

Network theorists, when they study an abstract pattern of dots connected by lines are concerned with the pattern, that is, the "architecture of relationships, not the identities of the dots themselves. We can draw a metaphor with information, what it is and how it is dispensed and shared among people. László Barabási, a Transylvanian physicist, showed that the distribution of links on the Web is skewed to the left with a very long and heavy tail to the right. A handful of sites on the Internet are much more connected than others, with many more incoming or outgoing links than average, and billions of remaining pages languish in obscurity with no incoming links at all.[8]

What network theorists found is that the Internet—despite being an unregulated, unruly labyrinth where anyone can post anything and link it to any other page at will—is self-organizing. The Internet follows the same pattern that persists in the "small world" (with, for example, a tendency to "short cut" and cluster like brain cells). It also displays the kind of *scale-free* (wide range) patterns prevalent in Nature (e.g., "the food-web of species preying on one another, the meshwork of metabolic reactions in a cell, the interlocking boards of directors of a large corporation, even the structure of the English language itself,"[6] says Strogatz). Barabási showed that the Internet was both fragile and robust, with properties of resilience, and that sites acted much like living cells (in that, for example, in protein interactions, the most highly connected proteins were the most important ones for the cell's survival; not unlike CNN and Yahoo on the Web). The Web is also very fluid with "nodes" or clusters that change (not unlike a low budget hit that starts out slowly and builds by word of mouth).

Strogatz notes that, "we still have almost no clue how the interlocking activities of … genes and proteins are choreographed in the living cell."[6] He notes also that such phenomena, like most others in the Universe, are fundamentally non-linear.

In Chapter 4, I mention how Swiss psychiatrist Carl G. Jung created the concept of *synchronicity* in the 1920s to describe "meaningful

coincidences" that may have no apparent causal relationship, yet seem to be meaningfully related: a psychic factor independent of space and time, which both challenges and compliments the classical view of causality.[9] The choreography of meaningful coincidences and their gestalt relationships and emerging patterns certainly interested Jung.

Photo 6.3: Coastal dory shop in Lunenburg, Nova Scotia, Canada.

Photo by Nina Munteanu

Water and Cymatics

"When man is artistically engaged with tone, he puts his ear to the very heart of nature itself; he perceives the will of nature and reproduces it in a series of tones."

—Rudolf Steiner

Our world is composed of energy, light, sound and matter, all expressed at different frequencies. Everything that moves has an internal and external rhythm. All movement follows its own path and destiny, fulfilling a kind of rhythm that expresses its relationship with the world. Even things that aren't moving have a potential for rhythm, an internal clock that beats its particular message.

"We are all vibrational beings comprised of systems of vibrating particles,"[10] Pangman and Evans share in their book *Dancing with Water*. "Vibration provides the music in water's dance." Each part of our body, they add, resonates at a specific frequency. Additional frequencies add to each chord with increasing levels of complexity and building in a kind of harmony. Nature builds in cycles, and each cycle adds harmonics that complement the chord of the existing frequency.

In 1967, Hans Jenny, a Swiss doctor, artist, and researcher, published a book on the structure and dynamics of waves and vibrations.[11] He created the term *cymatics* from the Greek word *kyma* (wave), to define the study of how sound affects gases, liquids, plasmas and solids and how vibrations, in a broad sense, generate and influence patterns, shapes and moving processes. When sound travels through non-solids, it moves in longitudinal waves called compression waves. In matter, such as water, the medium is displaced by sound waves, causing the water to oscillate at a frequency relative to the sound. Then visible patterns emerge.[11]

Leonardo da Vinci, Galileo Galilei, Robert Hooke, and musician/physicist Ernst Chladni all investigated the expression of sound waves in various materials in the 1400s, 1500s, 1700s, and 1800s, respectively. In the 1780s, Chladni's acoustical experiments included spreading sand on metal plates and recording the movement patterns of the sand on a surface as he ran a violin bow across the plate. The sand moved and

concentrated along the nodal lines where the plate surface remained still, outlining the nodal lines. These patterns are now called *Chladni sound figures.*

Two hundred years later, Jenny showed what happened when one took various materials (such as sand, spores, iron filings, water, and viscous substances) and placed them on vibrating metal plates or membranes. Shapes and moving patterns appeared that varied from nearly perfectly ordered and stationary to turbulently developing, organic and constantly in motion.

Using crystal oscillators and his invention (called a "tonoscope") to set plates and membranes vibrating, Jenny controlled frequency and amplitude or volume to demonstrate that simple frequencies and songs could rearrange the essential molecular structure of certain materials, including water. The flowing patterns reflected a variety of forms found in nature and provided the means to study invisible forces that underlie natural processes, from the movement of amoebae to the formation of galaxies.[12]

Jenny was convinced that biological evolution was a result of vibrations, and that the nature of the vibrations determined the ultimate outcome. He speculated that every cell has its own frequency and that a number of cells with the same frequency create a new frequency that is harmonious with the original. This possibly forms (or evolves into) an organ that may also create a new frequency in harmony with the two preceding ones. Jenny was saying that the key to understanding how we can heal the body with the help of tones or vibrations lies in our understanding of how different frequencies influence genes, cells and various structures in the body. In his book *Animal Landscapes*, Jenny writes, "Animals are hieroglyphs born out of a cosmic language; they are also the [symbols], pointing to the universe and its reflections."[13]

Boldly extending his tonoscope research into voice and language, Jenny discovered that when the vowels of ancient Hebrew and Sanskrit were pronounced, the sand took the shape of the written symbols for

Illustration 6.1: Drawings of A) a turtle shell and B) Chladni sound arrangement of an oscillating elliptical plate at 1088 Hz, showing similarity to markings on the turtle. Interpreted from: "Water Sound Images" (2007) by Alexander Lauterwasser.

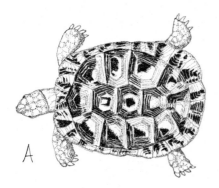

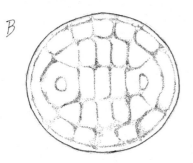

Illustration by Nina Munteanu

these vowels, while modern languages didn't generate the same result. This led spiritual philosophers to ponder if "sacred languages" (including Tibetan and Egyptian) have the power to influence and transform physical reality, to create things through their inherent power, or can they, through recitation or singing of sacred texts, heal a person who has gone "out of tune"?

Cymatics photographer and author Alexander Lauterwasser photographs water under the influence of sound vibrations. Lauterwasser raised tortoises as a child in Heiligenberg, Germany, and when he discovered the illustrations of *Chladni sound figures*—some of which bore a striking resemblance to the patterns on his tortoises' shells—Lauterwasser sought to investigate the relationship of frequency and sound with the shapes in nature.[14]

Lauterwasser's beautiful and thoughtful book *Water Sound Images* is rich with vibrant imagery of natural formations and structures that reveal similarity of vibration—clouds, a melon, waves, cut agate.[15] Fascinated and eager to elucidate the fundamental processes that shape nature, Lauterwasser concludes that, "the similarities of structure, design and pattern of many types of *Chladni sound figures* with those … of natural phenomena is quite surprising and suggests a certain kinship or commonality of origin."[15] He then quotes Goethe's lectures on colour: "With any phenomenon in nature, especially those that are important and noticeable, one should not stop, not attach oneself to it, not stick to it, and not view it as isolated. Instead one should look around at all of nature to see where we find something similar, something related; because only through compiling the related does an "all-ness" develop bit by bit, one that expresses itself and requires no further explanation."[3]

Working with water and other materials, Lauterwasser showed that higher frequencies created more intricate and complex patterns. The water or sand typically formed radial, spherical or elliptical shapes that repeated the outer form of the perimeter. And when asymmetrical shapes developed at certain frequencies, symmetrical shapes always formed in between.[13] A perfect ellipse materialized when the sand was exposed to the frequency of a Hindu OM chant. A Buddhist prayer evoked a multiple circular wave pattern.[15]

When Lauterwasser subjected elliptical plates to a high frequency of over 12,000 Hertz, the shapes arranged themselves into both longitudinal and lateral symmetry that resembled the silica "ribs" of the diatom *Cocconeis*, the ubiquitous periphyton diatom that I studied in a fast-flowing Quebec stream, which is found all over the world.

Illustration 6.2: Drawing of a Cocconeis placentula, an elliptically shaped diatom with silica ribs similar to Chladni sound arrangement at 12,000 Hz.

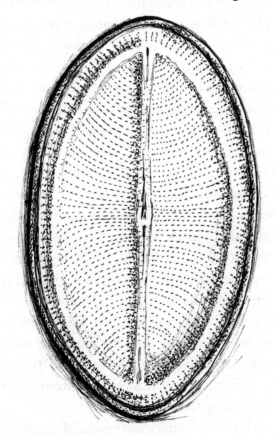

Illustration by Nina Munteanu

Form, Pattern & Meaning
水

"Knowing the Form without form, you can go everywhere and fear no evil."

—*Lao Tsu*

Lauterwasser draws on the wisdom of biologist Brian Goodwin to suggest that current biology has moved on from seeing an organism as a machine with parts. Biology is beginning to recognize an organism as "a living being that 'just like art, represents value by itself'"[15] ... and is itself a continually developing perception of life,"[16] constantly oscillating on the edge of chaos and permanently searching for emerging order.[17] He sees a living being as a composition of moving "morphic resonance."

Goodwin used the term *robust morphogenesis* to describe a principle of formation that endured eons of resisting arbitrary, random mutation. Goodwin gives as examples the periodic repetition of vertebrae in higher animals and the whorl in higher plants. I also saw such periodic repetition in my studies of algae, and of diatoms particularly. I learned in botany class how virtually all arrangements of branches, leaves, petals and sepals exist in the form of a spiral or whorl. It is simply that some are more observable, given the tightness of the formation. Goodwin writes that, "every leaf is shifted relative to the previous one by a constant angle of divergence ... of which ... 137.5 degrees is the most common." Lauterwasser adds that this angle is significant, given that it corresponds to the Golden Mean ratio (see Chapter 3).

Mathematician Ian Stewart suggests that, "the patterns of nature are emergent phenomena—emerging from the process of nature herself, as a new quality,"[18] and surfacing, Lauterwasser adds, "from the ocean of complexity—just as Botticelli's Venus emerged from the shell—unannounced and transcending their own origin."[14]

In his work with water, Lauterwasser noted that quiescent patterns form at distinct frequencies, in what he called a "rest of higher order" or a "standing wave" that evolves out of the centre of a "chaotic wave" or dynamic oscillation—that is, *rest founded in movement*. He distinguished two types of waves: (1) concentric ring waves that propagate outward from the centre to the rim and return back to the centre; and (2) radial waves that move along the rim, their wave crest edges passing through the centre like rays. Lauterwasser noted a signature of structuring, ordering and creative process. He proposed that any particular arrangement (e.g., number) is an expression of its structured relationship to the whole.[15]

Videos of a water drop's changing wave pattern with progressively higher frequencies can be seen on several sites on the Internet. It is stirring and worthwhile to watch. I first saw this frequency progression in a talk given by American author Greg Braden[19] and was fascinated by the symmetrical shapes water drops took on. As the frequency increased, the complexity of the water drop's wave pattern also increased.

The water drop begins to show concentric patterns. As a key threshold resonance is approached, the wave pattern changes into a more complex expression of itself, then oscillates in a kind of stable chaos. With each threshold, as frequency is increased, the standing wave transforms from two, three, four, five, six rays to a 10- or 12-pointed "star"—then into polar star tetrahedron or *merkaba* (an Egyptian word for light, body and spirit, also known as Metatron's Cube), icosahedron, octahedron, and finally something resembling the "flower of life."

At 28.9 Hz, the oscillation picture of a water drop shows a hexagonal pattern (actually two polar triangles) that resembles the blossom of a lily. Many cultures consider the mutual penetration of two polar triangles to represent the most fundamental principle of creation—the successive unification and harmonization of all opposites.[13] Polar opposites of 4- and 5-fold structures occur in both water and plants. At 24.24 Hz, for instance, a 4-fold standing wave in a water drop reflects the blossom of *Paris quadrifolia* and, at 38.45 Hz, a 5-fold standing wave reflects the

Photo 6.4: Common milkweed (Asclepias syriaca) flowering umbel, showing flowers with 5 reflexed petals and 5 raised hoods with horns, Credit River, Ontario, Canada.

Photo by Nina Munteanu

blossom of the wax flower. At 79.7 Hz, water's 7-fold standing wave, while more rare in nature, can be found in the plant *Siebenstern* (Seven Star). At 102.5 Hz, the ultimate standing form—the spiral or whorl—expresses. This form is a ubiquitous and universal form in nature and in the universe from sunflowers to galaxies. Lauterwasser's 14-arm spiral emerged at this frequency.[15] At 102.5 Hz, the pattern of opposing spirals seen in a water drop is consistent with the pattern of a sunflower seed head. The pattern expresses at 137.5 degrees, or the Golden Mean ratio.

It seemed as though in those few minutes of watching that video of the water drop expressing its morphic resonance with increased frequencies, I saw the entire universe express itself through rhythms in "a process of becoming"[11]—from the primal binary impulse to the progressively more complex patterns that quivered and trembled in a wondrous polyphonic symphony of flow—in search of harmony. It was truly as though the water drop had "come alive."

Photo 6.5: Clematis jackmanii *showing 8-sepal arrangement, Mississauga, Ontario, Canada.*

Photo by Nina Munteanu

Hegal, in his discourse *Aesthetics*, insightfully described vibration and the sounding of musical instruments as a process of overcoming the "hitherto quietly within-itself existing materiality" and birthing motion through an "inner quivering of the body."[20] Hegal writes that, "the result of this oscillating quiver is the tone." He adds that through this quivering within itself, the quiet material form loses its exclusive identity, so that suddenly something more embracing, something deeper, "more ideal than the physicality," can emerge.[15,20]

Lauterwasser suggests that a rhythmical ordering or even a creative force is at work within numbers.[15] This is why, he says, there have been so many different numbering systems throughout our history. He gives the examples of the decimal system, with 10 as the unit; and the binary system developed by W. Leibniz with 2 as the unit. From Babylon, the Sumerian sexagesimal system (based on the number sixty) has continued relevance in the 360 degrees of a circle and hours, minutes and seconds. Similarly, the Chinese use hexagrams in the canonical *I Ching* (a divination manual), with their sexagenary cycle of sixty terms for recording days or years. Water's "sensitive chaos"[21,4] opens water to nature's numerical rhythms, revealing astonishing similarities in geometry, including the arrangements of flower petals, leaves, cactus heads, fruit, sea urchins and sand dollars, diatoms, and many other natural forms (both animate and inanimate) on Earth and elsewhere.

When observing pattern and form, Lauterwasser reiterates the limitations of *reductionist science* (i.e., trying to construct a comprehensive understanding of an organism atomistically, by adding together the smallest parts to arrive at the organism as a whole). According to Goodwin, shapes of life mirror "a profound pattern of orderly relations."[15] Lauterwasser describes the prevalence of two opposing spirals in nature and in the motion of water. Reflected in many forms in nature (e.g., the water vortex), the Golden Mean ratio (which I talk about in Chapter 3) expresses a fractal relationship, whereby every part carries the whole within it. Anthropologist and mathematician Ernst Bindel describes it this way: "The whole, which carries the image of the whole undetached within itself, yet which makes the grace and power of the whole stand out even more through the act of separation."[22] Surely, this is Bohm's "Implicate Order" and "Holomovement" (see Chapters 3 and 11).

The Music of the Spheres

Two hundred years before Jenny worked with the rhythms of water and sand, Johannes Kepler discovered that the velocities of the planets correspond to musical intervals. The virtual symphony they create is known as the *Music of the Spheres*. The Music of the Spheres (*Musica universalis*) is based on mathematical relationships that express "tones" of energy through numbers, visual angles, shapes and sounds—all connected by proportion.[22] The symphony supplies the creative and sustaining tones of the entire universe. The tones that each celestial body expresses change with the cycling seasons and the journey through space. Kepler found that the difference between the maximum and minimum angular speeds of a planet in its orbit conforms to a harmonic proportion.[23] And, as I mention in Chapter 3, the symphony evolves and communicates throughout the universe by vortices.[8]

Pythagoras had originally shown how the pitch of a musical note resulted from the length of the string that produced it and how the intervals between harmonious sound frequencies form numerical ratios.[24] He suggested that the Sun, Moon and the planets each emit a unique *hum* (orbital resonance), based on their orbital revolution and that their "tones" correlated with their celestial movements. He posited a relationship between celestial and terrestrial events based on musical harmonics. Both he and Kepler believed that the link was in the harmony of music. Kepler then used the concept of the music of the spheres in his 1619 *Harmonice Mundi* (*Harmony of the Worlds*).[23]

The note of the open string is called the *fundamental*. When the octave is sounded, it can be heard in the same pitch as the fundamental only in a different place in the whole spectrum: the fundamental and

the octave are different, but also the same. Both Pythagoras and Kepler found this of mystical significance. They saw it as essential proof that there is a cognitive, creative link between the one and the many, the Creator and the Creation. "As above, so below."[25]

When a string vibrates, the space around it fills with rotating *lines of force* (vortexes) interspersed with *nodes* (where there are no vibrations)—as shown in Lauterwasser's experiments that subjected sand and water to different frequencies. For instance, sand gathers in the node spaces of a vibrating plate, forming lines along the non-vibrating places on the plate. Vibratory physicist Dale Pond suggests looking at our backbone, "as an image of the harmonic vibrations that surround the vibrating notochord of the embryo. Matter, in the form of somites or embryonic vertebrae, is deposited in concentric vortices along the notochord like pearls on a string. Each vertebra in cross section can be seen to be in the form of a vortex. These vertebral vortices are suspended in the active centers of vibration. Where intervertebral disks will be formed in the fetus, the string of the monochord has a silent node."[25]

When I was pregnant with my son, I felt an overwhelming urge to listen to classical music (mostly Beethoven, Debussy, Ravel and Mozart) and soft "new age" Celtic music (mostly Enya). What I'd intuitively felt is now known: music calms or stimulates the movement and heart rate of a baby in the womb. It has also been shown that children who receive regular music training demonstrate better motor skills, math ability, and reading performance than those who don't. High school students who sing or play an instrument score up to fifty points higher on Student Aptitude Test scores than those who don't.[26]

These observations are borne out by another observation: that adult musician's brains generally exhibit more EEG (brainwave) coherence than those of non-musicians.[26]

Music is a language understood instinctively by all peoples because it communicates directly to the soul. Darwin suggested that music may have played a role in the evolution of language, comparing the sounds of speech to the way birdsong is used in courtship.[26] Tecumseh Fitch in Mark Liberman's online "Language Log" says, "Some have referred to this as a 'musical proto-language'."[26]

Don Campbell, author of *The Mozart Effect*, eloquently described *music* as "the sounds of earth and sky, of tides and storms. It is the echo of a train in the distance, the pounding reverberations of a carpenter at work. From the first cry of life to the last sigh of death, from the beating of our hearts to the soaring of our imaginations, we are enveloped by sound and vibration every moment of our lives. It is the primal breath of creation itself, the speech of angels and atoms, the stuff of which life and dreams, souls and stars, are ultimately fashioned."[28]

Cymatics demonstrate the role of *chaos* (destruction) as Nature's bridge to creation. Jenny and Lauterwasser showed that as the amplitude or frequency rose, old patterns broke down and new patterns emerged, reflecting more complex levels of organization. Their observations harmonize with the polarity of creative destruction seen throughout Nature and the Universe. Below, I talk about *Nataraja*, the Lord of Dance, who depicts the Hindu God Shiva, the divine cosmic dancer who destroys a weary universe in preparation for *Brahma*'s creation.

Photo 6.6: The Credit River at Belfountain, Ontario, Canada.

Photo by Nina Munteanu

Water's Sounds & Rhythms

I'm a bit of a bohemian. A gypsy poet perhaps. I travel a lot and often move from place to place. I come by my itinerant lifestyle naturally: I'm Romanian. In truth, teaching and writing for a living has provided me with a lifestyle that allows me to wander and explore the planet, something I have always dreamed of doing from childhood (when I played "let's explore" games with my sister). I realized after a while that I conduct a virtual checklist whenever I first move into a new home or residence. My wandering soul checks for three things: a diverse and interesting food market; a café with character and ambience with great coffee, of course; and a large park with water. During my most recent residence in Mississauga, I felt unsettled until I discovered and walked the length of the Credit River.

My spirit soars with a resonating lightness of being when I walk along water of any kind. Rivers and creeks in a forest are particularly magical. There is nothing quite like the sound of liquid water making its way along a landscape, with the commiseration of birds and trees. Flowing water is so alive and gestalt, dancing and laughing over the rocks, bubbling, gurgling, rushing and trickling.

The sounds of Nature that resonate with us stay with us and speak through us.

Rhythms of "Home"

Perhaps best known these days for his melancholic stories of fatalistic, ironic tyrannies, Victorian author Thomas Hardy wrote with a tender and poetic sensibility about nature, and particularly the heath where he grew up. All of Hardy's writings strongly embody a sense of place as does his "Wessex," the embodiment of Dorset where he grew up and lived. His novel *Return of the Native* is one of his best examples of the meaning of place. In the following passage, Thomas Hardy writes about the beloved (and cursed) Egdon Heath and how its natives grasped its subtle minutiae:

> *"The wind, indeed, seemed made for the scene, as the scene seemed made for the hour. Part of its tone was quite special; what was heard there could be heard nowhere else. Gusts in innumerable series followed each other from the northwest, and when each one of them raced past the sound of its progress resolved into three. Treble, tenor, and bass notes were to be found therein. The general ricochet of the whole over pits and prominences had the gravest pitch of the chime. Next there could be heard the baritone buzz of a holly tree. Below these in force, above them in pitch, a dwindled voice strove hard at a husky tune, which was the peculiar local sound alluded to. Thinner and less immediately traceable than the other two, it was far more impressive than either. In it lay what may be called the linguistic peculiarity of the heath … Throughout the blowing of these plaintive November winds that note bore a great resemblance to the ruins of human song, which remain to the throat of fourscore and ten. It was a worn whisper, dry and papery, and it brushed so distinctly across the ear that, by the accustomed, the* material minutiae *in which it originated could be realized as by touch. It was the united products of infinitesimal vegetable causes, and these were neither stems, leaves, fruit, blades, prickles, lichen, nor moss. They were the mummied heath bells of the past summer, originally tender and purple, now washed colourless by Michaelmas rains, and dried to dead skins by October suns."[29]*

In his treatise on author Thomas Hardy, Henry Charles Duffin suggested that Hardy considered trees the interpreters between Nature and

man.[30] From the "sobbing and stertorous breathing"[31] of a fir plantation to a the stillness of trees in a quiet fog, standing "in an attitude of intentness, as if they waited longingly for a wind to come and rock them."[32] Trees, meadows, winding brooks and country roads formed the backdrop for both Hardy's world and his stories. Amazon reviewer Darragh O'Donoghue expressed Hardy's deep connection with Nature's embedded rhythms personified: "In its animation of the sexually charged woods, the lanes, glades, fields, sunsets, dawns, storms, drizzles, winds, breezes, nature is the true hero, full of almost supernatural agency." This was deeply Hardy's world, where he grew up and lived. And where his heart rejoiced.

I grew up in a small town in the pastoral Eastern Townships of Quebec, a place of gently rolling hills and dairy farms. I remember listening to the soft thumps and slaps of rain falling on the leaves of the maple–beech forest behind our house and, lying in bed at night, to the soothing chirp of crickets and singing frogs in the garden and woodland out back. I remember spending much of my time as a child on the ground, usually sitting or crouched or even lying there to watch life unfold. Nature came to me in the buzz of the bees, the recursive clap of a grasshopper, the lyrical notes of robins, cardinals, wrens and sparrows, and the clanking of lanky poplars in a moaning wind. I lived in a suburb, surrounded by the familiar sounds of an occasional barking dog, the distant roar of a lawn mower, or hum of a propeller plane or car. These were the pervasive sounds of "home."

Photo 6.7: Baby robin rests on a lawn chair shortly after emerging from the nest of a maple tree, Mississauga, Ontario, Canada.

Photo by Merridy Cox

My naturalist friend Merridy Cox relates her experience with the resonance of "home" through her memories of birdsong by her family cottage near Ottawa, Ontario. She tells me how, since the 1950s, the cottages where she spent many summers sat cheek-by-jowl along Lake Mississippi:

"In that time, the ash and maple soared to great heights, allowing both sun and shade for cottagers to lounge and swim in the summer. Late in the season, the treetops reverberate with an all-encompass-

ing sound, as striking and beautiful as can be found in the tallest cathedral. The source of this amazing antiphony is small birds hidden in the highest canopy. Goldfinches! Those tiny, mouse-like birds that feed on thistle seed and fly in wild swoops are congregating. Now their instincts are starting to prepare them for a great migration. Now they are singing themselves together into a cohesive choir, a symphony of ululation. Tomorrow, they may be gone. For me, sitting beneath the trees on the lakeshore, the sound catches at my soul like a miracle."

We imprint on the sounds of our birthplace ecosystem. I noticed this when I moved from the mixed deciduous forest of Quebec to the temperate rainforest of the British Columbia coast, where I raised my son. In Quebec, the varied notes of the wind rustling through maples and beeches are joined by a birdsong symphony. The breeze through B.C. rainforest conifers has a cooler, more unified sound dominated by the strident caw of crow or starling. While I have made the west coast of British Columbia my home and feel a deep and tender connection to it—I raised my family there—the sounds of my childhood in the Eastern Townships still resonate with me in the sweetest of notes.

Photo 6.8: Mixed deciduous forest in southern Ontario, Canada.

Photo by Merridy Cox

Polarity & Creative Destruction

Over twenty years ago, I conducted a limnological study in central British Columbia of a lake affected by both natural-made and human-related landslides.[33] The initial challenge involved the elucidation of human-related impact to determine the actions toward, costs of, and responsibilities for habitat restoration and compensation. However, the human-related impact was entwined within the ecosystem's own evolutionary tendency and natural succession. The question of what was already naturally occurring and what was exacerbated by humanity's interference remained unresolved. In a world of "who's to blame and therefore pays," these are key questions continually debated among government regulators, various stakeholders and their environmental consultants. The definition and realizable benchmark for what constitutes "pristine" is complex, providing the dilemma: to what level of "natural" can we conceivably and reasonably "restore"? When we do not always recognize "natural change," assigning responsibility and action becomes an insurmountable challenge; one in which most environmental scientists find themselves deferring to politics.

Amid the political and social debate of who was responsible for what, I ran across the ground-breaking papers of C.S. Holling on the ecological model of *creative destruction*.[34,35,36] Economist Joseph Schumpeter introduced the term in 1942 to describe the process of industrial transformation that accompanies radical innovation. According to Schumpeter's view of capitalism, innovative entry into the market by entrepreneurs sustained long-term economic growth, even as it destroyed the value of established companies that enjoyed some degree of monopoly power. Xerox, for example, saw profits fall

"Chaos is another name for opportunity."

—*I Ching*

and its dominance vanish as rivals launched improved designs or cut manufacturing costs, drawing customers away. Similarly, ecologists describe the seral stages of plant colonization: initial monopolization of pioneer opportunists in the landscape (e.g., fireweed) that give way to increased diversity and niche partitioning of resources. Creative destruction is a matter of scale.

Holling suggested that the experience of instability in Nature maintains the structure and general patterns of ecosystem behaviour; in other words, that Nature "learns" and accommodates with time. In his classic paper, entitled "Simplifying the Complex: the Paradigms of Ecological Function and Structure,"[36] Holling's model recognized ecosystem behaviour as non-linear, self-organizing, and continually adapting through cycles of change from expansion and prosperity to creative destruction and reorganization. Holling described four phases of natural ecosystem succession in his "nature evolving" paradigm, starting with the *exploitation* phase, in which new opportunities are realized through rapid colonization of new ground and competition. Then, natural forces of *conservation* (e.g., nurturing, consolidating) eventually lead to a vulnerable system (e.g., an old growth forest), as stabilizing factors lose strength and the ecosystem evolves from having few interrelationships to having many. The result is often an abrupt change that both destroys the ecosystem and creates *opportunity* (*creative destruction*) through fire, storms, pests, senescence. *Mobilization* of bound, stored "capital" (e.g., carbon, nutrients and energy) through physicochemical and biological processes (e.g., decomposition and mineralization) completes the dynamic cycle of a functional ecosystem.[34,35,36] Then the exploitation phase begins again. So, while these phases with increasing diversity reflect "instability" and change, overall they reflect a kind of stable chaos, marked by resilience, elasticity, and balance.

It is interesting to note that in the Chinese *I Ching*, the *hexagram* (a six-lined symbol that represents an ancient energy pattern) for "crisis" is the same as that for "opportunity."

I used the ecological model of creative destruction to describe the elastic resilience of cyclical lake ecosystem evolution (or succession). I argued that *stochastic change* (involving random bahaviour) and *elastic stability* (ability to regain its original quality as soon as impact is removed) underpin the long-term effects of sediment loading and nutrient input from natural disturbances in aquatic ecosystems (e.g., debris torrents, landslides and rock falls). Drawing on evidence from long-term studies of landslides and artificial reefs, I posited the concept of disturbance and change as an integral and necessary part of lake ecosystem structure, function and evolution.[33] My take-home message was that behind every natural disturbance lies opportunity. Life creates life—through death. Of course, on the larger scale of evolution, this means that one ecosystem replaces another. So, an *oligotrophic* lake (with low plant nutrients and high in oxygen) naturally transforms into a *mesotrophic* lake (with moderate nutrients), then a *eutrophic* lake (rich in nutrients supporting dense plant growth and depleting lower oxygen levels), as nutrients enter the water or are created by lake metabolism. Eutrophic lakes often give way to a marsh or a bog, depending on environmental characteristics and natural processes at work. Ultimately the marsh or bog may fill in and become a field, then a forest.

Destruction in creation and creation in destruction are ingrained in the life cycles of everything on this planet and in the universe. A forest fire can destroy life but in so doing creates a more vibrant, healthier forest. Holling and I, in our separate studies, were really drawing on the ancient knowledge of polarity and cycles in nature. The opposing forces of polarity generate ongoing cycles of creation and destruction. The Ouroboros, remembering.

The *Ouroboros* is an ancient symbol that depicts a serpent or dragon swallowing its own tail to form a circle. As a serpent devouring its own tail, the Ouroboros symbolizes the cyclic nature of the Universe: creation out of destruction, Life out of Death. The Ouroboros eats its own tail to sustain its life, in an eternal cycle of renewal. In the Gnosis

Illustration 6.3: The Ouroboros, snake eating its tail, symbolizes eternity.

Illsutration by Kerste Voute

scriptures, it symbolizes eternity and the soul of the world.

The Hindu God Shiva, whose statue sits outside of CERN headquarters in Geneva, Switzerland, is known as the Destroyer or the Transformer. He is often depicted as Nataraja, the cosmic dancer performing a divine dance to destroy in order to create. Shiva is limitless, transcendent, unchanging and formless; encompassing paradox and existing—like water—in three states: destruction, desolation, and rebirth. "Modern physics," writes Austrian physicist Fritjof Capra in his book *The Tau of Physics*, "has shown that the rhythm of creation and destruction is not only manifest in the turn of the seasons and in the birth and death of all living creatures, but is also the very essence of inorganic matter …Shiva's dance is the dance of subatomic matter."[37]

In the final analysis, it is a matter of scale. Scale is something you can't see or easily measure and assess, especially if you are in it. Scale is like hindsight. And perspective is connected to scale. According to researchers at the University of Bristol, a major extinction event (and climate change) at the end of the Permian (about 250 million years ago) killed over 90 percent of life on Earth, including insects, plants, marine animals, amphibians, and reptiles. Called the *Great Dying*, ecosystems were destroyed worldwide, and life was nearly completely wiped out. According to the Bristol study, ecosystems took apparently 30 million years to fully recover.[38]

The Great Dying & Opportunity

Using the Great Dying as an example, palaeontologist Peter Ward argued in his book *The Medea Hypothesis* (named after the sorceress who destroyed her children) that life has self-destructive tendencies. The hypothesis challenged and contradicted the Gaia Hypothesis (named after another goddess, the Greek goddess of the Earth—see below), which posits that organisms can and do adapt their environment "to

Photo 6.9: Statue of Shiva as Nataraja in front of CERN, Geneva, Switzerland.

Photo by Kenneth Lu, Wikimedia Commons

suit themselves." According to Ward, the Permian "Great Dying" was caused by sulphur-generating marine bacteria that poisoned sea and land. Hardly behaviour of self-interest, Ward contested.[38]

Perhaps it is a matter of definition. For instance, what is "self" and, therefore, "self-interest"? Where does "self" end and "other" begin? Bring in fractals, autopoiesis, synchronicity, self-organization, and altruism, and it all begins to blur. Bring in notions of cellular intelligence and concepts of "external mind" and morphic resonance, and our traditional precepts of self-interest lose themselves within the greater complexity of stable chaos. I coined the term *stable chaos* in my science fiction book *Darwin's Paradox* to describe the apparent chaotic behaviour of Nature and the Universe that is, in fact, stable—but we generally cannot perceive the stability, mainly because of our lack of perspective and problems with scale.[39] Scale is the lens for perceiving our fractal landscapes and how they are interconnected and interact and loop into one another.

Lee Kump, professor of geosciences at Pennsylvania State University, noted that the primary organs of Earth's system—photosynthesis, respiration, and associated greenhouse gas production and destruction—remained intact and continued uninterrupted through the cataclysm of the "Great Dying." Animal life eventually recovered and achieved levels of diversity and complexity that far surpassed what existed before, says Kump.[40] In other words, the cataclysm of the "Great Dying" provided an "opportunity" for life to regenerate, establish and diversify. It is only scale that separates the colonization of a valley devastated—but nourished—by a forest fire from a mass-extinction of global proportions.

The Gaia Hypothesis

When James Lovelock and Lynn Margulis hypothesized in the 1970s that living organisms actively modified their environment to keep the Earth habitable, they were following in the footsteps of James Hutton (the father of modern geology), who in 1785 imagined the planet as a kind of metaphoric "super-organism."[41] As a result of their discussions about the role of micro-organisms as links to life and the Earth, Lovelock and Margulis' Gaia Hypothesis ironically hinged yet again on sulphur and its essential role in living things. The concept of "feedback mechanisms" lies at the heart of it. Changes in external conditions trigger responses that counteract the imposed changes. Living organisms regulate global environmental change through behaviour that creates a dynamic "equilibrium" of sorts. I compare this to the homeostatic behaviour of organisms at the cellular and tissue level. In fact, biochemists have applied Gaia-like rationale to the study of human biochemistry, such as the body's impressive ability to regulate glucose production to demand.

The Gaia Hypothesis attracted hostile criticism from the traditional scientific community. They claimed that it contravened Darwinian evolution, required organisms to "know" and have "purpose" and ridiculed its associated New Age overtones. Richard Dawkins, one of the community's chief objectors, criticized the hypothesis on the grounds that it demanded global altruism among organisms—a feature that counters Darwinian natural selection, according to those same scientists. It is interesting to note that Dawkins had similarly dismissed Margulis' theory of *endosymbiosis* (which posited that cells evolved through co-operation)—itself a challenge to the neo-Darwinist concept of natural selection and also to Dawkin's concept of the "selfish gene"—only to retract his criticism later, when the theory was proven fact.

The systems of Gaia are complex, from the tiniest cell to the com-

plex planet itself. Weather, for instance, is a "chaotic system" that displays a fractal structure and a range of chaotic behaviour on many scales. Temperature, air pressure, wind speed and humidity are all sensitive to initial conditions and interrelated in multi-scales. Brian Arthur, professor at Stanford University, shares that the complex approach is total Taoist. In Taoism there is no inherent order. "The world starts with one, and the one become two, and the two become many, and the many lead to myriad things."[42] The Universe in Taoism is perceived as vast, amorphous, and ever changing. You can never nail it down. The elements always stay the same, yet they are always arranging themselves. So, it's like a kaleidoscope: the world is a mosaic of patterns that change, that partly repeat, but never quite repeat, that are always new and different and yet the same. It is the paradox that embraces strange attractors, stable chaos and quantum entanglement in a constant flow.

Western scientists are just beginning to appreciate self-organizing paradox through the application of complexity theory and chaos theory, something the eastern world has "known" since ancient times: humility before nature, respect for richness and diversity of life, the generation of complexity from simplicity, and understanding the whole to understand the part—Bohm's Implicate Order.

Photo 6.10: Scarborough Bluffs overlook Lake Ontario, Scarborough, Ontario, Canada.

"Network theory, a hot new discipline where mathematics intersects with sociology, looks at the Internet and other complex networks as powerfully self-organizing systems, both generating and managing complexity out of a few simple rules,"[43] writes Steven Shaviro, American cultural critic and author of *Connected, Or What it Means to Live in the Network Society.* "The brain is described, in connectionist accounts, as a self-organizing system emerging from chaos; today we try to build self-learning and self-organizing robots and artificial intelligences, instead of ones that are determined in advance by fixed rules. "Genetic algorithms" are used to make better software; Brian Eno devises algorithms for self-generating music. Maturana and Varela's autopoiesis is taken by humanists and ecologists as the clear alternative to deterministic and mechanistic biology."[43]

Photo by Nina Munteanu

Polarity, Piezoelectricity & Embracing Paradox

Austrian philosopher and naturalist Viktor Schauberger described the attraction and the repulsion of polarized forces as the dance of creation. *Polarity*, according to Schauberger, is Nature's engine (Nature uses opposing forces and cycles to create). Polarity is perhaps more like a song; a rhythmic dance that cycles through its own opposing forces. Like two dance partners shifting as one to a synchronizing tune.

In his book *Water Sound Images*, Alexander Lauterwasser writes how "Life" swings back and forth between two extremes in an attempt to mediate balance and harmonize; from losing oneself through dissolution to finding a firmer order through solidifying concentration. He suggests that water best portrays this oscillating dynamic between chaos and order. "It swings back and forth, perpetually changing between its diverse states of condensation, evaporation into the air, streaming and flowing in its liquid state, and freezing as ice; unifying all of the different regions of our planet in one perpetual circular flow."[13]

There are many examples in nature of cycling polar forces of creation and destruction. Electricity and magnetism form polar forces that unite into an electromagnetic whole. As water circulates in the weak *piezoelectric* (able to generate an electric charge) and magnetic fields of the Earth, it achieves coherent structure. The organizing energy of coherence, coupled with spiral movement, ions, and the natural properties of light and sound, create full-spectrum, *living water* (water that is alive with its own pulses and harmonics). Unsurprisingly, it is this water that is the most beneficial for health.

As I mention in Chapter 2, many of the healing waters on Earth come from places where natural energy vortices occur. These places often possess the rhythm of stronger piezoelectric and magnetic fields. I talk more about this in Chapter 10, *Water is Prayer*.

Photo 6.11: A long tail boat speeds amid the steep karst islands of the Indian Ocean off Phuket, Thailand.

Photo by Nina Munteanu

Opposing Forces (Yin & Yang)

"Everything is dual; everything has an opposite, and opposites are identical in nature but different in degree."
—Hermes Trismegistus (Thoth)

The ancient Chinese used the principle of yin and yang to describe the cycles of opposing forces—polarity—in nature.[4] *Yang* brings about disintegration and *yin* gives shape to things. Yin energy is described as feminine, passive, downward, cool, dark, soft, negative, contracting and creative. Yang energy is masculine, active, upward, hot, light, hard, positive, expanding, and disintegrative. Neither is complete without the other, represented by the dot at the centre of each teardrop shape in the symbolic circle, both making up the whole. Yin and yang are still the basis of Traditional Chinese Medicine practised today.

The ancient Chinese also believed that in order for the cycle of breaking down and rebuilding to favour creation, the ratios of feminine to masculine tended toward 60:40. This is, in fact, what water's polar covalent bond exhibits. Hydrogen represents the feminine component and oxygen the masculine, in a ratio that approximates the geometric ratio of *phi*, a ratio found in virtually all living things and iterated in the numerical sequence developed by medieval mathematician Leonardo Fibonacci. The nature of the interconnected molecules in polarized water gives it many of its unusual properties.

Paradox and opposites lie in everything. "Opposition (polarity) is the power in the universe that creates growth,"[4] Pangman and Evans tell us. It is the force behind two oppositely charged atoms bonding to form a third substance, or the creation of new life, when male and female energies unite. Pangman and Evans assert that water must cycle to be healthy and life-giving.[10] When unrestricted and permitted to flow freely, water regenerates through a "feminine" spiral movement that cultivates structure, ionization, and other life-giving qualities. After discharging its energy, water takes on "masculine" qualities and draws minerals and other replenishing constituents. It is a cycle of opposites that feed a greater whole.

Bartholomew suggests that, "Nature is founded far more on cooperation than on competition, because it is only through harmonious interplay that physical formation can occur and structures can be built. At the heart of the creative process in Nature are polarities, such as positive and negative, chaos and order, quantity and quality, gravitation and levitation, electricity and magnetism. In every case, for any natural process to be harmonious, one polarity cannot be present without the other, and each needs the other to make up the whole."[44]

Dialectic Thought & Stable Chaos

In response to the apparent paradoxes in dualistic thinking, German philosopher Hegel promoted *dialectic thought*, which integrated opposite extremes of logical thought to come to an understanding of the underlying Unity behind them.

Hegel's dialectic reconciled paradoxes to arrive at absolute truth. Based on his belief in the connection of all things universal, "the apparent self-subsistence of finite things appeared to him as illusion; nothing, he held, is ultimately and completely real except the whole."[45]

Following a three-step process, from (1) thesis, to (2) anti-thesis, to (3) synthesis, Hegel's dialectic "actualizes itself by alienating itself, and restores its self-unity by recognizing this alienation as nothing other than its own free expression or manifestation."[46] Hegel's dialectic suggests Campbell's "Hero's Journey" (Chapter 9) and Bohm's "Holomovement" (Chapter 11). It follows a teleological path because "each later stage of dialectic contains all the earlier stages [and] none of them is *wholly* superseded, but is given its proper place as a moment in the whole."[47]

Illsutration 6.4: The Taijitu, Taoist Yin-Yang symbol describes balanced complementary-opposing forces that give rise to each other and codepend (e.g., shadow cannot exist without light).

Illustration by Kerste Voute

Hegel described dialectic thinking as a process of thought by which "such contradictions are seen to merge themselves into a higher truth that comprehends them." Therefore, yin is balanced by yang; magnetism by electricism, frequency by wavelength, and chaos by order toward a whole.

Science writer James Gleick, author of *Chaos: Making a New Science*, pointed out that life is created from chaos,[48] or in the terms of Hegel, from anti-thesis.

Water is an ideal medium for chaos, given its unpredictable and turbulent behaviour. Theodor Schwenk writes that water, "by renouncing every rhythm of its own becomes the carrier of each and every rhythm."[4] Japanese philosopher and researcher Masaru Emoto writes, "The water flowing within us is part of the water flowing through nature and part of the rhythm of life being played out throughout the Universe."[49]

Rhythm undulates—at once turbulent and calm—signaling its fractal presence. Rhythm scours and builds its music with infinite patience and precision. Spiralling. Oscillating in successive rushes, glides, surges and trickles. Self-organizing. Coherent. Viscous.

Rhythm is water.

References

1. Smaaland, R. 1996. "Circadian Rhythm of Cell Division." *Prog Cell Cycle Res.* 2: 241–66.
2. Oehmke, M.G. 1973. "Lunar Periodicity in Flight Activity of Honey Bees." *Journal of Interdisciplinary Cycle Research* 4(4): 319–335.
3. Goethe, J.W. (1980)."Farbenlehre (A Doctrine of Colour)." Verlag Freies Geistesleben, Stuttgart, Germany.
4. Schwenk, Theodor. 1962. "Sensitive Chaos: The Creation of Flowing Forms in Water and Air." *Rudolf Steiner Press*. 288 pp.
5. Wilkens, Andreas; Michael Jacobi; and Wolfram Schwenk. 2005. "Understanding Water." *Floris Books*, Edinburgh. 107 pp.
6. Strogatz, Steve. 2003. "Sync: The Emerging Science of Spontaneous Order." *Hyperion*, NY. 338 pp.
7. Winfree, A.T. 1967. "Biological Rhythms and the Behavior of Populations of Coupled Oscillators." *J. Theor. Biol.* 16: 15–42.
8. Barabási, Albert-László, and Albert Réka. 2002. "Statistical Mechanics of Complex Networks." *Reviews of Modern Physics* 74: 47–97.
9. Jung, Carl G. 1973. "Synchronicity: An Acausal Connecting Principle." *Princeton University Press*, New Jersey. 152 pp.
10. Pangman, M.J. and Melanie Evans. 2011. "Dancing with Water: The New Science of Water." *Uplifting Press*. 255 pp.
11. Jenny, Hans. 1967. "*Wellenund Schwingungenmitihrer Strukturund Dynamik / Cymatics*" (The Structure and Dynamics of Waves and Vibrations). *Basilius Press*, Basel, Switzerland.
12. Jenny, Hans and Peter Guy Manners. 1986. "Cymatics: The Healing Nature of Sound." *Macromedia*. YouTube Video. Newmarket, NH. 80 min.
13. Jenny, Hans. 1992. "Tierlandschaften (Animal Landscapes)." *Raffael Verlag*, Ittigen, Switzerland.
14. Lauterwasser, Alexander. 2012. In: "The Sound of Sacred Geometry—Alexander Lauterwasser." YouTube video: https://www.youtube.com/watch?v=9R4Bkwh9h9c

15. Lauterwasser, Alexander. 2006. "Water Sound Images: The Creative Music of the Universe." *Macromedia Publishing*. 172 pp.

16. Goodwin, Brian. 1997. "Der Leopard der seine Fleckenverliert." *Piper Verlag*, Munchen.

17. Portmann, Adolf. 1965. "Die Tiergestalt." *Herder Verlag*, Freiburg, Germany

18. Stewart, Ian. 1998. "Die Zahlen der Nature: Mathematikals Fensterzur Welt." *Spektrum Akademischer Verlag*, Heidelberg, Germany.

19. Braden, Gregg. 2012. In: "Gregg Braden— Vibration." YouTube video. Online: https://www.youtube.com/watch?v=ykO9aQFxYpE

20. Hegel, G.W., Fr. 1986. "Vorlessungenüber die Ästhetik III." *Suhrkamp Verlag*, Frankfurt.

21. Novalis. 1957. "Werke und Briefe." *Lambert SchniderVerlag*, Wasmuth, Heidelberg.

22. Bindel, Ernst. 1980. "Die geistigen Grunlagen der Zahlen." *Verlag Freies Geistesleben*, Stuttgart.

22. Kepler, Johannes. 1619. "Harmonices Mundi (Harmony of the Worlds)." *Johann Planck*, Austria.

24. Weiss, Piero and Richard Taruskin. 2008. "Music in the Western World: a history in documents". Cengage Learning.

25. Pond, Dale. 2000. "It Really Is a Musical Universe." *The Cosmic Light*, University of Science and Philosophy. Online: http://pondscience-institute.on-rev.com/svpwiki/tiki-index.php?page=1.21%20-%20It%20Really%20Is%20a%20Musical%20Universe

26. Woodwind & Brasswind. 2015. "Music Enhances the Mind". Woodwind & Brasswind. Online: http://www.wwbw.com/The-Woodwind---Brasswind---Music-Makes-You-Smarter-g26057t0.wwbw

27. Fitch, W. Tecumseh. 2009. "Musical Protolanguage: Darwin's Theory of Language Evolution Revisited." In: *Language Log*. Online: http://languagelog.ldc.upenn.edu/nll/?p=1136

28. Campbell, Don. 2001. "The Mozart Effect." *Avon*. 352 pp.

29. Hardy, Thomas. 1878 (1999). "The Return of the Native." *Penguin Classics*. 496 pp.

30. Duffin, Henry Charles. 1962. "Thomas Hardy: A Study of the Wessex Novels, the Poems, and the Dynasts Anmols Literature Series." *Manchester University Press*. 356 pp.

31. Hardy, Thomas. 1887 (1998). "The Woodlanders." *Wordsworth Collection*. 336 pp.

32. Hardy, Thomas. 1874 (2003). "Far from the Madding Crowd." *Penguin Classics*. 480 pp.

33. Munteanu, N. and G.P. Thomas. 2001. "The Role of Disturbance in Lake Evolution and Implications to Restoration and Management." In: 28th ATW Symposium, Winnipeg, October 2001.

34. Holling, C.S. 1973. "Resilience and Stability of Ecological Systems." *Annual Rev. Ecol. Syst.* 4: 1–23.

35. Holling, C.S. 1977. "Myths of Ecology and Energy." In: "Proceedings, Symposium on Future Strategies for Energy Development." Oak Ridge, Tenn., 20–21 October, 1976. *Oxford University Press*, New York, N.Y.

36. Holling, C.S. 1987. "Simplifying the Complex: The Paradigms of Ecological Function and Structure." *Eur. J. Oper. Rel.* 30: 139–146.

37. Capra, Fritjof. 2010. "The Tau of Physics". *Shambhala*. 368 pp.

38. Ward, Peter. 2009. "The Medea Hypothesis." *Princeton University Press*. 208 pp.

39. Munteanu, Nina. 2007. "Darwin's Paradox". *Dragon Moon Press*. 320 pp.

40. Kump, Lee. 2011. "The Last Great Global Warming." *Scientific American*, June 29.

41. Lovelock, J.E. and L. Margulis. 1974. "Atmospheric homeostasis by and for the biosphere: the Gaia hypothesis". *Tellus Series* A 26 (1-2): 2-10.

42. Arthur, Brian. 2004. In: Mitchel M. Waldrop (author), "Complexity: The Emerging Science at the Edge of Order and Chaos". *Simon & Schuster Paperbacks*, New York. p. 333.

43. Shaviro, Steven. 2009. "Against Self-Organization". *The Pinocchio Theory*. Online: http://www.shaviro.com/Blog/?p=756

44. Bartholomew, Alick. 2010. "The Spiritual Life of Water." *Park Street Press*. 368 pp.

45. Caygill, Howard. 1995. "A Kant Dictionary." *Blackwell Publishers*, Cambridge. 464 pp.

46. Bottomore, Tom. 1995. "A Dictionary of Marxist Thought." *Blackwell Publishers*, Cambridge. 647 pp.

47. Russell, Bertrand. 1945. "The History of Philosophy." *Simon & Schuster*, New York. 895 pp.

48. Gleick, James. 2008. "Chaos: Making a New Science." *Penguin Books*, revised edition. 384 pp.

49. Emoto, Masaru. 2005. "The Secret Life of Water." *Atria Books*. 178 pp.

7. Water is Vibration

Photo 7.1: Water patterns in flowing water of the Upper Credit River.

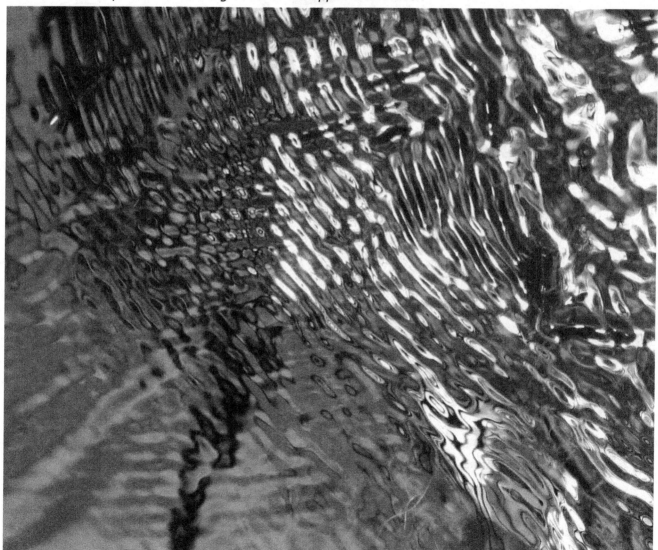

Photo by Nina Munteanu

"If you want to find the secrets of the universe, think in terms of energy, frequency and vibration."
—Nikola Tesla

Where I grew up in a small Quebec town, I used to tag along behind my older brother and sister to the parks and undeveloped scrub to play. We frequented a woodland just down the street. We would spend the whole day there. We made up games using Nature's materials; we played hide-and-seek among the trees; and we concocted magic potions from various things nature provided: sticks, leaves, flowers, sap and water.

I was blessed as a child; my parents, while they were strict about certain social activities like going to parties and drinking, let us go to the local river and play there the whole day. I grew up hearing the songbirds of eastern North America. I grew up with the wind rustling through the trees and the howling cold of winters. I fell asleep on hot summer nights to the hypnotic murmur of crickets.

In the previous chapter I write how the familiar sounds from my childhood give me comfort today. Whenever I hear a small propeller plane overhead, a part of me remembers the warm and relaxing summer days of school holidays. I am remembering where I came from and who I was—and still am. To this day, when I feel stressed or anxious, I seek a natural place where Nature's sounds caress my ears and feed my soul with invigorating energy and the feeling of "home." Quite simply, they give me joy, like a poem from heaven. I am re-aligning myself to Nature's intimate frequency.

Frequencies that bring balance to living organisms on Earth are those that were in the background during their creation, say science writers Pangman and Evans.[1] The frequency of the Sun (hydrogen) and the frequencies of Earth (e.g., Schumann resonance) act together to balance all organisms on the planet in a harmony of existence.

Rudolf Steiner, Austrian philosopher and founder of biodynamics and anthroposophy (a spiritual philosophy of freedom), contended that the sounds and vibrations of birds and insects are fundamental to life. He shared the same worldview with Johann Wolfgang von Goethe, who posited that, "thinking … is no more and no less an organ of perception than the eye or ear. Just as the eye perceives colours and the ear sounds, so thinking perceives ideas."[2]

"There will come a time," Steiner wrote, "when a diseased condition will not be described as it is today by physicians and psychologists, but it will be spoken of in musical terms, as one would speak of a piano that was out of tune."[3] Nostradamus foretold the healing of cancer through pure tones; George Gershwin suggested that music's vibration resonates physically with people and that eventually the right vibration for each person will be found and used; American mystic Edgar Cayce called sound the medicine of the future.[4]

In their book *Secrets of the Soil* researchers P. Tomkins and C. Bird reported on experiments that suggested that plant growth increased notably when exposed to the sounds and frequencies of birds, over their control counterparts.[5]

"Quantum physicists reveal that underneath apparent physical structure there is nothing more than energy, that we are energy beings,"[6] cell biologist Bruce Lipton tells us. "That means that we interact with everything in the field. This has an important impact on health care. Quantum physics reveals that energies are always entangled with

Photo 7.2: Trees reflecting in pooling water in a Quebec woodland, Canada.

Photo by Nina Munteanu

each other. In an energy universe, waves are always flowing through and interacting with all other waves."

Lipton argues that when we don't pay attention to our vibrational energies, we miss important read-outs from our environment. "While medicine does not train its doctors to recognize that energy is part of our systems, they very easily adapted to using the new scan systems to determine what is going on inside the body. It is humorous that they read their scans as 'maps,' but do not have the fundamental understanding that their maps are direct readouts of the energy present in the body."[6]

Japanese intuitive researcher Masaru Emoto imagined that the human body is like a universe of its own, made of over 60 trillion cells and each carrying out its specialized functions, while harmonizing with other cells to make us who we are. "The organs, nerves, and cells of the body have their own unique frequency," says Emoto. "The body is like a grand orchestra consisting of the harmonization of various sounds."[7]

Photo 7.3: Common thistle (Crisium vulgare) *in the Credit River marsh, southern Ontario, Canada.*

Photo by Nina Munteanu

Quantum Vibration

"What we have called matter is energy, whose vibration has been so lowered as to be perceptible to the senses. There is no matter."

—Albert Einstein

Herbert Fröhlich of the University of Liverpool introduced the idea that some sort of collective vibration helped proteins cooperate with each other and carry out instructions of DNA and other proteins to achieve quantum coherence. Fröhlich predicted that certain frequencies just beneath the cell membrane (now called *Fröhlich frequencies*) could be generated by vibrations in these proteins through wave communication.[8] He showed that once energy reached a certain threshold, molecules vibrated in unison until they reached a high level of coherence.[9] Fröhlich hypothesized that cells could recognize one another at a distance and be attracted or repelled; as well, they could trigger coherent electric vibrations with feedback and amplification potential.[10,11,12]

The Italian physicist Renato Nobili of the Università degli Studi di Padova demonstrated that electromagnetic frequencies occur in animal tissues. His experiments showed that cell fluid holds currents and wave patterns that correspond to wave patterns in the brain cortex.[8]

According to science journalist Lynne McTaggart, physicist Fritz-Albert Popp considered homeopathy as a "resonance absorber." (I describe homeopathy in Chapter 5.) Briefly here, *homeopathy* is based on the premise that "like treats like," which in Western medicine is the basis for vaccinations. The only difference is that in homeopathy, the substance is diluted to "zero concentration." The notion behind homeopathy, however, is that the effect is not based on chemistry, but on information—in this case, frequency. "If a rogue frequency in the body could produce certain symptoms, it followed that the high dilution of a substance which would produce the same symptoms would still carry those oscillations," writes McTaggart in her book *The Field*. "Like a tuning fork in resonance, a suitable homeopathic solution might attract and then absorb the wrong oscillations, allowing the body to return to normal."[8]

According to this theory, says McTaggart, two molecules that are tuned into each other, even at a long distance, may resonate to the same frequency. These two resonating molecules would then create another frequency, which would continue in a chain reaction to produce radical changes based on tiny initial effects.

In Chapters 4 and 5, I talk about epitaxy and the work by Del Guidice and others, who demonstrated that water molecules create coherent domains. To reiterate, they describe water's tendency to polarize around a charged molecule—storing and carrying its frequency so that it may be read at a distance. "This would mean that water is like a tape recorder," writes McTaggart, "imprinting and carrying information whether the original molecule is still there or not."[8] McTaggart concludes that water is a natural medium of cells, acting as an essential conductor of a molecule's signature frequency in all biological processes and that water molecules organize themselves to form a pattern on which wave information can be imprinted. As I write in Chapter 5, water may not only send the signal but may amplify it.

In the 1930s, British bacteriologist Edward Bach developed essences from flowers (later known as Bach Flower Remedies). A form of ancient healing, this kind of homeopathic treatment dissolves the flower components in water until very little, if anything, is left of the actual material. The treatment is said to contain only the vibration of the original flower. These solutions, described as vibrational medicines, are considered pseudoscience, given that they rely on the concept of water memory. Other researchers, including Masaru Emoto in Japan and Bernd Kröplin in Germany, have looked at the effects of flower essences on the structure and appearance of water (see Chapter 5).

Water is capable of carrying a wide spectrum of frequencies, write Pangman and Evans. Particularly in its fourth phase (see Chapter 2), water supports coherence and a way for complex organisms to stay "in tune." Signals transmitted as vibrations in the fluid connect each cell to the whole organism. "This is perhaps the most important function of

Photo 7.4: Apple blossom in Prince Edward County, Ontario, Canada.

Photo by Nina Munteanu

the body's extracellular fluid,"[1] Pangman and Evans write. On a larger scale, they add, vibrations connect everything in the Universe.

The ancient Shinto of Japan is a religion of vibration, writes Masaru Emoto in his book *The Secret Life of Water*.[7] *Shintoism*, Emoto tells us, is mostly about raising the vibrational rate to drive out negative forces and create holy places. Ancient temples were placed in areas considered pristine that emitted a high energy. New Age philosophy considers such places to occupy junctions where *ley lines* (sources of power or energy) converge, such as Glastonbury in the United Kingdom.[13]

"Shinto does not claim one founder or one god," writes Emoto. "Mountains, rivers, oceans, animals, trees and flowers are all gods, and along with people, all elements of a single, unified universe. The soul of Shintoism is harmony."[7] According to Shinto belief, nothing is inferior or superior in Nature. Everything has a role and responsibility, with one part of the Universe serving all other parts "by best being who and what it is."

Photo 7.5: A honeybee feeding on the nectar of a flower, southern Ontario, Canada.

Photo by Nina Munteanu

Resonating Water & Schumann Resonance

Bumblebees fascinate me. I love to watch them buzzing around a flower, collecting nectar. Their fuzzy black and yellow bodies tremble as they make their way along the flower with their legs clothed in pollen. Then they spring into flight, wings a-blur. Bees have an amazing sense of navigation, enabling them to fly the shortest route possible between flowers—something we are still trying to figure out. According to scientists, they use the sun as a compass and navigate by polarized light. Bees can also recognize individual faces using feature recognition. When bees change jobs, they change their brain chemistry. And researchers at the University of Illinois found that they even have personalities. Bees have also evolved a uniquely efficient way to store honey and raise their young: the hexagonally shaped honeycomb.

A honeybee flaps and rotates its wings 240 times a second, creating a vortex that lifts it into the air. Honeybees use short wing strokes of less than 90 degrees and a high number of flaps every second to stay aloft. When challenged by difficult conditions, the bees use wider strokes (increasing their wing amplitude) but maintain the same frequency. This stroke pattern is less efficient than the broader strokes and slower flapping of fruit flies and other insects, but it allows the bee to generate more lift when it needs to carry a heavy load, such as a cargo of nectar or larvae and to fly in a straight line, rather than the fanciful flight of the butterfly. Pollen, which the bee collects on its hind legs is a source of protein for the hive and is needed to feed the baby bees (larvae) to help them grow.

"Everything in life is vibration."
—Albert Einstein

The nectar that the bee collects is a sweet, watery substance that the bee processes and then regurgitates into waxy honeycomb cells in the hive. After they fan it with their wings to remove excess moisture, honey results. Bees are the only insects in the world that make food that humans can eat. And honey is the only insect-created food with therapeutic, medicinal, and nutritional value.

When, as a child, I watched a bumblebee flit from flower to flower like a jet-propulsion dirigible, I wondered what brought the bee to a particular flower. I eventually learned in school that scent, shape, pattern and colour play a role, given that bees can see visible and ultraviolet light and have precise olfactory receptors. Recent scientific evidence from the University of Nevada shows that bees also detect the electric fields that flowers emit. Flowers have a slight negative charge relative to the air around them, and bumblebees have a positive charge, due to friction of their body parts in the air.[14] It's what helps the pollen grains stick to the bee's legs—a little like shuffling across a static carpet in wool socks.

Nature communicates with itself through resonance. "It is the language of communication and response, the law of attraction bringing the bee to the lemon blossom and the moss to the damp earth,"[15] Alick Bartholomew writes.

The word *resonate* comes from the Latin for "resound." Objects, charged particles and mechanical systems tend to vibrate at certain natural frequencies, known as their *harmonics*. These natural standing waves are also called *resonant frequencies*. Resonance occurs when one object, vibrating at the same natural frequency of a second resting object, forces that second object to vibrate in turn. The amplitude of one object's oscillations increases by the matching vibrations of another object.

When we enjoy a particular piece of music, we resonate with its dynamic energy. From molecule to cell to tissue and sense of self, our whole body participates in a state of sublime resonance with the sound.

Like the soft caress of two lovers, resonance celebrates communication of two attractive energy patterns. "For millennia people have sung and played music to their crops, streams, lovers, children, and animals," Bartholomew shares. He adds that resonance and vibrational rate of water movement lies at the heart of natural medicine, homeopathy, bio-communication and husbandry. Mechanical and acoustical resonance—from the rhythmic marching soldiers and the constant pitch of their *shofars* (ram's horn)—may have played a role in bringing down the walls of Jericho.

The Earth's surface conducts electricity, which is maintained at a negative potential by a global electrical circuit.[15] The circuit has three main generators: the solar wind, which enters the magnetosphere; the ionospheric wind; and thunderstorms, which emit thousands of lightning strikes per minute around the globe. The earth's surface, therefore, provides an abundant source of free electrons. When a human is in direct contact with the earth (e.g., barefoot), free electrons run freely into the body, allowing it to maintain the same electrical potential as the earth. This is called *Earthing*, which I introduce in Chapter 2. Experiments conducted by measuring changes in electroencephalagrams, surface electomyograms, and blood volume pulse suggest that Earthing affects human physiology and reduces overall levels of stress and tension.[16,17]

The resonant frequency of the Earth's atmosphere, between the surface and the densest part of the ionosphere, is called *Schumann Resonance*. Named after German physicist Winfried Otto Schumann, who predicted it mathematically in 1952 (and first detected it in 1954—an auspicious year for me), this global electromagnetic resonance occurs as a set of peaks in the extremely low frequency (ELF) portion of the Earth's electromagnetic field spectrum.

The normal standing wave created in the Schumann Cavity occurs at a wavelength equal to the circumference of the Earth, and at a base frequency (and highest intensity) between 6–8 Hz (7.83 Hz). Some

Photo 7.6: Kite surfing on Lake Ontario, Cherry Beach, Ontario, Canada.

Photo by Nina Munteanu

call this base frequency the Earth's "heartbeat" or the "tuning fork" of the planet. This coincides with alpha rhythms produced by the human brain during meditation, relaxation and creativity. Many biological systems appear to resonate at this same frequency range. Dolphins produce sound waves that coincide with Schumann Resonance frequency.

Nikola Tesla intuited that energy waves in the earth and the atmosphere could be used to transmit power to any point on the globe. He understood that the surface of the Earth, the ionosphere and the atmosphere together form one electrical circuit. Tesla was able to transmit power and energy wirelessly over long distances (via transverse waves and longitudinal waves). He transmitted ELF waves through the ground and between the Earth's surface and the Kennelly-Heaviside layer of the ionosphere. Tesla patented wireless transceivers that developed standing waves, and it was he who discovered that the resonant frequency of the Earth was about 8 Hz, in the range of the Schumann Resonance.

Ancient Chinese teachings tell us that humans balance two environmental signals: the yang (masculine) signal from above and the yin (feminine) signal from below. These correspond, respectively, to the relatively strong signal of the Schumann wave and the weaker geomagnetic waves originating from the planet. To achieve perfect health, say the teachings, both signals must be in balance.

Universal Frequencies

In 1953, the International Standards Organization (ISO) promoted a change to the musical scale, and since then the note "A" has been tuned to 440 hertz. Some musicians now argue that this pitch is disharmonious with the resonance of Nature and may even generate negative effects on human behaviour and consciousness. Prior to this worldwide standardization, music was often tuned to A=432 Hz. Known as Verdi's A, this tuning was used by many classic musicians including Mozart, Chopin, Bach, and Debussy. The Stradivarius violin was tuned this way. This tuning was standard throughout cultures of the ancient world: ancient Egyptians and Greeks tuned their instruments to this pitch.

An initial effort to make A=440 Hz the basis of standard pitch occurred in 1910, when the Rockefeller Foundation issued a grant to the American Federation of Musicians to popularize the concept. In the 1930s, research in musical frequencies funded by the Rockefeller Foundation and involving the U.S. Navy and, oddly enough, the Nazi regime, focused on how musical frequencies affected human behaviour. Studies apparently determined that 440 Hz music promoted hard work.[18,19] Behavioural scientist Leonard G. Horowitz argued that the British Standards Institute (BSI) adopting the A=440 Hz standard just prior to going to war and the US adopting the standard in 1940 were connected with the findings mentioned above. The International Standards Organization (ISO) finally endorsed A=440 Hz in 1953. Unsubstantiated claims have circulated that the Nazi regime had promoted this pitch as a standard, after research established that the 440 Hz pitch encouraged population herding and greater aggression, psycho-social agitation and emotional distress.

"Everything is energy and that's all there is to it. Match the frequency of the reality you want and you cannot help but get that reality. It can be no other way. This is not philosophy. This is physics."

—Albert Einstein

Horowitz suggested that consciousness is affected through vibration—and hydro-sonically, through the effects of sound on water. He argued that water functions as a liquid crystal superconductor and hydro-sonic signals communicate within and between cells through a liquid-crystal *proteoglycan matrix* (consisting of a protein bonded to glycosaminoglycan groups) usually found in human connective tissue.[20]

Proponents of a return to the standard pitch to 432 Hz claim that it vibrates with the universe's Golden Mean (*phi*) and unifies properties of light, time, space, matter, gravity and magnetism with the DNA code, and consciousness.[21,22] The number 432 is reflected in ratios of the Sun, Earth and Moon, as well as in the precession of the equinoxes, and dimensions of the Great Pyramid of Egypt, Stonehenge, and the *Sri Yantra* (sacred chakra), among other sacred sites.[23] Proponents of A=432 Hz also claim that it resonates with the heart chakra, repairs DNA and restores both spiritual and mental health. When our atoms and DNA start to resonate in harmony with the spiralling pattern of Nature, our sense of connection to Nature is said to be magnified. Some have suggested that 432-tuned music stimulates the right brain, responsible for many desirable human traits.[24]

Intrigued by the arguments and claims regarding these two standards, whose difference is merely 8 Hz, I searched the Internet and found several examples of the same musical piece tuned to both, for comparison. I was amazed at how different the pieces sounded. Initially, the music tuned to A=432 Hz felt a little muted compared with the sharper, more highly-defined A=440 Hz. But, the overall experience of the A=432 Hz music was a warmer, softer and richer experience. I would describe the difference between the A=440 and A=432 metaphorically as a sharp high-definition news video versus a warm, richly experienced movie film. The A=440 *tells* and you *listen*; the A=432 *shows* and you *experience*.

Musicians and music lovers have variously noted that music tuned in A=432 Hz induces a more inward experience that is felt inside the

Photo 7.7: Footprints in the snow at Port Credit, Ontario, Canada.

Photo by Nina Munteanu

body, at the spine and the heart. "Music tuned in A=440 Hz is felt as a more outward and mental experience, and is felt [in] the head." [23] Audiophiles have also stated that A=432 Hz music seems to be non-local and can fill an entire room, whereas A=440Hz can be perceived as directional or linear in sound propagation. One guitarist noted, "The overall sound difference was noticeable, the 432 version sounding warmer, clearer and instantly sounded more listenable, but the 440 version felt tighter, with more aggressive energy."[23]

The 8 Hz difference between these two pitch standards may have other connections. Eight Hz is the fundamental "heartbeat" of the planet, known as *Schumann Resonance*, a global electromagnetic resonance originating in electric discharges of lightning within the cavity between the Earth's surface and the ionosphere. The frequency of 8 Hz also resonates with the frequency of 432 Hz, creating a harmonic. This harmonic is related to the physical laws that govern our universe.

The frequency range around 8 Hz (e.g., from 4-13 Hz) is associated with the *theta* and *alpha* brainwaves that are most associated with whole brain synchronization, also referred to as "whole brain functioning" or "hemispheric synchronization."[25]

The human brain during creativity, relaxation, or meditation resonates in and around this frequency range: including 1) *theta waves* of dreaming sleep or deep meditation (4-8 Hz), characterized by increased creativity, super-learning, integrative experiences and increased memory; 2) *alpha waves* (8-14 Hz) of deep relaxation, associated with super-learning, focus, and increased serotonin production; and even the lower frequency *delta waves* (0.1-4 Hz) of dreamless sleep (or waking trance), associated with a non-physical state and access to the "collective unconscious" mind.[25]

In 1973, Gerald Oster, and shortly after Robert Monroe (founder of Hemi-Sync), demonstrated that not only did the brain entrain to a frequency equal to the difference between two tones, resonating to that frequency (a difference tone called a "binaural beat"), but that the entrainment (e.g. a "Frequency Following Response" or FFR) happened in both hemispheres and showed identical frequencies, amplitude, phase and coherence.[26,27,28] For instance, frequencies of 200 Hz and 210 Hz produce a binaural beat frequency of 10 Hz, which will feel relaxing. The brain then "produces increased 10 Hz activity with equal frequency and amplitude of the wave form in both hemispheres."[28] The differences between the two frequencies must be small (less than 30 Hz) for the effect to occur; or else the two tones will be heard separately and no beat will be sensed.

Further research showed that hemispheric synchronization and brain entrainment can be induced by binaural beats.[29] The balance between the two hemispheres of the brain correspondingly increased as the wave patterns slowed from beta to alpha to theta to delta.[25] "Hemispheric synchronization represents the maximum efficiency of information transport through the whole brain," says Lester Fehmi, director of the Princeton Biofeedback Research Institute. "You become less self-conscious and you function more intuitively."[30] Meditating develops the ability to use one's whole brain toward a more balanced state, characterized by brain synchronization and whole brain functioning, leading to improved coherence and intelligence.[31,32] Some of the most brilliant scientists, technologists and artists showed a high degree of "whole brain synchronization," including Einstein, Picasso and Lewis Carol.

There are "two main effects of reorganization and increased synchrony in the brain. One is an increase in various mental capabilities: increased learning ability, creativity, mental clarity, intelligence, intuition, and so on. Second, each time the neural structure changes, positive changes in mental and emotional health occur."[25]

Known as the "scientific pitch" or "philosophical pitch," A=432 Hz was proposed by the French physicist Joseph Sauveur in 1713, and later endorsed by Giuseppe Verdi in the 1800s. A movement to return to the 432 Hz tuning was spearheaded by Dutch journalist Richard Huisken in 2008.[33]

Photo 7.8: The dividing line where Fraser River freshwater meets the saltwater of the Pacific Ocean, off Sand Heads in Georgia Strait, BC, Canada.

Photo by Nina Munteanu

According to Brian T. Collins, a Canadian musician and researcher, the new standard pitch (A=440 Hz) does not harmonize with cosmic movement, rhythm, or natural vibration. Collins writes, "Some of the harmonic overtone partials of A=432 Hz appear to line up to natural patterns and also the resonance of solitons. *Solitons* (wave packets or pulses) need a specific range to form into the realm of density and span from the micro to the macro cosmos. Solitons are not only found in water mechanics, but also in the ion-acoustic breath between electrons and protons." Collins adds that, "our inner ear works on the basis of *phi* dampening. The waters of our inner ears rely on Fibonacci spiral dampening through the seashell-like structure of the cochlea to keep us feeling balanced, centred or grounded. This Fibonacci spiral shape helps cancel out certain inertial standing-wave interference patterns, just like a Helmholtz resonator, in order to keep us properly balanced with the natural environment around us ... The difference between A=440 Hz and A=432 Hz is only 8 vibrations per second, but it is a perceptible difference in the human consciousness experience."[24]

Author and cymatics researcher Robert Boerman captured water–sound images taken at 432 Hz and 440 Hz.[34] As with the difference in overall musical sound, I was amazed at the differences in water's standing wave patterns between these two frequencies. Water's sound image at 432 Hz expressed a radial pattern of 28 arms in clear pulses and intervals. The 440 Hz wave pattern displayed a "smudged" image in which concentric rings, rather than radial arms, dominated.[34] Boerman's stunning water images can be found on several Internet sites, including his own.

Spiritualist and cymatics researcher Dameon Keller writes that, "A=432 Hz ... places C# at 136.10 Hz [or] 'Om,' which is the main note of the Sitar in classical Indian music and the pitch of the chants of Tibetan monks, who tell us that, 'It comes from nature.'"[35]

The Names of God ...

The Sufi sect of Islam attaches great significance to sound, starting with the abstract sound called *saut-e-sarmadhi* (the eternal sound). "The philosophy of form may be understood by the study of the process by which the unseen life manifests into the seen,"[36] writes Sufi master Hazrat Inayat Khan. "As the fine waves of vibrations produce sound, so the gross waves produce light. This is the manner in which the unseen, incomprehensible, and imperceptible life becomes gradually known, by first becoming audible and then visible, and this is the origin and only source of all form."

According to Khan, the *saut-e-sarmadhi* was the sound heard by many spiritual figures during moments of revelation. It is the sound that Mohammed heard in the cave of Ghar-e-Hira when lost in the divine ideal; Moses heard it on Mount Sinai while communing with God; Christ heard it during prayer and fasting in the wilderness; and Shiva heard it in a Himalayan cave, as the *Anahad Nada* (the "unstruck sound") during his *Samadhi* (the highest state of consciousness one can reach).

We are not only formed of vibrations, Khan writes, but we live and move in them; they surround us as aquarium fish are surrounded by water, and we contain vibrations within us as the tank contains water. Our different moods, inclinations, successes and failures depend on vibration, whether in thoughts, emotions or feelings.[36]

As with the Sufi tradition, Jewish Kabbalists recognize the power of sound as a key influence on the human psyche. The ancient Jewish wisdom of the Kabballa makes extensive use of sound in meditation to gain spiritual insight and an esoteric knowledge of God. *Haggadah* (e.g., legend) was passed along orally for centuries. *Kabballa* means "oral tradition."

"The goal of Kabballa is to clear and align the total human be-ing,"[37] writes Carlisle Bergquist, author of *The Coyote Oak*. "The pro-cess of healing and repairing is not an individual goal. The mastery of Kabballa allows one to better serve humankind and the planet. The primary aim of Kabballa is *tikkumolam*—to repair the world." The study of the Kabballa is made up of *Atzilut*, the spiritual body; *Beriyah*, the mental body; *Yetzirah*, the emotional body; and *Assiyah*, the physical body. Each of these bodies contains the "Tree of Life" on which are ten energy centres called *Sefirot*. "These 40 Sefirot are a vibrant sys-tem through which the divine comes into manifestation. The Kabbalist works to empty these centers of negative influence, and thus bring more Divine Light into the world. Sound is an effective means of clearing and vivifying these centers, since they are themselves vibration and thus express sound," writes Bergquist.

According to Kabbalist Mark Malachi, "Each thought creates something, for energy is not wasted. As we are taught in physics, the first law of thermodynamics states that energy cannot be created or de-stroyed. Therefore, we must conclude that the energy of thought must go somewhere. Indeed it helps create the arrangement of particles in the physical world ... Thought is vibration. It manifests itself as a wave ... Since it is vibratory in nature, it has sound ... We have the sound as tone, effected by sound as letters, effected by sound as thought or kavvanah—the power of focused intention. The degree to which one masters each of these, is the degree to which the Kabbalist masters the arts of revelation and creation. Kabbalah works to repair the world in co-creation with the *Most High*."[38]

A few years ago, an insightful friend of mine passed me a book by Rabbi Yehuda Berg called *The 72 Names of God: Technology of the Soul*. The square bright orange-covered book looked too trendy and fun to contain anything worthwhile. But what I found inside was great wis-dom. The 72 Names are sequences of three Hebrew letters that act like an index to specific spiritual frequencies that may elicit spiritual insight

Photo 7.9: Junk boats glide among steep karst islands in Phuket, Thailand.

Photo by Nina Munteanu

and transformation. The Names usually involve some permutation of the Sacred Name (YHVH) or the association of the ten *Sefirot* of the "Tree of Life" with certain attributes of God. The 72 Names work like tuning forks to connect to frequencies through sympathetic transference, all aimed to help repair you at the soul level.

Harvard language researcher Uri Harel investigated the five holy books of the *Torah* (the five books of Moses) to elucidate music as one of the layers of meaning in the texts. Harel first assigned a frequency to each of the letters in the Hebrew alphabet using the science of *Gematria* (an Assyro–Babylonian system of numerology that assigns numerical value to words or phrases). This allowed him to unlock the musical patterns encrypted in the original Hebrew texts, and he was able to produce beautiful classically arranged compositions. Harel found that the musical effect did not translate well from one language to another. The universal language of music and frequency, however, preserved the meaning and understanding.[39]

The *Bamidbar Rabbah* (a rabbinical holy text also known as the *Numbers Rabbah*), studied and interpreted the biblical *Book of Numbers*, part of the *Torah*. The interpretations stated that when the Universe was created, the frequencies of the Hebrew alphabet were used to bring it into existence, using sacred geometry as the blueprint.[39] This reflects the Christian Bible verse in John 1:1: "In the beginning was the Word, and the Word was with God, and the Word was God."

Photo 7.10: Looking upstream at the Credit River in Meadowvale, Ontario, Canada.

Photo by Nina Munteanu

Water's Paradox of Harmony

Tone results from a periodic harmonization of rest and motion in an oscillation (or a given frequency). A violinist strokes the string, causing it to tremble and vibrate—springing back and forth from its initial equilibrium. A barista deftly jiggles out the velvety microfoam milk over espresso, then pours a line across, drawing a swirling vortex-tree pattern. The actions of both violinist and barista represent a meeting of two poles of movement and stillness. "The resulting exchange leads to a 'dialogue' between the two polarities," writes Lauterwasser, "which culminates in a dynamic equilibrium of rhythmically swinging or whirling processes and forms. Something new evolves," he adds, "the harmonizing and integration of stillness and movement, of permanence and change as a structured movement and dynamic gestalt. The moment of movement has integrated itself into the principle of stillness, which introduces the aspect of permanence of structure into the continuous change. The moment of stillness has integrated into itself the principle of movement, which changes the firmly rigid into a streaming dynamic."[40]

The Language of Water's Vibration

It makes sense that humanity in its infancy created language by listening to the various sounds—the vibrations and frequencies—created by Nature. Interestingly, in Sanskrit, the word for sound is *Nada–Brahman*. *Nada* means "wide river" and *Brahman* means "the source." Sound, then, means "the source of the river." The location of a spring was likely one of the most important sounds for early humankind.

Ancient peoples listened to Nature to communicate important concepts. Through time, the sounds of Nature became our sounds, and eventually our many languages—each reflecting its own unique environment. Japanese researcher Dr. Masaru Emoto suggests that, "Nature emits sounds with vibrations distinctive to the particular location and environment, accounting for the many different languages spoken by the various peoples of the Earth."[7]

In his work with water crystals, Emoto demonstrated that water exposed to the same word, but in various languages, created similar crystals. If the crystal structure is a function of vibration and frequency, then it follows that, although the English is *thank you*, the Japanese is *arigato*, the French is *merci*, and the German is *dankeschon*, all of these words carry a similar vibration and frequency. Emoto suggests that "all the different words are perhaps nothing more than different ways of hearing the same thing." Although words of each source language will vary in looks and sound, they are formed according to the principle of Nature and its source environment. When water is exposed to words with similar meanings and vibrations—regardless of language—the crystals formed are similar.[7]

In his book *The Miracle of Water*, Emoto discusses his years of re-

Photo 7.11: Snow-covered trees ("snow ghosts") on Whistler Mountain, British Columbia, Canada.

Photo by Kevin Klassen

search using photographs of crystals made by freezing water. Emoto first exposed water to written words before he froze it, and then compared the resulting crystals. He found, time and again, that the same water formed different crystal structures when exposed to different word combinations. These remarkable results are based on his premise that words carry "vibration" and a specific "frequency" that allows water to fulfill the unique role of resonance in all things.[41]

Since our bodies—like the planet—consist of [over] 70 percent water, says Emoto, "we can infer from the crystals that the water within us also contains the energy of words."[41]

When asked about what words create the most beautiful crystal, Emoto unreservedly responds, "love and gratitude." He tells the story of how, on a whim, he combined the two words instead of using them separately in his crystal experiments. The effect was synergistic and spectacular. He explains it this way: "Love is the energy that we give to others, and gratitude is the love that we receive from others ... The greatest form of energy results from the harmony between the energy of giving and the energy of receiving."[41] This is surely a universal truth of balance and resonance. The energy from only giving is not enough, Emoto, tells us, and neither is the energy resulting from only taking. The two form a covenant of reciprocal action that moves the earth and the universe.

It is the resonating harmony of altruism.

Photo 7.12: Stellar-plate snowflake, Moscow Russia.

"Love and gratitude create the harmony found in all of Nature," shares Emoto, who proposes a radical notion. He posits that lack of love and gratitude can throw the harmony of the entire human race into chaos, manifested in natural disasters such as earthquakes or tsunamis. His theory, totally unproven, is that "disastrous phenomena are the result of disruptions in the energy of love and gratitude." This is an incredible notion, one that suggests so much about the power of human thought and intention in the Universe. I talk more about this in Chapters 10 and 11.

Photo by Alexey Kljatov

It also suggests something else, something about who and what we are, and the commonality of our existence, based largely on water. For instance, Emoto tells us that the Japanese word for cosmos, *uchu*, supposedly came from the sounds the stars made.[7]

The water within us carries the power and resonance of words, says Emoto. He tells us that "love comes from the inside and spreads out, and that gratitude is the feeling felt by the receiver of this vibration ...The person who receives love feels confidence and will then be in a position to emit love, and in this way, love and gratitude spread throughout the world with the vibration of this beautiful energy."[7]

Resonance is basically vibration resulting in more vibration. Resonance requires the interaction of two complimentary phenomena, being expressed in the same frequency. In Chinese culture, these are referred to as yin and yang or light and dark and, as Emoto believes, love and gratitude. "The love given and the gratitude returned resonate with each other through vibration."

Emoto's experiments further demonstrated that water shown the characters for "peace" formed crystals in a shape that resembled the joined crystals that formed when water was exposed to the words "love" and "gratitude" together. Emoto concluded that when love harmonizes with gratitude, you get peace. "When you heap love on top of thanks, your soul will be at peace," says Emoto. "The water outside of you resonates with the water within you."[30]

The important part to take away from this is that to vibrate in a positive way requires that you resonate with someone else's positive vibrations. This is why it's so important to find something positive in anyone and anything. "Resonance is what we use to share our energy with each other,"[41] says Emoto. "In the same way, when we align our words and thoughts to the grand principles of Nature and the Will of the Creator, we can experience positive vibration and happiness. This energy makes us feel alive and full of energy." It is the very basis for altruism. We can resonate with all the sounds in each octave, Emoto tells us, as well as

with higher and lower octaves. "This is why we are capable of resonating with and giving energy to anything and everything that is," he says.

Further to this, in Chapter 10, I discuss the scientific evidence and ongoing discussion for a phenomenon known as "the Maharishi Effect." Briefly here, the Maharishi Effect describes how a small percentage of people can change the world through individual consciousness affecting the coherent collective wave consciousness of the whole. It was named so, based on the 1960 prediction of the Maharishi Mahesh Yogi that one percent of a population practicing Transcendental Meditation, within the alpha frequency of 8-10 Hz or even the delta frequency of 4-8 Hz, would produce measurable improvements in the quality of life for that population.[42]

Photo 7.13: Blue Rocks, Nova Scotia, Canada.

Photo by Nina Munteanu

Resonating with the Universe

Does art imitate life or does life imitate art? Do we dream about our past or of another reality? What is *déjà vu* ... really? What came *before* the Big Bang? Did time even exist before we defined it? In the King James version of Genesis 1:3, God said, "Let there be light: and there was light." Which came first? Story or reality?

The most frequent question asked of writers is "Where do you get your ideas?" to which we often bumble some inadequate reply and invoke that indefinable abstruse term, muse. But what is muse ... really? Intuition? Divine inspiration?

In a quote from his autobiographical essay, author Philip Pullman says, "It's important to put it like that: not 'I am a writer,' but rather 'I write stories'. If you put the emphasis on yourself rather than your work, you're in danger of thinking that you're the most important thing. But you're not. *The story is what matters and you're only the servant*, and your job is to get it out on time and in good order."[43] But, where do they come from?

In my 2012 historical fantasy *The Last Summoner*, the young Baroness Vivianne discovered that she could alter history. Having travelled into the future (to the year 2010 from 1410 Poland), she used hindsight in an attempt to recreate a new path for humanity, one devoid of two world wars and the evils consequently unleashed. Vivianne travelled back in time and tried to subvert critical events involving Emperor Wilhelm II, Annie Oakley, Nikola Tesla and others. In each case, her interference failed to alter the event in the way she had hoped. In fact, while the details of history differed, the end result remained pretty much the same. For instance, it seemed that no matter what she did to prevent World War I, it happened anyway.

Vivianne discovered that she was unable to alter history in the way she'd intended. She found, to her dismay, that every time she set out to alter a crucial event, quirky consequences ensued and events did not yield to her clever manipulations—as though History had an uncooperative conscience and a predetermined destiny to fulfill.[44]

Okay … that's just me being the writer, subverting the protagonist with obstacles played out in ever-twisting plots and subplots. But, what if …

What if History (as in any realized reality) is predetermined through its harmonic relationship with other realizable realities? Given that all mass and energy is governed and expressed through frequency, and given that in physics (and music) frequencies exist as multiples of some fundamental frequency—then does it not follow that threads of realizable realities, intertwined around a fundamental path (of history), would move inexorably toward a common destiny?

A recent article I ran across on a writers' forum discussed how artists tend to mimic each other's ideas, or come up with the same ideas at the same time. Aside from outright stealing (which happens a lot less than people think), multiple and independent formulation of same ideas is more common than people think—and it's increasing. Multiple independent discoveries (and inventions) have greatly increased in society since the nineteenth century. Columbia University sociologist of science Robert K. Merton, defines *multiple discoveries* as similar discoveries simultaneously made by scientists working independently of each other. Examples of what is now currently termed the "multiples effect" include the independent formulation of calculus by Newton and Leibniz or the theory of the evolution of species by Charles Darwin and Alfred Russel Wallace and McFadden and Pocket independently but at the same time coming up with electromagnetic fields being the seat of our consciousness.[45] Steven Bancarz lists dozens of examples of the "multiples effect" and notes that in many cases the discovery or formulation occurs on the same day.

Some posit a "great man" or "genius" theory of history; others forward a "social determinist" or "zeitgeist" argument; and others argue "chance" based on probabilistic models is responsible for the phenomenon.[46] Some followers of Jungian thought suggest that this is because the fabric of our society is acting more and more like a neural network, learning, interacting and sharing toward the achievement of a common zeitgeist. This is in keeping with the idea shared by physicists Michio Kaku, John Hagelin and others of a shared consciousness as a non-local field and eloquently expressed by Erwin Schrödinger: "The total number of minds in the universe is one."

Suggesting that "multiple discoveries" resonate like rippling waves of water, Jacob Devaney writes in the Huffington Post, "For many years, people thought it was impossible for a runner to break the four-minute mile. As soon as Roger Bannister did it, he gave dozens of other athletes "permission" to do the same within the same year. What is apparent is that there is a collective field of thought/belief that dictates, to some degree, what is possible and these limits are continuously being expanded."[47] The many learning from the few.

What if the whole of our society behaves like an autopoietic system, self-organizing, adapting, evolving and tapping into—and possibly influencing—a common super consciousness? One related to a fundamental frequency?

Ray Tomes of the Alexandria City discussion group in 1996 suggested that "the pattern of cycles found in every field of study on Earth, in astronomy and also in music are all explained by a simple rule that says that a single initial frequency will generate harmonics and each of these will do the same."[48]

Why do galaxies and stars form where they do? Toss a handful of sand on a drum and then beat it (but not at the centre); you will find that the sand moves to certain places and congregates into predetermined patterns. These are the nodes of the standing waves in the drum. Electromagnetic waves (e.g., radio, light and x-rays) form stand-

Photo 7.14: Ice formations on the shoreline of Lake Ontario, Canada.

Photo by Nina Munteanu

ing waves. Standing waves appear everywhere. Consider the "prede-termined" beauty of natural phenomena. Consider Fibonacci numbers and the golden mean in Nature. Consider fractals and the Mandelbrot Set, quantum entanglement, and Schumann Resonance. Consider syn-chronicity, autopoiesis, and self-organization.

Einstein tells us that, "everything in life is vibration." Schrödinger's wave function describes *us* as vibrating waves.

As I mentioned above, the normal standing wave created in the Schumann Cavity occurs at a wavelength equal to the circumference of the Earth. The standing wave averages 7.83 Hz as the base frequency or Earth's "heartbeat," and, as I write in Chapter 10, is significantly connected with prayer and meditation, and may generate healing prop-erties when we are entrained to its rhythm.

"Vibrations are dynamic things not unlike living things," Dale Pond, researcher in harmonics, adds. "They are active and prolific in their dynamics, as are their harmonic offspring. These discrete tones of the harmonics interact with each other ... They will in a very natural way mix, merge and divide among themselves just like living cells."[49]

In *Outer Diverse*, the first book of "The Splintered Universe Trilogy," Galactic Guardian Rhea Hawke speaks with Ka, an alien mystic, about music, frequency and harmony. And "the music of the spheres." Says Ka:

"The particular tone of the planet's song is dependent upon the ratio of its orbit, just like the relationship of a keynote to its octave. The cos-mic beauty of the octave is that it divides wholeness into two audibly distinguishable parts, yet remains recognizable as the same musical note ...We, of course, now know that ratios in frequencies of spectra of elements compare to intervals in a musical chord," Ka went on, leaning forward on his massive feathered arms. "Given that a pitch of sound is analogous to the color of light, both being caused by the frequencies of their waves, we can characterize entire worlds based on these properties," he ended, beak-mouth breaking into a beam-ing grin that showed his round little teeth. "It was your Kepler—a

scientist I believe—who suggested that when planets formed angles equivalent to particular harmonic ratios, a resonance was created both in the archetypal 'Earth soul' and in the souls of individuals born under those configurations … He called it a celestial imprint," Ka continued, now leaning forward with his cup in both hands, *"and said that in the vital power of the human being, ignited at birth, that remembered image glows. That geometric–harmonic imprint is the music that impels each listener to dance … from the particle to the cosmic. Your own heart finds its shifting harmony between excessive order and complete randomness, encompassing complex variability—a symphony—in its beating pattern. Sound—vibration—is the language of the mind and the secret to creation."*[50]

Remember the "tuning fork" idea?

We are creatures of this planet, co-evolved with Earth's environment through the helix structure of our DNA and the water coursing through us; this is reflected in our behaviour, culture, intelligence and beliefs. Our entire bodies resonate with all other life at a similar frequency as the planet Earth. Our brains in their most divine state of creativity, prayer or meditation reflect the same frequency. We are a gestalt culmination of light, wave-pulse and motion resonating with this beloved planet Earth. Our minds, bodies and souls "sing" its choral aria. What is muse, then, if not this wonderful "intent"?

So, which came first? Story or reality?

Vibration hides and reveals its entangled energy. Vibration drifts on the tidal tapestry of the soul. Resonating in synchronous tones as it courses down gravity waves, vibration writes its unique sound and story.

Vibration is water.

References

1. Pangman and Evans. 2011. "Dancing with Water: the New Science of Water". *Uplifting Press*. 256 pp.

2. Steiner, Rudolf. 1883. "Einleitung Zu Goethes Naturwissenschaftliche Schriften (Geothean Science)." *Rudolf Steiner Gesamtausgabe GA1.*

3. Kurtz, Michael. 2015. "Rudolf Steiner and Music." *Goetheanum, Dornach.* 608 pp.

4. Arem, Gaerth. 2015. "The Future of Sound Therapy". *Sound as Medicine.* Online: http://gaearth.com/sound-as-medicine/the-future-of-sound-therapy/

5. Tompkins, Peter and C. Bird. "Secrets of the Soil." 1998. *Earthpulse Press.* 422 pp.

6. Lipton, Bruce. 2012. "The Wisdom of Your Cells." *Bruce Lipton Website.* Online: https://www.brucelipton.com/resource/article/the-wisdom-your-cells

7. Masaru, Emoto. 2005. "The Secret Life of Water." *Atria Books.* 187 pp.

8. McTaggart, Lynne. 2003. "The Field: The Quest for the Secret Force of the Universe". *Element.* 384 pp.

9. Fröhlich, H. 1968. "Long-range Coherence and Energy Storage in Biological Systems." *Int. J. Quantum Chem.*, 2(5): 641–649.

10. Fröhlich, H. 1975. "The Extraordinary Dielectric Properties of Biological Materials and the Action of Enzymes". *Proceedings of the Natural Academic Sciences of the USA 72*: 4211–5.

11. Fröhlich, H. 1978. "Coherent Electric Vibrations in Biological Systems and the Cancer Problem." *IEEE Transactions on Microwave Theory and Techniques* MTT–26(8): 613–7.

12. Fröhlich, H. 1981. "The Biological Effects of Microwaves and Related Questions." *Advances in Electronics and Electron Physics*, 53: 85–152.

13. Cowan, David. 2003. "Ley Lines and Earth Energies: An Extraordinary Journey into the Earth's Natural Energy System". *Adventures Unlimited Press.* 252 pp.

14. Cole, Adam. 2013. "Honey, It's Electric: Bees Sense Charge on

Flowers." *NPR*, February 22. Online: http://www.npr.org/2013/02/22/172611866/honey-its-electric-bees-sense-charge-on-flowers

15. Bartholomew, Alick. 2010. "The Spiritual Life of Water: Its Power and Purpose." *Park Street Press*. 368 pp.

16. Chevalier, G., K. Mori and J.L. Oschman. 2006. "The Effect of Earthing (Grounding) on Human Physiology." *European Biology and Bioelectromagnetics*, January 31: 600–621.

17. Ghaly M, Teplitz D. 2004. "The Biological Effects of Grounding the Human Body during Sleep, as Measured by Cortisol Levels and Subjective Reporting of Sleep, Pain and Stress." *J Altern Complement Med* 10 (5):767–776.

18. Tobias J. 2009. "Composing for the Media: Eisler and the Rockefeller Foundation Music Projects." *Rockefeller Archive Center Research Reports*. Online: http://www.bibliotecapleyades.net/archivos_pdf/composing-the-media-eisler-rockefeller.pdf

19. Horowitz, L.G. 2001. "Death in the Air: Globalism, Terrorism & Toxic Warfare." *Tetrahedron Press*, Sandpoint, ID. 530 pp.

20. Horowitz, L.G. 2004. "DNA: Pirates of the Sacred Spiral." *Tetrahedron Press*, Sandpoint, ID. 544 pp.

21. St-Onge, Elina. 2013. "Here's Why You Should Consider Converting Your Music to A=432 Hz." *Collective Evolution*. Online: http://www.collective-evolution.com/2013/12/21/heres-why-you-should-convert-your-music-to-432hz/

22. Vey, Gary. 2014. "It Hertz so Bad: The 432 vs. 440 Controversy." *Viewzone*. Online: http://www.viewzone.com/432hertz222.html

23. Zweerts, Boudewijm. 2015. "Sounds of Silence." Online: http://www.soundsofsilence.eu/frequency/

24. Collins, Brian T. 2015. "The Importance of 432 Hz Music". *Omega432*. Online: http://omega432.com/432-music/the-importance-of-432hz-music.

25. Centrepoint Research Institute. 1995. "Scientific Research Validates Holosync's Benefits". Centrepoint Research Institute. Online: http://www.centerpointe.com/articles/articles-research

26. Oster, Gerald. 1973. "Auditory beats in the brain." *Scientific American*, 229, 94–102.

27. Hutchison, Michael. "Megabrain". *Ballantine Books*: New York, 1986, p. 25.

28. Morris, Suzanne. *The Facilitation of Learning*. Privately published manuscript, p. 15. 1989.

29. Hutchison, Michael. "Megabrain". *Ballantine Books*: New York, p. 219. 1986.

30. Fehmi, Lester F., and George Fritz. "Open Focus: The Attentional Foundation of Health and Well-Being." *Somatics*, Spring 1980.

31. Pagnoni, Giuseppe and Milow Cekic. 2007. "Age effects on gray matter volume and attentional performance in Zen meditation". *Neurobioogy of Aging* 28: 1623-1627.

32. Holzel, Britta K., James Carmody, Mark Vangel, Christina Congleton, Sita M. Yerramsetti, Tim Gard, and Sara W. Lazar. 2011. "Mindfulness practice leads to increases in regional brain gray matter density". *Psychiatry Res* 191 (1): 36-43.

33. Dutch Progress. 2008. "Terug naar 432 Hz". Dutch Progress. Online: http://www.terugnaar432hz.org

34. Boerman, Robert. 2012. "Water Sound Images: A=432 Hz and A=440 Hz." *Water Sound Images*. Online: http://www.watersoundimages.com/news/432hz.htm

35. Keller, Dameon. 2014. "Sound's Good: The Spiritual Science of Sound & Vibration." *CreateSpace*. 80 pp.

36. Khan, Hazrat Inayat. 2000. "The Sufi Message of Hazrat Inayat Khan: the Mysticism of Sound, Music, The Power of the Word, Cosmic Language." *Library of Alexandria*. 256 pp.

37. Bergquist, Carlisle. 1997. "Doorways in Consciousness: An Exploration of Resonant Being—Part 1". Vantage Quest. Online: http://www.vantagequest.org/trees/door1.htm#.VfY1oUtgrlw

38. Malachi, Mark. 1995. "From the Depths of Silence." In: Edward Hoffman (ed.), "Opening the Inner Gates: New Paths in Kabbalah and Psychology." *Shambhala*. 320 pp.

39. Harel, Uri. 2010. "Torah, the Word." In: The Awakening. Online: https://hiddenlighthouse.wordpress.com/category/the-torah/

40. Lauterwasser, Alexander. 2006. "Water Sound Images: The Creative Music of the Universe". *Macromedia Publishing*, Eliot, ME. 172 pp.

41. Emoto, Masaru. 2011. "The Miracle of Water." *Atria Books*. 160 pp.

42. Maharishi University of Management. 2015. "Maharishi Effect". Maharishi University Website. Online: https://www.mum.edu/about-mum/consciousness-based-education/tm-research/maharishi-effect/

43. Pullman, Philip. 2008. "Phillip Pullman". His Dark Materials. Online: http://www.hisdarkmaterials.org/pages/philip-pullman

44. Munteanu, Nina. 2012. "The Last Summoner." *Starfire World Syndicate*. 406 pp.

45. Simonlon DK. 1979. "Multiple discovery and invention: zeitgeist, genius, or chance?" *J. Personal. Sot. Psycho* 37:1603-16.

46. Bancarz, Steven. 2014. "Scientific Proof Our Minds Are All Connected". Spirit Science and Metaphysics, February 14, 2014. Online: http://www.spiritscienceandmetaphysics.com/scientific-proof-our-minds-are-all-connected/

47. Devaney, Jacob. 2014. "A Moment Shared Around the World, the Collective Field". The Huffington Post. Online: http://www.huffingtonpost.com/jacob-devaney/a-moment-shared-around-th_b_5276804.html

48. Tomes, Ray. 1996. "Harmonics, Music, Pythagoras and the Universe." From: *Alexandria City discussion group*. Online: http://ray.tomes.biz/alex.htm

49. Pond, Dale. 2000. "It Really is a Musical Universe." *The Cosmic Light*, University of Science and Philosophy. Winter Edition.

50. Munteanu, Nina. 2011. "Outer Diverse." Book 1, The Splintered Universe Trilogy. *Starfire World Syndicate*. 324 pp.

8.
Water is Beauty

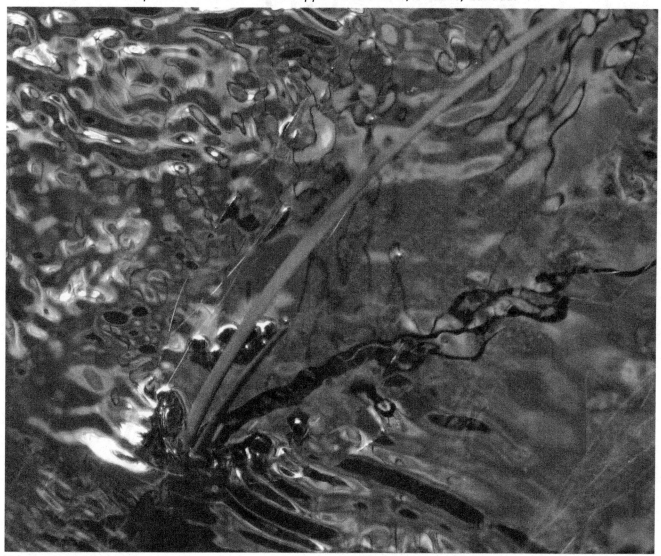

Photo 8.1: Water flow pattern around a reed in Upper Credit River, Ontario, Canada.

Photo by Nina Munteanu

"Those who contemplate the beauty of the earth find reserves of strength that will endure as long as life lasts."
—Rachel Carson

What is beauty?

The classic theory defines *beauty* in terms of order and harmony of form. Beauty possesses unity-in-variety: something considered beautiful presents a variety of details combined into a unity of general effect. In this definition, variety without unity is confusing, and unity without variety is monotonous and boring; order unifies and creates harmony.[1] Aesthetic idealism attempts to further define beauty through the harmony between the ideal (its significance) and the observer.

"To be beautiful, a living creature, and every whole made up of parts, must ... present a certain order in its arrangement of parts,"[2] wrote Aristotle over 2300 years ago. Aristotle added that, "The chief forms of beauty are order and symmetry and definiteness, which the mathematical sciences demonstrate in a special degree."[2] This view implies certain mathematical formula. As with Aristotle, Plato's idea of beauty ultimately reduces to mathematics, with one's appreciation of beauty depending on one's recognition of the mathematical behaviour of the universe.[3] The *golden section* (i.e., Golden Ratio or *phi*) is often evoked as one of beauty's principles; Plato describes five regular solids (now known as the *Platonic solids*) which relate to the Golden Ratio. I mention the Golden Ratio in Chapter 3, and talk about it more below, in this chapter. Briefly here, the *Golden Ratio* describes a mathematical relationship in which the ratio of two quantities is the same as the ratio of their sum to the larger of the two quantities. Also known as the golden (or divine) proportion, the golden cut and the golden number, its properties were studied by mathematicians since Euclid. The golden proportion was incorporated in many classical works of art and architecture from the Greek Parthenon to da Vinci's "Vitruvian Man." It is recognized in many patterns in nature, including the spiral arrangement of leaves and other plant parts.

There is beauty, writes 18th century aesthetic realist Francis Hutcheson, "in the knowledge of some great principles, or universal forces, from which innumerable effects do flow, such as gravitation, in Sir Isaac Newton's scheme."[4]

Photo 8.2: View of a red barn and snow-covered field from the author's house in Ladner, British Columbia, Canada.

Photo by Nina Munteanu

Neither beauty of form nor beauty of idea sufficiently applies to its definition, because beauty is, as we all know, "in the eyes of the beholder."

Beauty—like love—is not so much a quality as a relationship.

In 1942, philosopher of aesthetics Jared Moore described complete beauty as three varieties of harmony combined: (1) objective harmony (i.e., harmony among the elements that make up the "beautiful object" through form, idea and its expression); (2) objective–subjective (i.e., harmony between the beautiful object and the contemplative mind through spiritual and psychophysical [empathetic] means); and (3) psychological (i.e., its meaning).[1] Moore writes that complete aesthetic harmony—expressed by psychological or purely subjective harmony—is achieved only when the first two harmonies are attained. He describes this complete sense of harmony as "a sense of pleasure" which not merely adds itself to the sense of beauty, but "enters into and becomes a part of it." This "inner harmony" brings the personality into a state of "unity and self-completeness."[5] A unity of the subjective, not only with the object, but with itself.[1]

We recognize beauty, and, in feeling it, are beautiful.

In 1933, Harvard mathematician George David Birkhoff—interested in the qualities that make a painting, sculpture, musical composition or poem pleasing to the eye, ear, or mind—sought a mathematical measure that would capture an object's beauty. He created a formula that encapsulated his insights in a theory: $M = O/C$, where M equals aesthetic measure; O, aesthetic order (or symmetry); and C, complexity. Birkhoff favoured symmetry over complexity.[6] With no way to objectively measure symmetry and complexity, Birkhoff's theory was forgotten but has been revived with recent biological studies, which show how humans and other animals are highly attuned to symmetry. Sensitivity to symmetry appears ingrained in animal behaviour.[7]

British artist and educator John Lane, author of *Timeless Beauty*, describes beauty this way:

"Although the complexities of both nature and beauty have a subtle mathematical basis, reason by itself cannot tell us why beauty exists nor what is beautiful ... There is often something spontaneous, even 'illogical' about these emotions; like love, they can never be predetermined, let alone dictated. But neither can the otherwise and splendid things which are most significant in human life, to which the greatest of the human race have contributed most, and in which our real refreshment consists—the love of truth, the sources of inspiration and the production of great works of art."[8]

"These, like beauty," says Lane, *"ultimately pertain to the unconscious, the heart and the soul. They pertain to the heart because it is love which discerns the mystery inherent in those things we see as beautiful; love which abandons arrogance and stands in awe before the mystery of life. It is love that sees beauty which, in turn, is always loved."[8]*

"Except in the vaguest limits, beauty cannot be described,"[3] writes Eric Newton, art critic and author of *The Meaning of Beauty*. "It cannot be measured either in quantity or quality ... Nonetheless, it would seem reasonable to stalk the word, to outflank it and creep up on it from behind. Eventually one must have the courage to meet it face to face."[3] After some self-discourse, Newton wisely concludes—like Lane—that it comes down to love: "Surely the mechanism of love, that delicate relationship between the lover and the object of his affections, provides a kind of key to this locked door at which so many philosophers have hammered."[3]

"Beauty and grace are performed, whether or not we will sense them. The least we can do is try to be there,"[9] says Annie Dillard, author of *Pilgrim at Tinker Creek*.

Beauty is slow. To notice beauty, we must slow our mind and sense with our soul. We may "see" beauty all around us, but we do not "feel" it until we open to it, let it touch us and let it stroke our inner soul.

Beauty, like water, flows.

Photo 8.3: Winter stream on the road to Wolfville, Nova Scotia, Canada.

Photo by Nina Munteanu

Beauty of Nature's Being

The beauty of motherhood flows both deep and wide. Being with my young son slowed my world and returned to me a great sense of wonder. A walk to the little store with young Kevin was an expedition. He'd amble, explore, poke, then suddenly squat and study something on the pavement that I'd missed.

Love makes an object beautiful.
—Eliseo Lagano

He brought me back to the ground, to the extra-ordinary mundane—to the quiet details and the fragrant light. Acting like a macro lens, he pointed me to the little things, Nature's nuanced designs that I'd forgotten in the larger paradigms of my hurried life.

He brought me back to the immediate, to Nature's elegant silence and beauty. He showed me the fractal wonders of tree branches, exploding seeds, glorious reflections in puddles, strange mud waves and odd moss-covered rocks. We crouched in halted silence to watch a bee feast from a flower's nectar then launch itself—a dirigible laden with pollen—into the sky. We followed the brilliant Fibonacci spiral of a sunflower or the circular gossamer web of a spider, both mimicking the greater spiral of our own Milky Way Galaxy. We stuck our tongues out to taste the snow as it cascaded down in heaps or caught hexagonal snowflakes on our sleeves and sadly watched them melt. We stomped in road puddles or threw rocks and watched the circles of waves feed outward, changing the colour and texture of everything. We collected flotsam in nebulous forest pools and made magical potions. We wrote stories in the ocean sand, then leapt from dry rock to dry rock until the sea trapped us in its rushing embrace.

Photo 8.4: The author exploring in British Columbia with her son.

At the heart of all of these was glorious Nature celebrating Beauty.

Photo by Herb Klassen

Water's beauty spans the subtle dewdrops on a suburban lawn to the extravagant and powerful surges of a tropical sea.

"It's hard to find anything more beautiful than dew on flower petals and leaves," writes Masaru Emoto in *The Secret Life of Water*. "A single drop of dew falls off the tip of a sprouting leaf on a branch and makes its descent, through the forest canopy, and lands on the back of a frog … Water spreads itself … to shower love on the frog and the new sprout—and to be loved in return. Just as a mother instinctively loves her newborn, water in infancy is loved by all of nature."[10]

In his book *The Holy Order of Water: Healing the Earth's Waters and Ourselves* William E. Marks writes, "The mysteries flowing from water are with us in many ways—in the life surrounding us; in thoughts generated by our water-filled minds; the smells and rhythms of our oceans; the soothing sounds of gurgling streams and fountains; the beat of our hearts; the gift of sight from our watery eyes; the ever-changing clouds above; the misty fog that lightly kisses our faces; the sight of an awe-inspiring tornado; the vortex swirl of water disappearing down a drain."[11]

Beauty does not lead to satiety and eventual disgust from over-indulgence. Think of a bowl of cherries and cream: one is good, several satisfy, a dozen is too much and two dozen make us sick. But we do not tire of beauty. "Each experience of it enjoys an exquisite singularity but there can never be enough,"[8] says Lane. It is like love, whose quality refreshes the soul and never runs dry.

Photo 8.5: Raindrops on a hosta leaf, Mississauga, Ontario, Canada.

Photo by Nina Munteanu

Beauty of Truth

What did Keats mean when he wrote those arcane lines in *Ode on a Grecian Urn*? Mathematician and author Martin Gardner asked this question in a 2007 *Scientific American* article and quoted T.S. Eliot who called the lines "meaningless" and "a serious blemish on a beautiful poem." A rather pithy remark, I thought, considering the lines spoke of beauty. Gardner further described how great theorems and great proofs, such as "Euclid's elegant proof of infinity of primes, have about them what Bertrand Russell described as 'a beauty cold and austere' akin to the beauty of great works of sculpture."[12]

Ian Stewart, professor of mathematics at the University of Warwick in England and author of *Why Beauty is Truth: a History of Symmetry*, suggested that symmetry lay at the heart of beauty—in relativity theory, quantum mechanics, string theory, and much of modern cosmology. He concluded his book with two maxims: (1) in physics, beauty does not automatically ensure truth, but it helps; and (2) in mathematics beauty must be true—because everything false is ugly.[13]

Neither beauty nor truth (certainly in all its facets) can be remotely described or "proven" through science—certainly not in the language of traditional science. Both are perceived through the soul. When one is truthful, about oneself particularly, then one is also beautiful. To see the truth about a person or phenomenon is to recognize their inherent beauty—and ours—where we are one and the same.

We are each a unique universe, within whom resides a world of aesthetic truths. Beauty—like truth—is recognized and expressed from within, where our soul meets God. It is found when we look beyond the shallow shores of deception into the deep abyss of truth. Divine grace. Forgiveness. Compassion. Humility. Altruism. These are all expressions of Beauty and ultimately expressions of Truth.

"Beauty is truth, truth beauty— that is all ye know on earth and all ye need to know."

— John Keats

"The water in a vessel is sparkling; the water in the sea is dark. The small truth has words which are clear; the great truth has great silence."
—Rabindranath Tagore

In her 2003 foreword to John Lane's book *Timeless Beauty*, Kathleen Raine writes, "Of Plato's three verities, the Good, the True and the Beautiful, none can be understood in terms of the materialist values of modern Western civilization, and beauty least of all."[8] She adds, "Keats saw [beauty] as the highest value—because its reality can be known only to the soul … If beauty is the highest of Plato's verities this is because it is in accordance with our nature: Plato did not invent that need. And did not Dostoevsky in *The Idiot* affirm his believe that the world can be saved only by beauty? We disregard and undervalue the beautiful at our peril."[8]

Photo 8.6: the Matterhorn seen from Zermatt, Switzerland.

Photo by Nina Munteanu

Beauty of Mind and Art

In his book *Timeless Beauty*, John Lane shares that, "Whatever else that beautiful may be is certainly neither cerebral nor egotistic; it has a quality of innocence and purity. Smelling a batch of freshly baked bread, regarding a photograph of Henri Cartier-Bresson, appreciating the serene austerity of mediaeval plainsong and the fierce elegance of a thrush. I am not thinking why the bread smells good, why the photograph is perfect or the bird so beautiful. It is enough to breathe the perfection of their being and stand in awe before the miracle of life. To marvel is enough."[8]

Some of the most beautiful things ever made, says Lane, were created by those who had no conscious desire to make them beautiful: the painted walls of the Stone Age, the folk pottery of Japan, or the barns and furniture of the Shakers. Japanese philosopher Soetsu Yanagi argued that for a craft to be beautiful, the maker had to be free of self. According to Yanagi, no craftsperson had within himself the power to create beauty; the beauty that came from "self surrender" was incomparably greater than that of a work of art produced by individual genius. "For work to be beautiful," writes Lane, "its maker should get out of the way of his or her ego, and let nature do the creating."[8]

Vinoba Bhave, a follower of Gandhi, wrote in *Talks on the Gita*, "On the action performed with pure heart and unstinted effort, the Lord sets the seal of His approval. His grace. When the Lord, well-pleased, touches the action with the hand of love, beauty appears there … If our mind is beautiful, its image in the medium of action will also be beautiful. We should judge the purity of outward action by the purity of mind, and the purity of mind by the purity of outward action."[14]

"The hours when the mind is absorbed by beauty are the only hours when one is really alive."
—Richard Jeffries

In describing Botticelli's painting *Primavera* in the Uffizi Gallery in Florence, Lane invokes flowing harmony: "... each curvature, each repetition, each rhythm, enjoys its own exquisite beauty: the interwoven arms and hands ... the pattern of their movements ... how the hair tumbles down their backs like the natural flow of racing waters; how the diaphanous draperies ebb and flow like tides in a whirlpool; how their feet and the flowers on their dresses dance like an incoming tide ..."[8]

How perfectly water's metaphors describe the beauty of art!

Several years ago I visited Paris for the first time to research my historical fantasy *The Last Summoner*. Much of my research involved walking the streets of Paris. Of course I visited the Louvres. But my favourite museum was le Musée d'Orsay, housed in a magnificent former Beaux-Arts railway station located on the left bank of the Seine. Le Musée d'Orsay showcases a large collection of Impressionist art.

One need only visit le Musée d'Orsay, or walk the streets of Paris to observe the nuances and great diversity of beauty and personal taste. While I naturally gravitated to the later Impressionist works of Renoir, Pisarro, Van Gogh and Monet, my friend preferred the more current avant-garde artwork down the hall. Is one more beautiful than the other? Of course not! What matters is why one appeals to you. It's a matter of resonance. And connection.

Figure 8.2: Bal du Moulin de la Galette *painted in 1876 by Pierre Auguste Renoir.*

Musée d'Orsay, Paris, France.

Figure 8.1: Stagecoach to Louveciennes *painted in 1870 by Camille Pissarro.*

Musée d'Orsay, Paris, France.

Beauty in Connection

In 1974 James Lovelock and Lynn Margulis proposed the *Gaia Hypothesis*, which described life on Earth as part of a single, self-regulating system acting to preserve the conditions that make life possible.[15] Some contemporary thinkers such as Patrick Harpur, Rupert Shelldrake, and David Chalmers argue that the human psyche extends beyond the physical confines of the body in what Chalmers calls the "extended mind."[16,17,18] Harpur and others posit that the soul—which includes qualities of beauty—resides in the Universe, in all life, and even in other elements of Earth, such as soil, minerals, and water.[16] He cites Plato's reference to the collective *anima mundi* (the soul of the world), in *Timaeus*, in which he describes the world as a living being with intelligence and a soul "woven right through from the centre to the outermost heaven."[2] Harpur suggests that this image usually expresses as a feminine archetype and, as Jung would say, personifies the "collective unconscious" of the World–Soul.

"That the universe is alive, a living entity, there can, it seems, be less and less doubt, and that it is beautiful there can be none at all,"[8] says Lane.

"We perceive beauty in the harmonious intervals between the parts of a whole."

—Aldous Huxley

Beauty of Shape, Pattern, Flow & Symmetry

"Nature uses only the longest threads to weave her patterns, so each small piece of her fabric reveals the organization of the entire tapestry."

—Richard Feynman

"Nature provides very few instances of form whose mathematical basis the eye can grasp in its entirety and at a glance,"[3] writes Eric Newton in his book *The Meaning of Beauty*. "One of the few," he says, "is the logarithmic spiral of the nautilus shell whose mathematical formula is dependent upon the rate of growth of the nautilus … Another is the perfect sphere of the soap bubble, which owes its shape to Nature's determination to enclose the maximum volume of air within the minimum area of containing surface."

However, Newton wisely adds, "If anyone doubts that an underlying orderliness is at work even in the most apparently chaotic patch of natural form, let him try the effect of interfering with such a patch. Let him, for example, tie up against a wall a stem of bramble that has been lying along the ground, or let him blast out a quarry from a hillside. Immediately his eye is afflicted with a sense of something amiss, of a pattern disturbed. The leaves that had arranged themselves so carefully to catch the sunlight are now disarranged, and they will require at least a week to reorganize themselves. The curvature of the hillside, the product of centuries, has lost its inevitability. At least a century will be required to repair these interferences with Nature's formulae. Under such circumstances it is evident that science and mathematics can do no more than offer a set of rough, though valuable, pointers. They can open a door to the jungle, but, once through the door, only intuition can find the way."[3]

"Sand dunes are something of an archetype,"[19] Philip Ball writes in his book *Flow*. They are "an exemplary demonstration of how such patterns lie in wait in systems of many interacting parts, even though no amount of close inspection of the components will reveal them."[19] Sand dunes, like most wave patterns, are self-organized. "Sand ripples and dunes are a conspiracy of grains, a pattern that emerges from the interplay of windborne movement, collision-driven piling up, and slope-shaving avalanches."[19] These sand waves and ripples also occur on beaches due to water's action in a similarly self-amplifying self-organized sequence of transport and settling.

The fascination of water's beauty in motion has run the gamut of appreciation from painting and sketching to photography and more. In the 1870s, the high-speed photographs by British physicist Arthur Worthington captured water in mid-splash. He discovered that a splash—from a pebble dropped in the water, for instance—erupted into "a corona with a rim that broke up into a series of spikes, each releasing micro-droplets of their own."[19] In his 1917 book *On Growth and Form*, D'Arcy Wentworth Thompson saw a connection between these fluid flow splash-forms, and a more general patterning process that could be seen in the shapes of soft-tissue living organisms. For instance, he drew likenesses between the splash form and a *hydroid* (a marine animal related to the jellyfish and sea anemones).[20] Similarities may relate to frequency.

"It is fair to say," Ball writes, "that most Chinese artists have attempted to imbue their works with *Chi*, the vital energy of the universe, the Breath of the Tao."[19] Ball draws on the 17th century painter's manual *Chieh Tzu Yüan* ("The Mustard Seed Garden"), which explains that "circulation of the Chi produces movement of life." This evocation of basic simplicity beyond shape and form sounds Platonic, but differs fundamentally in being alive with spontaneity. "He who uses his mind and moves his brush without being conscious of painting touches the secret of the art of painting," wrote ninth-century writer Chang Yenyüan. In Chinese art everything depends on the brushstrokes and the source of Chi, writes Ball. It is no wonder, he adds, that one of the brush

Photo 8.7: Water splash in a kitchen sink captured using a Canon Powershot SD110, 2006.

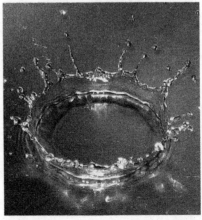

Photo by Omegatron, Wikimedia Commons

stroke types is called *T'anwots'un* (brushstrokes like an eddy or whirl-pool). This is very Tau: dynamic, in motion, fleeting and spontaneous. Chinese art depicts the inner life of flow and what Chinese critic Tung Yü called "the fundamental nature of water."[19] Many East Asian artists, like Hokusai and his *The Great Wave* (which I talk about in Chapter 4), represent the flow of water in a series of lines that show the trajectories of floating particles, "like the streamlines employed by fluid dynamicists," says Ball. The strokes are more "schematic" than "realistic", Ball continues, who then compares Leonardo da Vinci's precisely-lined water sketches to East Asian drawings.

In Chapters 4 and 5, I talk about da Vinci's fascination with swirls, eddies and vortices. Both artists and scientists, such as myself, share the fascination. For instance, if you stand, as I often do, in the middle of a stream and watch water flow around a large boulder, turbulence will appear as if from nothing. An eddy will suddenly appear, form and develop, then dissolve. Within moments another will appear and, in turn, dissolve—followed by another. Where do the vortices come from? And "whence this apparently irrepressible tendency of a liquid to swirl and coil?" asks Ball. Why this need, "to circulate back on itself, flowing (or so it seems) *uphill?*" Turbulent flow—contrary to everyday thought—is not synonymous with disorganized or even chaotic or unpredictable flow. Fluid turbulence is stable chaos in action.

In the early 1900s Ludwig Prantl and his team of scientists in Germany studied cylinder wakes and found trains of alternating vortices. Now called Kármán vortex streets, these alternating swirls arise from a phenomenon called "eddy shedding," caused by the unsteady separation of flow of a fluid around a blunt body such as a rock or piling.[19] Vortex streets are common in nature, Ball writes. The wake of a bubble forms vortex streets as it rises through water, "pushing the bubble first to one side and then the other as the vortices are shed." This explains why bubbles in champagne often follow a zigzag path. Bees use vortex or eddy shedding from their wingtips to help them keep

Photo 8.8: Kármán vortex street caused by wind flowing around the Juan Fernández Islands off the Chilean coast.

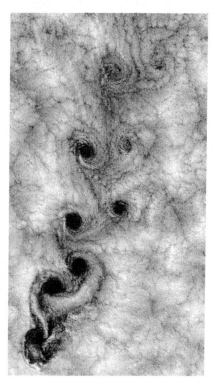

Photo by Bob Cahalan, NASA GSFC

aloft. Vortex streets are also responsible for the "singing" of suspended power lines and the vibration of a car antenna at certain speeds. Vortex streets aren't necessarily turbulent; the pattern is an alternating separation of flow that is periodic and "unsteady." The wake generated by the propellers of a ship creates a constant movement of alternating motion.

Another fascinating fluid pattern is the transformation of smooth, laminar flow into a wavy pattern due to shear instability. This happens when two layers of fluid (at different speeds or in different directions) slide past one another and experience shear force. The boundary becomes unstable, and eventually waves curl into vortices in a process called the *Kelvin–Helmholtz instability*. Given the self-amplifying nature of boundary instability, a regular series of waves that roll over into vortices are formed. A stunning example occurs in the atmosphere of Saturn, captured by NASA's *Cassini* spacecraft, where two bands of clouds with different densities, velocities and flow directions meet. The instability at the boundary creates a series of swirling vortices of dark on light.[19]

Whirlpools, from the spiralling of your bath water to the powerful funnels of tornadoes and hurricanes are self-organized coherent structures of symmetry. Vortices can express in different forms from monopoles (e.g., a single sphere with axial symmetry) to dipole, tripole and quadrupole structures. A *dipolar* vortex (one with two oppositely spiralling fluids in mirror-symmetry) forms when a two-dimensional fluid system encounters a Kelvin–Helmholtz instability. Dipolar vortices commonly occur in meteorological and coastal flows (caused by atmospheric phenomena) and in the trailing vortices from aircraft.[21,22]

Not all whirlpools are round: some are triangular, square, hexagonal, or shaped like other regular polygons. A decade after I graduated from Concordia University in Montreal, Quebec, Georgios Vatistas—a researcher there—demonstrated how vortices could change from circular to many-lobed. Vatistas set a layer of water rotating in a cylindrical tank by spinning a disk on the bottom of the tank. As the disk sped up, the

Photo 8.9: Kelvin-Helmholtz instability on Saturn, formed at the interaction of two bands of the planet's atmosphere.

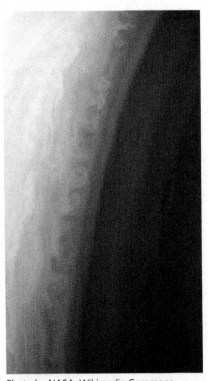

Photo by NASA, Wikimedia Commons

core of the vortex changed from circular to wavy and ultimately changing shape to a successive number of lobes. Vatistas suggested that, given the comparability of rotating gas clouds and dust in spiral galaxies to vortices in fluids, these many-lobed vortex cores may explain why some galaxies appear to have several dense cores (e.g., the double core of the Andromeda galaxy).[19]

I mentioned Saturn's hexagonal shaped storm in Chapter 3. Hurricane Ivan in 2004 took on a square eye wall as it approached the US east coast.[19] Natural convection, which occurs in a fluid layer heated from below, develops an upwelling with a regular (and hexagonal, if surface-tension driven) pattern of convection cells known as *Benard cells*. D'Arcy Thompson, in observing these self-organizing, nonlinear systems, thought of the preponderance of hexagonal patterns in the layers of living cells, in soap froths, in the pores that perforate the shells of marine micro-organisms, in the cloud patterns of a "dappled or mackerel sky."[20]

In Chapter 3, I talk about how Van Gogh's mental "turbulence" gave him the ability to accurately intuit the forms of real turbulent flow. We have seen this wild pattern before, says Ball.

When sharp gradients develop in temperature, moisture, and momentum (i.e., wind shear), strange things happen and wild phenomena present themselves. I recall on one of my many trips through the mid-western states of America, I found myself being followed by a very dark weather system. Behind me, a dark shroud of charcoal cloud chased me. Ahead of me, spread out for kilometres, was the strangest cloud formation I'd seen: beneath a sheet of cumulonimbus, pouches of lighter clouds hung in a series of braids, like balloons. I later learned that these were called *mammatus* clouds (from *mamma*, which means "udder" or "breast"). True to their ominous appearance, mammatus clouds often mean that a particularly strong storm or even a tornadic storm is coming. Given that I was in Wyoming, where I'd encountered tornadoes before, I would not have been surprised. However, in this

Photo 8.10: Mammato-cumulous clouds over Wyoming, USA.

Photo by Nina Munteanu

case, it was just a severe thunderstorm. I stopped driving and settled at the roadside to enjoy the full onslaught of the thunderstorm—complete with hail. The storm passed through quickly and out from it emerged my prize—a double rainbow.

Rainbows appear when light is reflected off the back of a raindrop; a second usually dimmer rainbow appears when light is reflected twice in a more complicated pattern. The colors of the second rainbow are inverted, with blue on the outside and red moved to the inside. Many rain droplets of different sizes—possibly a bazillion—make a rainbow visible to the human eye.

Beauty comes in all forms and moods. Sometimes we must inhale it in halting gulps, edged in the thrill of fear, to appreciate its depths.

Figure 8.3: Bain à la Grenouillère *painted in 1869 by Claude Monet.*

New York Metropolitan Museum of Art

Beauty of Snow

I grew up in southern Quebec, where the first snow of the season often came from the sky in a thick passion. Huge flakes of unique beauty settled on my coat sleeves and within minutes I was covered in snow. I would stand enraptured and study each one as I could.

Snow wraps everything in a blanket of soft acceptance. It creates a dazzling face on a dark Earth. It refuses to distinguish between artificial and natural. It covers everything—decorated house, shabby old car, willowy trees, manicured lawn—beneath its white mantle. It quiets the Earth.

Have you ever gone for an evening walk in the fresh crisp snow, boots crunching, snow glistening in the moonlight? Each step is its own symphony of textured sound. A kind of collaboration with the deep of the night and Nature's own whisperings.

Snow is a shape shifter, charging down in a fierce blizzard and as hoarfrost that forms as water vapour migrates up through the snow base on cold, clear nights. Snow is a gypsy, conspiring with the clever wind to form mini-tornadoes and swirling on the cold pavement like misbehaving fairies. It drifts like a vagabond and piles up, cresting over the most impressive structure, creating phantoms out of icons. Some people, fearful of the chaos and confusion that snow brings, hide indoors out of the cold. Others embrace its many forms, punching holes through the snow crust to find the treasure of powder beneath or ploughing through its softness, leaving behind an ivory trail of adventure.

Snow is magic. It reveals as it cloaks. Animals leave their telltale tracks behind their silent sleuthing. No two snowflakes are alike. Yet every non-aggregated snowflake forms a six-fold radial symmetry, based on the hexagonal alignment of water molecules when they form ice. Tiny perfectly shaped ice-flowers drift down like world peace and settle

Photo 8.11: Snow banks along a trail in Manning Park, British Columbia, Canada.

Photo by Nina Munteanu

in a gentle carpet of white. Oddly, a snowflake is really clear and colourless. It only looks white because the whole spectrum of light bounces off the crystal facets in diffuse reflection (i.e., at many angles). My son, who skies, extols "champagne powder"—very smooth and dry snow, ideal for gliding on. On powder days, after a fresh snowfall, mountain trees form glabrous Henry Moore-like sculptures. Skiers wind their way between the "snow ghosts," leaving meandering double-helix tracks behind them.

Snow is playful. It beckons you to stick out your tongue and taste the clouds. Snow is like an unruly child. Snow is the trickster. It stirs things up. Makes a mess. It is the herald of change, invigorating, fresh and wondrous. Cars skid in it and squeal with objection. Grumpy drivers honk their horns, impatient to get home; while others sigh in their angry wake. Brown slush flies in a chaotic fit behind a bus and splatters your new coat. Boys and girls too (of all ages) venture outside, mischief glinting in their eyes, and throw snowballs. Great battles are fought in backyards where children build awesome forts and defend them with fierce determination.

Photo 8.12: Freshly fallen snow covers trees in Ladner, British Columbia, Canada.

Photo by Nina Munteanu

The Snowflake

As a child, I marvelled at the snowflake. I discerned even then that most snowflakes had a six-fold radial symmetry that displayed an elaborate and unique pattern. Foreshadowing my later scientific pursuits, I tried to classify them by shape and size. I intuitively realized that snowflakes looked different under different conditions of temperature, humidity and wind. Their type and size depends on the humidity and temperature present when they form. That's why the flakes are small when its very cold and they get larger when it's closer to zero degrees Centigrade.

Snowflakes are crystals of pure ice. They grow from frozen water droplets (in the form of water vapour as opposed to much larger raindrops). Water vapour in the air condenses and freezes to add more ice to the newly born snowflake. About a hundred thousand cloud droplets make a single snowflake heavy enough to fall to Earth, says Caltech physicist Kenneth Libbrecht, author of *The Secret Life of a Snowflake*.[23]

Photo 8.13: Stellar-plate snowflake, photographed with a Canon Powershot A650 and 44M-5 Helios lens.

Photo by Alexey Kljatov

Snowflakes have six sides because a water molecule lines up that way, based on its tetrahedral arrangement (e.g., the oxygen—oxygen links form the structural framework for all ice structures, with hydrogens distributed at random throughout the oxygen—oxygen framework, following the Bernal–Fowler rules).[24] While snowflakes are completely symmetrical with themselves, they don't match any other snowflake. A single snow crystal consists of millions of molecules of water and the number of ways that these molecules can arrange themselves into six-sided crystals is huge. Each snowflake is unique—just as each person is unique—because it encounters unique atmospheric conditions during its descent. Each one of a snowflake's six arms undergoes the same micro-condition; but no two snowflakes experience that same condition.

You may find it worthwhile to view lovely photos of snowflakes on-line.[24] Table 8.1 describes different classes of snow and how they form.

Table 8.1: Morphology of Snow	
Snow Crystals	Single ice crystals, often with six-fold symmetrical shapes. These grow directly from condensing water vapour in the air, usually around a nucleus of dust or some other foreign material. Typical sizes range from microscopic to a few millimetres in diameter.
Snowflakes	Collections of snow crystals, loosely bound together. These can grow to a large size (up to about 10 cm across in some cases), especially when the snow is wet and sticky. A snowflake consists of up to 100 snow crystals clumped together.
Rime	Super-cooled tiny water droplets (typically in a fog) that quickly freeze onto whatever they come in contact with. An example is small droplets of rime that sometimes form on large snow crystals.
Graupel	Loose collections of frozen water droplets, sometimes called "soft hail." Graupel makes for dangerous driving.
Hail	Large, solid chunks of ice.

Reference: www.SnowCrystals.com

Photo 8.14: Stellar-dendrite snowflake, photographed with a Canon Powershot A650 and 44M-5 Helios lens.

Photo by Alexey Kljatov

While no two snowflakes look alike, you can still recognize types of shapes. Just as aggregated snow varies according to temperature and humidity, so do individual snowflakes. Those who study snowflakes classify them into four main groups: dendrites; columns, needles; and rimed snow.

The *dendrite* or ice fern is the classic snowflake and the shape most of us imagine for a snowflake. It's a "plate" snowflake that looks like a star or flower, with small side branches crystallizing from each of the six main branches. Some dendrites display a more intricate fractal arrangement, resembling a fern. Dendrites form in a wide temperature range, depending on saturation of the cloud, from just below freezing (low saturation) to minus 20°C (high saturation).

Ice needles are snow crystals, still with six sides, but in the shape of long "columns" or needles. Resembling pencils, they fall when the temperature is just below freezing, from around minus 5°C to minus 10°C). On one mild winter day in Toronto, nothing but these needles dropped from the sky, covering everything from my coat to my car with white "hair clippings." This kind of snow is quite fluffy and develops when the cold air is drier.

Capped columns form when the weather is a little warmer. Capped columns are basically six-sided columns with two plates on their ends like two wheels on an axle.

Rimed snowflakes are partially or completely coated in tiny frozen water droplets called rime. Rime forms on a snowflake when it passes through a super-cooled cloud.[24]

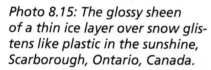

Photo 8.15: The glossy sheen of a thin ice layer over snow glistens like plastic in the sunshine, Scarborough, Ontario, Canada.

Photo by Nina Munteanu

Icicles and Other Miracles

Curious about patterns in nature, physicist Stephen Morris at the University of Toronto in Canada studies icicles. He set up an elaborate ice-making machine in his lab to watch them grow in different conditions and has created an online database for his large collection of data called the Icicle Atlas.[25]

When I came across Dr. Morris's work with icicles, I was delighted and fascinated. I grew up with icicles. Every winter, icicles formed on the roof edges of our house. Icicles formed on almost every object that provided a surface for water to collect and build and melt. During Quebec winters, devastating ice storms have covered trees in ice—and icicles.

Icicles are actually a rarity in our universe; while frozen water exists in virtually every part of our solar system—planets, comets, even space—icicles do not. Even on Earth they are mostly confined to the northern climates, and mostly in cities, where the right conditions of condensation, melting and ice-formation promote icicle formation. Icicles need two things: an atmosphere with water and the right conditions (like fluctuating temperatures) to make water drip and then transfer enough heat into the air to freeze. This only happens when water near the freezing point is in vertical motion: waterfalls, cliff faces and roofs. Our urban landscape of poorly insulated houses and overhanging eaves does a great job of promoting icicle formation.

Raymond Goldstein and his colleagues at the University of Cambridge in Britain demonstrated that icicles have hollow tips. Icicles in Nature typically have rippled surfaces, with the distance between each wave being fairly constant at one centimetre—regardless

Photo 8.16: Ice formation on the shore of Lake Ontario, Canada.

Photo by Nina Munteanu

of temperature and flow rate. Morris discovered that the icicle ripples are caused by impurities, such as salts, in the water. Morris's work with icicles has generated a lot of interest from various sectors, including artists, musicians, other scientists and entrepreneurs.

Consider the icicle, Stephen Morris says, and rejoice.

Saint Sebaldus, patron saint of Nurenberg, is traditionally invoked for protection against the cold. One miracle credited to him is known as the "miracle of the icicles." In his book *Lives of the Saints*, Reverend Alban Butler recounts the following story: Saint Sebald took shelter in a peasant's cottage one cold, snowy night. He found the fire low and the home as cold inside as outside. The peasant lamented that he could not afford fuel for the fireplace. Saint Sebald "turned to the housewife and asked her to bring in a bundle of the long icicles hanging from the eaves ... Sebald threw them on the fire and they blazed up merrily."[26] The miracle of the icicles is depicted in relief on the base of Saint Sebaldus' shrine at the church of Saint Sebaldus in Nurenberg, Germany.

Water's Hexagon & Other Sacred Shapes

In Chapter 2 and 3, I talk about EZ water and how water structures itself in tetrahedral clusters and hexagonal chains, as documented by water researchers Rustum Roy, Martin Chaplin, Mae Wan Ho, Gerald Pollack and many others.[27,28,29,30] I also mention how water aggregates and organizes into a hexagonal structure as ice and snowflakes.

The hexagonal shape—from a snowflake on Earth to a giant maelstrom on Saturn's north pole—appears to prevail in our world, our solar system and possibly the Universe. The hexagon is common in organic chemistry. Diamond and quartz crystals, epithelial cells in the human eye, the pattern of snake skin, and a bee's honeycomb are just some common hexagonal shapes. It is generally suggested that the number six symbolizes love, communication, balance, union and family.

The hexagon also forms the projection of each of the five Platonic solids: regular, convex polyhedrons with the same number of faces that meet at each vertex. Only five solids meet these criteria. The five Platonic solids are found in minerals, animated and organic life forms, sound, music, and language.

The Greek philosopher and mathematician Pythagorus initially described these unique solids. Plato elucidated them and associated each with a classical element, such as solid *"earth"* (cube or hexahedron), gas *"air"* (octahedron), liquid *"water"* (icosahedron) and plasma *"fire"* (tetrahedron), and the fifth element (the dodecahedron) being *ether*. According to Plato, "God used this solid for the whole universe, embroidering figures on it."[31] Plato felt that these perfectly symmetrically

"Water is the carrier of the life force matrix housed within the sacred geometric patterns of the flower of life."
—Pangman and Evans

Illustration 8.1: Drawing of an icosahedron, showing 20 faces and one of the platonic solids.

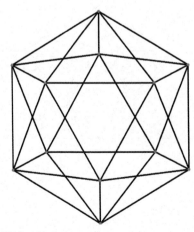

Wikimedia Commons

spatial shapes were the key to what he later developed as the "theory of everything" (based on two fundamental triangles) in his treatise *Timaeus*. Plato regarded the solids as the "atoms" or "corpuscles" of the various forms of substance that comprised what he called the *plenum* (i.e., space that is full of "matter").

According to spiritual mavens, the hexagon is the most common form of sacred geometry, as a basic feature of Platonic Solids, the Flower of Life and Metatron's Cube. The hexagon also delineates the geometry of Buckminster Fuller's vector *equilibrium*, a fractal arrangement of adjacent tetrahedrons and octahedrons in a 64-tetrahedron grid. Buckminster Fuller designed Montreal's Expo 67 geodesic dome or biosphere, a Class 1, Frequency 16 Icosahedron.

According to Marshall Lefferts of *Cosmometry*, "the quantity of 64 is found in numerous systems in the cosmos, including the 64 codons [sequence of three nucleotides] in our DNA, the 64 hexagrams of the *I Ching* (Chinese 'Book of Changes'), the 64 tantric arts of the Kama Sutra, as well as in the Mayan Calendar's underlying structure. It appears that the 64-based quantitative value is of primary importance in the fundamental structure of the Unified Field and how that field manifests from its implicate (pre-manifest) order to its explicate (manifest) order, both physically and metaphysically."[32]

The *tetrahedron* (with 4 triangular faces), *cube* (with 6 square faces) and *octahedron* (with 8 triangular faces) occur naturally in crystal structures.

Among Ernst Haeckel's prolific and articulate drawings in his 1904 collection *Kunstformen der Natur*, he drew a number of species of *Radiolaria* (amoeboid protozoa). These tiny creatures grow intricate mineral skeletons, shaped in various polyhedra, including *icosahedrons* (with 20 faces) and *dodecahedrons* (with 12 faces).[34] According to the Virus Research Group at UCLA, many viruses display icosahedral symmetry, apparently because the icosahedron is the easiest shape to assemble using the repeated protein subunits to build a virus.[33]

Illustration 8.2: Drawing of Metatron's Cube, a sacred geometric figure made of 13 equal circles with lines from the centre of each extending out to the centres of the others; derived from the Fruit of Life and begets the five Platonic Solids.

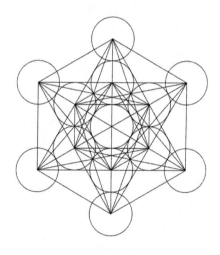

Wikimedia Commons

Sacred geometry underlies a worldview of pattern recognition that attributes the significance of fundamental structures and their relationships to space, time and form in a Great Design. Based on mathematical ratios, harmonics, light, frequency and sound properties, sacred geometry has informed the design of sacred architecture and art since ancient times. The Knights Templar used sacred geometry when building their holy structures. "Sacred" dimensions were used by medieval stone masons to build churches and cathedrals. An example is Chartres Cathedral, a magnificent medieval thirteenth-century structure located ninety kilometres southwest of Paris. Harmonic ratios were translated into its splendid Gothic architecture. Not only do these ratios define physical proportions of beauty; they define the harmonic sounds we find pleasing. Goethe described architecture as "frozen music," no more literally relevant than in this beautiful structure. A notable number of musical proportions—associated with sacred geometry—were embedded into the design of the Chartres Cathedral to bring humanity closer to God.

Photo 8.17: Vitruvian Man drawn in 1492 by Leonardo Da Vinci, currently in the Academia of Venice.

The patterns, forms and ratios of sacred geometry can be found throughout Nature from the cornea of our eye, strands of DNA, pinecones, flower petals, tree branches, and stars to galaxies.

The *Flower of Life* is a geometric figure composed of multiple evenly-spaced and overlapping circles. The circles are arranged in a flower-like pattern with a six-fold symmetry. The centre of each circle lies on the circumference of six surrounding circles of the same diameter. Some spiritualists consider the Flower of Life to carry a blueprint of the universe[35] and an *Akashic* record of basic information for all living things. *Akasha* (a Sanskrit word for "sky", "space", "luminous" or "ether") translates loosely into "light-carrying ether." Theosophists believe that the *Akashic* records are a collection of thoughts, events and emotions encoded in a non-physical plane. Leonardo da Vinci studied the mathematical patterns of the Flower of Life and used its geometry to create his *Vitruvian Man*, whose proportions also reflect the Golden Ratio (see below).

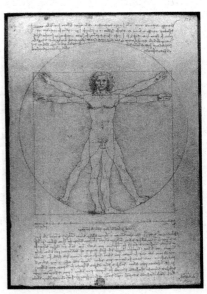

Photo by Luc Viatour

The *Flower of Life* form begins with the most basic and most common shape, the circle.

The circle divides once to form the *vesica piscis*, which is the intersection of the two circles with the same radius; the two circles overlap in such a way that the centre of each circle lies on the perimeter of the other. The *vesica piscis* symbolizes creation and what David Radcliffe of *Secular Freemason* calls, "a state of fractal holographic replication."[36] From the *vesica piscis*, one can produce the equilateral triangle, the hexagon, pentagon, square and so on. This sacred shape forms the basis of the building shapes that will eventually create the Seed of Life, Egg of Life, and finally the Flower of Life. *Vesica piscis*, described in Euclid's *Book of Elements*,[37] means "bladder of a fish" in Latin and is emblazoned on the cover of the Chalice Well in the sacred site of Glastonbury, UK.

The continued division of each circle creates the *seed of life*, a six-fold collection of circles with a six-fold dissected "flower" at the centre. Continued division of circles creates a second layer of dissected "flowers" and so on.

The Flower of Life symbol appears in ancient structures throughout the world. It can be found gracing the floors and rooftops of ancient houses in Ephesus, Turkey; it forms the mosaic of the water's-edge walkway and the marble floor of the Golden Temple (*Harmandir Sahib*), a Sikh holy shrine in Amritsar, India; it lies on the portal of an ancient Federici's house in Erbanno, Italy; in ancient synagogues, King Herod's palaces, and Masada, Israel; gracing the head of a Templar Knight's tombstone in St. Magnus cathedral in Kirkwall; in Buddhist temples in Japan; carved into rock in Assyria; flowering in the vaulted ceiling of la Mezquita cathedral in Cordoba, Spain; on the archways of the 14th century Tonning temple of Braedstrup, Denmark; on the ruins of Kabile in Bulgaria; and on the ceiling of a medieval house in Weitra, Austria. The Flower of Life has also appeared in Tibet, Greece, Morocco, Lebanon, Sweden, Lappland, Iceland and the Yucatan peninsula.

The oldest known depiction of the Flower of Life can be found at

Photo 8.18: The Golden Temple, Kyoto, Japan.

Photo by Nina Munteanu

The Temple of Osiris in Abydos, Egypt. The symbol appears burned into the granite rock. The geometry of the flower of life appears in the dimensions of Stonehenge and in the Great Pyramid of Giza.

In front of the ancient palace of Beijing's Forbidden City, China, the spherical form of the Flower of Life lies beneath the paw of the "Fu Dog." Also known as "Guardian Lions," *Fu Dogs* are considered guardians of knowledge and symbolize protection of the buildings and their inhabitants. In this case, the dogs are literally guarding "knowledge." And sacred geometry.

The most common form of the Flower of Life is a hexagonal pattern, where the centre of each circle is on the circumference of six surrounding circles of the same diameter, made of 19 complete circles and 36 partial circular arcs, all enclosed within a large circle. This complete flower (also called Nature's first pattern) encompasses the fruit, egg and seed of life. The Hebrew Kabbalist "Tree of Life," considered a "map" of creation, can also be derived from the Flower of Life.

Photo 8.19: A male Fu Dog, along with female (not pictured) guard a temple on Gerrard Street, Toronto and together manifest yin and yang. The male holds the flower of life with his right front paw; the female holds a baby cub representing the cycle of life.

When lines are drawn from the centre of each of the thirteen equal circles of the Fruit of Life, the 3-dimensional *Metatron's Cube*, which holds all the Platonic solids, emerges. The archangel *Metatron*, mentioned in Islamic, Judaic and Christian mythologies, was considered the scribe of God. Often depicted holding a cube, he was also known to the Egyptians as Thoth or Hermes Trismegistus (also a scribe of the gods). Metatron's Cube was first described by Italian mathematician Leonardo Fibonacci.

The *Merkaba*, two equal-sized and interlocked tetrahedrons, one pointing up and the other pointing down, is part of Metatron's Cube. It is also called a *Star Tetrahedron*, and can be viewed as a three-dimensional Star of David. The Merkaba is described by modern esoterics as the divine light allegedly used by ascended masters to connect with the higher realms. The word literally means light–spirit–body. According to Jewish mysticism centred on the Book of Ezekiel, the Merkaba is surrounded by counter-rotating fields of light (wheels within wheels).

Photo by Merridy Cox

Esoterics correlate these spirals of energy with the vector equilibrium of the *torus energy flow* (a geometric energy array), the *Shri Yantra* (Hindu "sacred instrument"), the *aura* (invisible emanated energy field), and *zero-point energy* (energy of the ground state of the zero-point field).

Upon his return from Egypt, Pythagoras founded a mystery school that encompassed a balanced learning of science and religion, in addition to conducting esoteric teachings for qualified initiates. The Pythagoreans believed that the Earth grid of electro-magnetic lines and vortices is composed in a fractal arrangement from the Earth throughout the cosmos to makeup the *plenum*. Also variously called the "akashic field," "Zero-Point energy Field", and "the metaverse," this cosmic ether is currently recognized by quantum physicists as not being empty space, but filled with "something." That "something" is currently called *dark energy*,[38] which supposedly permeates all of space. Following on the work of Nikola Tesla, systems theorist Ervin Laszlo described space as a vibrational "wave medium," within an information field.[39] Quantum physics predicts that all of space is filled with electromagnetic zero-point fluctuations (or a zero-point field), creating a universal sea of zero-point energy, which is the same as dark energy.[40,41]

While the Platonic solids were first named and described by Plato, these shapes existed in hundreds of carved prehistoric petrospheres in Scotland. These petrospheres are now also recognized arrangements of protons and neutrons in the elements of the periodic table.[42]

Photo 8.20: Three-petals and 3-sepals of a day lily flower.

Photo by Merridy Cox

The Golden Mean

Some of the greatest mathematical minds of all ages—from ancient Greece's Pythagoras and Euclid to medieval Italy's Fibonacci, and Renaissance astronomer Johannes Kepler, to present-day Oxford physicist Roger Penrose—have carefully studied the Golden Ratio, as Mario Livio writes in his book *The Golden Ratio: the Story of Phi, The World's Most Astonishing Number*.[39] The fascination with the Golden Ratio is not confined to mathematicians, Livio adds. Biologists, artists, musicians, historians, architects, psychologists, and mystics have reflected and discussed its ubiquity and appeal. "In fact," says Livio, "it is probably fair to say that the Golden Ratio has inspired thinkers of all disciplines like no other number in the history of mathematics."[43]

"All things come out of the one and the one out of all things."
—Heraclitus

Discovered by Pythagoras and later described by Euclid, Leonardo Fibonacci, and Luca Pacioli, the Golden Ratio—which roughly equals 1.618—is currently represented by the Greek letter *phi* or the letter *tau*. Johannes Kepler described the ratio as a "precious jewel."

In his 1509 book on mathematics called *De divina proportione*, and illustrated by Leonardo da Vinci, Luca Pacioli describes how the Golden Ratio applies to art and architecture, including the harmonics of dodecahedrons and icosahedrons.[44] Pacioli called this ratio the "Divine Proportion." Da Vinci later called it the *section aurea* (the "golden section"). The Golden Ratio was used to achieve balance and beauty in many Renaissance paintings and sculptures. Da Vinci used the Golden Ratio in his painting *The Last Supper*. The Golden Ratio also appears in da Vinci's *Vitruvian Man* and the *Mona Lisa*. Other artists who incorporated the Golden Ratio in their works include Michelangelo, Raphael, Rembrandt, Seurat, and Salvador Dali.

From the smallest to the largest, examples of *phi* in nature abound. These include the geometry of crystals and the spiral (often double spiral) of seed heads, such as a daisy or sunflower, the whorl of flower petals and leaves on a stem or branch, or seed heads, and pinecones. You can easily see the whorl design in pineapples and cauliflowers, for instance. Most seashells demonstrate the Golden Rectangle (whose sides are within the Golden Ratio) or logarithmic spiral. So do cyclones, whirlpools, hurricanes and many other weather phenomena. Faces of animals also display the Golden Ratio, as do animal bodies generally and parts such as fingers of hands and the uterus of a woman. The swooping flight path of a falcon stalking its prey also follows the same spiral. The double-helix spiral of DNA follows the Fibonacci series, with its ratio approximating *phi*. Researchers from the Helmholtz–Zentrum Berlin für Materialien und Energie (HZB), in cooperation with colleagues from Oxford and Bristol Universities, as well as the Rutherford Appleton Laboratory, UK, determined that the Golden Ratio is present at the atomic scale in the magnetic resonance of spins in cobalt niobate crystals. Coincidence? Radu Coldea of Oxford University doesn't think so. "It reflects a beautiful property of the quantum system—a hidden symmetry,"[45] he maintains.

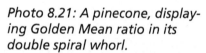

Photo 8.21: A pinecone, displaying Golden Mean ratio in its double spiral whorl.

Photo by Merridy Cox

The spiral arms of galaxies also follow the familiar Fibonacci pattern of the Golden Mean. It's interesting to note that spiral galaxies defy Newtonian physics: their radial arms do not wind around a galaxy as it turns as would be expected, given that the angular speed of rotation of a galactic disk varies with distance from the centre. Cosmologists have a name for it: the *winding problem*. Scientists postulated in the 1950s that magnetic fields may generate the spiral structure that is not fully developed. In the 1960s, Scientists Lin and Shu proposed that a galaxy's spiral arms maintained their form due to spiral density through wave amplification and resonance. Perhaps dark energy—and self organizing symmetry—will be determined to play a role.[46,47]

So, what does all this discourse have to do with water? Surely, water is all these things. Water embraces everything by simply being what it is.

Water is the ultimate altruist, taking on the form and shape of that which encompasses it, and, in turn, informs it with beauty.

Water makes everything beautiful.

Annie Dillard wrote in her book *Pilgrim at Tinker Creek*: "The texture of the world, its filigree and scrollwork, means that there is the possibility for beauty here, a beauty inexhaustible in its complexity, which opens to my knock, which answers in me a call I do not remember calling, and which trains me to the wild and extravagant nature of the spirit I seek."[9]

Beauty reflects Nature's flowing embrace. Deep and quiet, beauty captures divine radiance—refracting, magnifying, rejoicing—and bursts into a sparkling sea of serenity. Light personified.

Beauty is water.

Figure 8.22: A field of sunflowers in Missouri, USA.

Photo by Nina Munteanu

References

1. Moore, Jared S. 1942. "Beauty as Harmony." *The Journal of Aesthetics and Art Criticism* 2(7): 40–50.

2. Aristotle. 350 BCE (1984). "The Poetics" and "Metaphysics." In: "The Complete Works: The Revised Oxford Translation, Vol. 1. Bollingen/ Princeton University Press, N.J. 2512 pp.

3. Newton, Eric. 1950. "The Meaning of Beauty." *Whittlesey House.* 207 pp.

4. Hutcheson, Francis. 1725 (2004). "An Inquiry into the Original of Our Ideas of Beauty and Virtue." In: Wolfgang Leidhold (ed) Indianapois: Liberty Fund.

5. Puffer, Ethel. 1905. "Psychology of Beauty."*Houghton, Mifflin & Co.*, NY. 156 pp.

6. Birkhoff, George David. 1933. "Aesthetic Measure." *Harvard University Press.* 225 pp.

7. Livio, Mario. 2005. "The Equation that Couldn't Be Solved." *Simon & Schuster.* 368 pp.

8. Lane, John. 2003 "Timeless Beauty: In the Arts and Everyday Life." *UIT Cambridge Ltd,* , UK. 192 pp.

9. Dillard, Annie. 1974 "Pilgrim at Tinker Creek." *Harper Perennial.* 304 pp.

10. Emoto, Masaru. 2011. "The Miracle of Water." *Atria Books.* 160 pp.

11. Marks, William. 2001. "The Holy Order of Water." *Bell Pond Books.* 256 pp.

12. Gardner, Martin. 2007. "Is Beauty Truth and Truth Beauty?" *Scientific American*, March Issue.

13. Stewart, Ian. 2007 "Why Beauty Is Truth: The History of Symmetry." *Basic Books.* 304 pp.

14. Bhave, Vinoba. 1960. "Talks on the Gita." *The Macmillan Company.* 268 pp.

15. Lovelock, J.E. and L. Margulis. 1974. "Atmospheric Homeostasis by and for the Biosphere: the Gaia Hypothesis." *Tellus* Series A 26(1–2): 2–10.

16. Harpur, Patrick. 2002. "The Philosophers' Secret Fire: A History of the Imagination." *Penguin.* 384 pp.

17. Sheldrake, Rupert. 2003. "The Extended Mind." *Quest*. July–August Issue.

18. Clark, Andy and David Chalmers. 1998. "The Extended Mind." *Analysis* 58: 10–23.

19. Ball, Philip. 2011. "Flow." *Oxford University Press*. 208 pp.

20. Thompson, D'Arcy Wentworth. 1917. "On Growth and Form." *Cambridge University Press*. 793 pp.

21. Voropayev, Sergey I. and Y.D. Afanasyev. 1994. "Vortex Structures in a Stratified Fluid: Order from Chaos." *Chapman and Hall / CRC*. 240 pp.

22. Van Heijst, G.J.F. and J.B. Flor. 1989. "Dipole Formation and Collisions in a Stratified Fluid." *Nature* 340: 212–215.

23. Libbrecht, Kenneth. 2009. The Secret Life of a Snowflake. *Voyageur Press*. Minneapolis, MN. 48pp.

24. Libbrecht, Kenneth. 2015. "Snow Crystals." Online: www.SnowCrystals.com Caltech website online: http://www.its.caltech.edu/Ăatomic/snowcrystals/ice/ice.htm

25. Semeniuk, Ivan. 2015. "The Mysterious (and Cool) Science of Icicles." *The Globe and Mail*, March 2, 2015.

26. Butler, Rev. Alban. 1847 (2005)."Lives of the Saints." New edition. *Paraclete Press*. 400 pp.

27. Roy, R.; W. A. Tiller; I. Bell; and M. R. Hoover. 2005. "The structure of liquid water; novel insights from materials research; potential relevance to homeopathy." *Mat. Res. Innovat*. 9–4: 93–124.

28. Chaplin, Martin F. 2015. "Anomalous properties of water." Online: "Water Structure and Science": http://www1.lsbu.ac.uk/water/water_anomalies.html

29. Ho, Mae-Wan. 2008. "Living Rainbow: H2O." *World Scientific Publishing Company*. 380 pp.

30. Pollack, Gerald. 2013. "The Fourth Phase of Water." *Ebner & Sons*. 357 pp.

31. Plato. 360 BCE. "Timaeus." Translated by Benjamin Jowett. *MIT Classics*.

32. Lefferts, Marshall. 2014. "Vector Equilibrium & Isotropic Vector

Matrix." Cosmometry: Exploring the Fractal Holographic Nature of the Cosmos. Online: http://cosmometry.net/vector-equilibrium-&-isotropic-vector-matrix

33. UCLA. 2004. "The Origin of Icosahedral Symmetry in Viruses." The Virus Research Group, *UCLA Chem*. Online: http://virus.chem.ucla.edu/icosahedral_symmetry

34. Haekel, Ernst. 1904. "Kunstformen der Natur." In: Breidbach, Olaf. 2006. "Visions of Nature: The Art and Science of Ernst Haeckel." *Prestel Verlag*, Munich, 2006.

36. Radcliffe, David. 2012. "The Geometry of the Flower of Life." *Secular Freemason*. Online: http://secularfreemason.blogspot.ca/2012/02/geometry-of-flower-of-life.html

37. Euclid. 300 BCE (2010). "Thirteen Books of Elements," Book One. Digireads.com. 404 pp.

38. Peebles, P.J.E. and Bharat Ratra. 2003. "The Cosmological Constant and Dark Energy." *Reviews of Modern Physics* 75(2): 559–606.

39. Laszlo, Ervin. 2009. "Cosmic Memory." *Resurgence & Ecologist*, Sept/Oct Issue. Online: https://www.resurgence.org/magazine/article2914-cosmic-memory.html

40. Beck, Christian and Michael Mackey. 2007. "Measurability of Vacuum Fluctuations and Dark Energy." *Physica A* 379: 101–110.

41. Beck, Christian and Michael Mackey. 2007. "Electromagnetic Dark Energy." *Int. J. Mod. Phys.* D17: 71–80.

42. Hecht, Laurence. 1988. "The Geometric Basis for the Periodicity of the Elements." *21st Century*, May–June.

43. Mario Livio. 2003. "The Golden Ratio: The Story of Phi, The World's Most Astonishing Number." *Broadway Books*. 304 pp.

44. Pacioli, Luca. 1509. "De Divina Proportione." *Luca Paganinem de Paganinus de Brescia* (Antonio Capella), Venice.

45. Ouellette, Jennifer. 2010. "Symmetry in the Subatomic World?" *Discovery News*. Online: http://news.discovery.com/space/symmetry-in-the-subatomic-world.html

46. Lin, C.C. and F. H. Shu. 1964. "On the spiral structure of disk galaxies." *Ap J* 140: 646–655.

47. Lin, C.C. and F. H. Shu. 1967. "Density waves in disk galaxies." In:
Radio Astronomy and the Galactic System (Proc. IAU Symp. No 31,
Noordwijk 1966), H. van Woedden, ed. London & NY, *Academic
Press*. 313–317 pp.

9.
Water is Story

Photo 9.1: Water flow pattern in the Credit River, Ontario, Canada.

Photo by Nina Munteanu

"In the beginning God created the heaven and the earth. And the earth was without form and void; and darkness was upon the face of the deep. And the Spirit of God moved upon the face of the waters."
—**Genesis 1:1-2, King James Bible**

Water's primary role in the Creation is echoed in virtually every cultural myth; in many creation stories, the formation of Earth and life arises from a watery deep. "The story of water reaches from every individual cell to encompass the entire cosmos," writes scientist and philosopher Dr. Masaru Emoto, in *The Hidden Messages in Water*. "To understand water is to understand the cosmos, the marvels of nature, and life itself."[1]

We are all storytellers. We share our curiosity with great expression; our capacity and need to tell stories is as old as our ancient beginnings. From the Palaeolithic cave paintings of Lascaux to our blogs on the Internet, humanity has left a grand legacy of "story" sharing. Evolutionary biologist and futurist Elisabet Sahtouris tells us that, "whether we create our stories from the revelations of religions or the researches of science, or the inspirations of great artists and writers or the experiences of our own lives, we live by the stories we believe and tell to ourselves and others."[2]

The Journey

"To see a river was to be swept up in a great current of myths and memories that was strong enough to carry us back to the first water element of our existence in the womb. And along that stream were borne some of the most intense of our social and animal passions: the mysterious transmutations of blood and water; the vitality and mortality of heroes, empires, nations, and gods."
—Simon Schama, Landscape and Memory

As young girls, my sister and I conjured epic stories of thrilling adventure and discovery from interstellar travel in the far reaches of the Universe, to the exploration of the great Nile and Amazon Rivers of Earth. We'd never been out of Quebec, Canada, let alone on a space voyage; yet, we both shared a vivid idea of the characters of these exotic places. Without realizing it, we were tracing water's great journey.

The great rivers of the world stir thoughts of adventure, exploration and travel. Rivers such as the Seine, Volga, Thames, Danube, and Mississippi each carry their own myth and romance. Even with transportation less concentrated on waterways, we still think of our rivers as flowing networks that connect us. Pacific and Atlantic salmon well recognize that each river tells a unique story.

The four oldest civilizations sprang from the fertile floodplains of some of the world's greatest rivers, writes Philip Ball,[3] science writer and former editor of Nature. Mesopotamia (now Iraq) had the Tigris and Euphrates; the Harrapan culture (now Pakistan) had the Indus, shared with India; India also had the Ganges, Yamuna, and Brahmaputra, all originating in the Himalayas. China had the Yangtze and Yellow Rivers that came to them from the Tibetan plateau; and Egypt had the fertile Nile River.

The River Continuum & a River's Three-stage Journey

All rivers follow a journey of maturation from source to mouth. A river's journey can be described in three stages, corresponding to (1) a young *erosional* upper course, (2) a *transitional* mature and erosional–depositional mid-course, and (3) an old *depositional* lower course.[4,5] The river's journey, reflecting the hydrological cycle, is part of the circular path of all great journeys that return from where they came. The Ouroboros remembered. From the ocean's evaporation and plants' transpiration into clouds, to the torrential rains and percolating groundwater, to the roaring streams and placid lakes and rivers, water returns to its mother source, only to make the journey again.

The River Continuum Concept (RCC) was developed by water scientists to better study and illustrate the physical and biological characteristics of changes in rivers as they flow downstream from an erosional to transitional and finally depositional ecosystem. Some of the key features of the continuum model that help define a river's three-stage journey include a stream's mean flow velocity, its bed material (grain size), stream temperature, UV light penetration, and the representative biological community.[6] I talk more about the RCC in Chapter 3.

First Stage: Erosional. The upper course or headwaters is called a young river and is usually small with a steep gradient, a large-grain-size bed structure, and lower water temperature. Young river channels are typically V-shaped with steep sides. The high-energy rapid flow from the source down-cuts a narrow channel through rocky hills or mountains and picks up a lot of material. Waterfalls and scouring rapids are frequent features of upper courses.

Second Stage: Transitional. The mid-course of a river is called a mature river. It is slower and wider, forming a U-shape in cross-section through lateral erosion. It may meander, cutting a floodplain with a typical bed structure of medium grain size; and the river has higher water temperatures. While it may still scour banks and carry sediments, a mature river will drop larger materials, which creates fertile areas.

Third Stage: Depositional. The lower course of an old river slows and widens considerably, flowing down a very shallow gradient. Rich in dissolved and suspended materials, it drops suspended silt and forms muddy banks with a low-grain-size bed structure and higher water temperatures. The old river section has a broad U-shape and wide nutrient-rich floodplain. Oxbow lakes, sandbars and islands are often features of the old stage of a river. The river mouth may empty into a lake or the ocean, often forming vast deltas of deposited silt; it may form a marsh or swamp (an excellent filtration system); or transition into the sea under tidal influence through an estuary.[4,5]

Many of the world's greatest rivers empty into the sea via productive and diverse estuaries. Some that come to mind include the Amazon, Laguna Madre, Fraser, Thames, Hudson, Mississippi, Delaware, San Francisco Bay, Chesapeake, San Joaquin, Humber, Tugela, Orange, and Indian estuaries. There are, of course, many more. The banks of many estuaries are the most heavily populated areas of the world. Close to two-thirds of the world's population live near estuaries and on the coast near where a river empties.[6] My own city of Vancouver, British Columbia, is located on the Fraser River delta. In fact, the suburb where I raised my family is called Delta, B.C. We used to walk the dyke path, facing over 31,000 hectares of an estuary that provides an active nursery, forage, and refuge for diverse wildlife. Estuaries represent some of the most productive and valuable ecosystems in the world.

A river's three-stage journey metaphorically follows the same great journey of humanity, from the nomadic tribes of our ancient peoples through our transition to a modern global network. Rivers—indeed water in all its forms—reflect our evolving relationship with Nature and the Universe. A river's story is a story of its people.

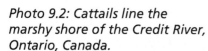

Photo 9.2: Cattails line the marshy shore of the Credit River, Ontario, Canada.

Photo by Nina Munteanu

Water's Three-Stage Journey

Our connection with water and its journey encompasses more than rivers. It embraces the entire water cycle, from tapping groundwater and torrential rains to great diversions and transformations and everything in between.

Early Garamantes (Libyan) farmers flourished for thousands of years in the Sahara Desert by using gravity to successfully mine and transport ground water through an elaborate underground irrigation system. In India's Cherrapunji, the people had adapted to the rhythms of extreme abundance and scarcity in a monsoon ecosystem. The ancient Khmer of Angkor (Cambodia) dug reservoirs and an underground irrigation system to store water from the monsoon rains throughout the drought season. Undoubtedly as a result of the water-harnessing ingenuity of the Khmer, Angkor became the largest pre-industrial city in the world.

Today, we control water on a massive scale. Reservoirs around the world hold 10,000 cubic kilometres of water; five times the water of all the rivers on Earth. Most of these great reservoirs lie in the northern hemisphere, and the extra weight has slightly changed how the Earth spins on its axis, speeding its rotation and shortening the day by eight millionths of a second in the last forty years.[7]

"Ten thousand years ago, we lived at the whim of the water cycle," geologist Iain Stewart tells us in the BBC program *How the Earth Changed History: Water*.[7] "Since then," says Stewart, "we have harnessed the power of rivers to advance our civilizations. We have extracted ground water from the depths of the most unlikely places. And we have learned to redirect and store water on a massive scale. Today we have unprecedented power over the planet's water. But one thing hasn't changed: there's still only a finite amount of water on Earth. It seems to me that water is the Achilles' heel of our modern civilization; it's the one resource, more than any other, with the potential to limit our ambition. The fundamental limits of the water cycle are still there. But the lesson of history is that the most successful civilizations learn to adapt to those limits."[7]

In his 2010 book *Elixir*, Brian Fagan tells the story of humanity's ingenious and utilitarian—and often abusive—relationship with water throughout the ages. It is a three-act story of humanity's separation, transformation and return—with water. Fagan describes the three ages of water that span five millennia. He begins with its sacred treatment in ancient Mesopotamia, leading eventually to its commodification, particularly during the Industrial Revolution. Now entering its third age, water is poised for humanity's enlightenment—and its return to a different relationship with water. As the global population approaches nine billion and ancient aquifers run dry, "to solve the water crisis of the future, we may need to [return to the] water ethos of our ancestors," says Fagan.[8]

In the writing courses I teach at university, I describe the three-act hero's journey whose roots come from the Ancient Greek play. The three acts correspond to three stages of a character's and a story's evolution: (1) *separation*, (2) *transformation*, and (3) *return*. All great stories follow these three acts to tell the tale of development, transcendence, and resolution. Water naturally follows this cyclical journey: (1) *separating* from its source, (2) *transforming* itself and its environment as it travels; and (3) *returning* to its source to undergo another journey. This is our story too.

Water's journey is really our journey, and it is ultimately our journey Home.

Figure 9.3: Freighter anchored in Port of Toronto, Lake Ontario, Canada.

Photo by Nina Munteanu

The Mythic Journey

For Joseph Campbell, perhaps our era's most influential student of mythology, myths express our basic need to explain, celebrate and immortalize the essence of life. Given that life itself has no inherent meaning—it simply is—it is our stories (pulled from the ethers of our muse) that give meaning to life. We tell stories about how the world began, our struggles to survive, and our victories against greed and evil. Each culture clothes its stories according to the place and time and its associated issues. And each defines its heroes and villains accordingly. At the root of all these lies a universal and timeless human experience. Where metaphor and the imagery of myth transcend culture, time, and place, they encompass all of humanity and our striving journey toward truth, grace and peace. This is why all myth, from Plutarch's *Theseus & the Minotaur* to George Lucas' *Star Wars*, resonates with us, regardless of whether it was created yesterday or thousands of years ago. Our relationship with water and water's relationship with us has been told over and over again in the myths and tales of each culture on our planet.

The Hero's Journey myth follows the three-act structure of the ancient Greek play, handed down to us thousands of years ago. Drawn from the depth psychology of Swiss psychologist Carl Jung and from scholar and mythologist Joseph Campbell, author of *The Hero with a Thousand Faces*, the Hero's Journey myth duplicates the steps of a rite of passage and is a process of self-discovery and self-integration.[9] "The emerging heroic ideal does not see life as a challenge to be overcome, but a gift to be received," Carol S. Pearson, author of *The Hero Within*, tells us.[10]

"The Universe is made of stories, not atoms."

—Muriel Rukeyser

The Power of Myth & Archetype

Joseph Campbell recognized that myths weren't just abstract theories or quaint ancient beliefs but practical models for understanding how to live.[9] Ultimately, the Hero's Journey is the soul's search for Home. It is a journey of transformation we all take in some form.

Jung proposed that symbols appear to us when there is a need to express what thought cannot think, or what is only divined or felt. Jung discovered reoccurring symbols among differing peoples and cultures, unaffected by time and space. He described these shared symbols as *archetypes*: irrepressible, unconscious, pre-existing forms of the psyche. Joseph Campbell suggested that these mythic images lie at the depth of the unconscious where humans are no longer distinct individuals—where our minds widen and merge into the mind of humankind—where we are all the same.[9]

Photo 9.4: Partially iced-over Highland Creek in Scarborough, Ontario, Canada.

Photo by Nina Munteanu

The Hero's Journey in Storytelling

Compelling stories resonate with the universal truths of metaphor that reside within the consciousness of humanity. According to Joseph Campbell, this involves an open mind and a certain amount of humility; and giving oneself to the story ... not unlike the hero who gives her life to something larger than herself: "Anyone writing a creative work knows that you yield yourself, and the book talks to you and builds itself ... you become the carrier of something that is given to you from ... the Muses or God. This is no fancy, it is a fact. Since the inspiration comes from the unconscious, and since the unconscious minds of the people of any single small society have much in common, what the shaman or seer [or artist] brings forth is something that is waiting to be brought forth in everyone."[11] I call this tapping into the universal truth, where metaphor lives. A story comes alive when these two, truth and metaphor, resonate.

Heroes are agents of change on a quest. The hero slays the dragon of the status quo. She enacts the ultimate sacrifice in her quest to change the world (and herself). The hero is the ultimate altruist, sacrificing her life for the greater good. The hero's task has always been to bring new life to an ailing culture,[12] says Carol S. Pearson, author of *The Hero Within*. Julia Cameron reiterates this in her book, *The Artist's Way*, when she describes the concept of art as a healing journey—not just for the individual, but for a culture. This is because the writer/artist changes society by changing themselves.[13]

Joseph Campbell describes a hero's twelve-step journey within a three-act play of transformation, influenced by five major archetypes (herald, mentor, threshold guardian, trickster, and shadow/shape-shifter). Our hero starts her journey in Act 1—in the Ordinary World—and will eventually *separate* from the Ordinary World in Act 2—entering the Special World, where she will *transform* through her many challenges. In Act 3, she *returns* to the Ordinary World, changed, with her gift, her elixir.

The hero's journey involves—in fact often requires—that the hero stray from the good path to learn the value of that good path. To transcend, one must understand and appreciate: one must grow to master oneself and one's journey in the world.

Evolutionary biologist and futurist Elisabet Sahtouris shares an allegory (attributed to Mark Twain, though never verified) of a youth who leaves home for his own adventures and returns surprised that his father has gained considerable wisdom in his absence. "We smile," says Sahtouris. "It is the son who has changed ... A youth cannot perceive the wisdom gained by experience until he becomes experienced himself."[2] This is the quintessential hero's journey of change. It recapitulates a river's journey of maturation, leaving its source to gain "wisdom" in its youthful turbulence, transition to a deep quiescence and return "home," to the oceans. According to Sahtouris, humanity now stands on the brink of maturity, still in adolescent crisis, but just mature enough to seek ancient wisdom for guidance.

Evolutionary Tipping Points toward Cooperation

Sahtouris tells a remarkable story of nearly four billion years of evolution that naturally follows a three-act maturation cycle from individuation to fierce competition and finally to mature collaboration and peaceful interdependence. According to Sahtouris, this narrative is punctuated by key tipping points in which a major evolutionary change took a potentially competitive situation and instead embraced a cooperative.[2]

The first tipping point, says Sahtouris, was the evolution of nucleated cells as giant bacterial cooperatives. In her 1981 book, *Symbiosis in Cell Evolution*, Lynn Margulis argued that eukaryotic cells evolved through a symbiotic union of primitive prokaryotic cells in a process she called symbiogenesis or *endosymbiosis*.[14] Her evolutionary theory posited that primitive cells gained entry into host cells as undigested prey or as internal parasites after which the "arrangement" became mutually beneficial to both partners (chloroplasts derived from cyanobacteria and mitochondria from bacteria—two examples). The theory challenged Neo-Darwinism by arguing that inherited variation, significant in evolution, does not come mainly from random mutations, but that new tissues, organs and even species evolve primarily "through the long-lasting intimacy of strangers."[15] The fusion of symbiosis followed by natural selection leads to increasingly complex levels of individuality, Margulis suggested, contending that evolution proceeds ultimately through *cooperation*, not *competition*: "Life did not take over the globe by combat, but by networking."[16] As far as "survival of the fittest goes," says Margulis, it is a "capitalistic, competitive, cost–benefit interpretation of Darwin"; even banks and sports teams must cooperate to compete.[14]

Photo 9.5: Mitochondria from mammalian lung tissue, showing matrix and membranes via electron microscopy.

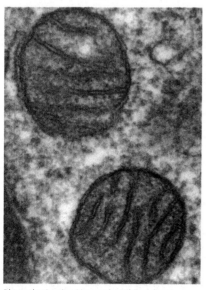

Photo by Louisa Howard, Wikimedia Commons

She saw natural selection as "neither the source of heritable novelty nor the entire evolutionary process."[15]

Co-evolution (and cooperation by default) is now an established theme in the biology of virus–host relationships. These relationships include the complex interaction between arboviruses and their vector mosquitoes; the malaria-causing plasmodium and humans; and the hantavirus and deer mice. Virologist Frank Ryan states that "today ... every monkey, baboon, chimpanzee and gorilla is carrying at least ten different species of symbiotic viruses."[17]

The second tipping point, says Sahtouris, heralded the evolution of multi-celled creatures. Eric Libby and William C. Ratcliff discuss why unicellular life evolved into multicellular life some 600 million years ago, despite the obvious successes of "unicellularity." The answer is co-operation; cells benefitted more from working together than they did from living alone.[18]

Humanity crossed a tipping point when tribes built the first city cooperatives to worship and trade, says Sahtouris. Cities, like the nucleated cells, became new entities that needed to evolve from youthful competition to mature cooperation. Now, after thousands of years of national and corporate empire-building we have reached a tipping point in planetary exploitation, "where enmities are more expensive in all respects than friendly collaboration."[2]

Sahtouris is describing the evolutionary strategies of populations (including humans) from an r-selected to a K-selected life-cycle approach. Coined by ecologists MacArthur and Wilson[19] and discussed by Pianka[20], r (for rate) and K (for *Konstante* or constant) define life-cycle strategies of populations reflecting an unstable and young density-independent environment to a maturing more stable and density-dependent one, respectively. Pianka describes r-selected strategists as generally small, of short life-expectancy and early maturation, and producing many offspring. Examples include annual plants, most insects and small rodents. Little investment, except to distribute widely, is made in the offspring. On the other hand, K-selected or equilibrium individuals are generally larger, longer lived, take longer to mature and produce few offspring but invest time and energy into nurturing their offspring to maturity. Examples include large mammals such as humans, and a climax forest. The K-selected strategy runs on a successive gradient of maturity, from initially competitive to ultimately cooperative.

Competition is a natural adaptive remnant of uncertainty and insecurity and forms the basis of a capitalist economy that encourages monopolization and hostile takeovers. Competition results from an initial antagonistic reaction to a perception of limited resources. It is a natural reaction based on distrust—of both the environment and of the "other"—both aspects of "self" separated from "self." The greed for more than is sustainable reflects a fear of failure and a sense of being separate, which ultimately perpetuates actions dominated by self-interest in a phenomenon described as "the Tragedy of the Commons."[21] Competition naturally gives way to creative cooperation as trust in both "self" and the "other" develops and is encouraged through continued interaction. "Communities with many co-operators and altruists do better than groups dominated by narrow and selfish thinking,"[22] writes Alain Ruche, strategist for the Secretary General of the European Union External Service. Ruche adds that a biological predisposition to cooperate appears to be independent of culture, relying instead on other factors, such as "the long-lasting intimacy of strangers," which I mention in the Preface and discuss later in this chapter.

Examples of creative cooperatives exist throughout the world, offering an alternative to the traditional model of competition. Creative cooperatives are changing the world, Ruche tells us. These creatives, while being community-oriented with an awareness of planet-wide issues, honour and embody feminine values (such as empathy, solidarity, spiritual and personal development, and relationships).[22] Mechanisms include reciprocity, trust, communication, fairness, and a group-sense of belonging. For instance, *We Day* is an Internet platform that celebrates youth making a difference in

Photo 9.6: Peggy's Cove at high tide, Nova Scotia, Canada.

Photo by Nina Munteanu

their local and global communities, by providing tools to create transformative social change.[23] Founded by social entrepreneurs Craig and Marc Kielburger to inspire youth to improve their communities and the world through daily actions, We Day is celebrated and organized all over the world through schools and community organizations. I give more examples of K-selected strategies and creative cooperatives below.

K-Selection & Creative Cooperatives

The American department store Nordstrom exemplifies a mature K-selected strategy in its customer service policy. The Nordstrom model of customer service is based on building a long-term relationship with returning customers, rather than the one-shot sale, and is very similar to reciprocal altruism. I've been told about people bringing in pairs of shoes that were years old, in poor shape, and definitely not from Nordstrom. They approached the sales desk and demanded a refund for the shoes they no longer cared for. They got what they asked for. Nordstrom refunds items at any time purchased from any Nordstrom store. And sometimes even from a competitor.

I can think of two examples of creative cooperative behaviour here in Canada, both in British Columbia, where I raised my family.

Train companies that operate in British Columbia cooperate. When I was working as an environmental consultant there some years ago, I consulted for several railway companies on environmental projects regulated by the provincial government. The companies (some national and others local) had banded together to better deal with issues that affected them all. They had entered a mutualistic, cooperative relationship, creating a kind of reciprocal altruism. Because all companies were present, meetings had a synergy in effectiveness and efficiency for both government and the rail companies. On one day, a company would share its experiences and help another; on another day I saw that reciprocated.

The second example is Vancouver's artisanal craft beer industry. I recently had a discussion on Skype with my son in Vancouver, who revealed that meeting socially in the tasting rooms of microbreweries with a growler-in-hand (it doesn't matter from which brewery—they honour each other) was the rage with hipsters, cyclists, business entrepreneurs and artists alike. Since 2013, twenty-seven new microbreweries had opened in the lower mainland with another dozen or more scheduled to open by mid-2015. Integrating itself into community life, each artisanal brewery exhibits confident niche partitioning through its unique nuances within a diverse and cooperative community of specialists. Confident, and operating sustainably within each other's "watershed" limits, the microbreweries celebrate both their individuality and the wholeness of their diverse community.

In my own writing community, perhaps the best example of mature K-selection is the maverick behaviour of colleague and fellow Canadian writer Cory Doctorow. He is renowned for his non-competitive strategy and for embracing the creative commons. Some thought this practice suicidal to his career and money-making potential. The opposite happened. "Not only does making my books available for free increase the number of sales that I get, but I also came to understand it artistically as a Science Fiction writer that if I was making work that wasn't intended to be copied, then I was really making contemporary work,"[24] said Doctorow in an interview with Greg Grossmeier, community development intern at Creative Commons. His rationale was based on the evolving role and power of copyright and its effect on the future freedoms of personal expression. "I believe that we live in an era where anything that can be expressed as bits will be," adds Doctorow. "I believe that bits exist to be copied. Therefore, I believe that any business-model that depends on your bits not being copied is just dumb, and that lawmakers who try to prop these up are like governments that sink fortunes into protecting people who insist on living on the sides of active volcanoes."

Photo 9.7: Whistler Mountain during the winter, British Columbia, Canada.

Photo by Nina Munteanu

Interspecies Cooperation & the Journey Home

Examples of interspecies cooperation, mutualism and altruism abound in Nature. (1) In Africa birds called ox-peckers perch on the backs of large animals, such as giraffes and cattle, and remove insects. The ox-peckers also warn of approaching danger through their cries and disturbed flight. (2) Defenceless fish live unharmed amid the stinging tentacles of jellyfish, and birds such as the wheatear may nest in rabbit burrows. (3) Many flowering plants are pollinated by insects, flitting from flower to flower for their nectar. Some flowers are shaped to suit a particular insect. (4) Seeds are distributed by animals. Birds eat fleshy seeds and transport them. The burrs on plants such as burdock have hooks that may catch on to fur and feathers. While these latter examples are not examples of altruism, *per se*, they exemplify the cooperative nature that is the hallmark of co-evolution.

Perhaps, one of the best examples of *interspecies cooperation* (or mutualism) is the bottlenose dolphin. In 2008, Aubrey Manning (Emeritus Professor of Natural History at Edinburgh University) writes in the Daily Mail of a female dolphin who selflessly saved a beached mother whale and her calf off Mahia Beach in New Zealand.[25]

Bottlenose dolphins off Laguna in Brazil have developed a cooperative relationship with the local fishermen. "Through highly synchronized behavior with humans, cooperative dolphins in Laguna drive mullet schools towards a line of fishermen and 'signal,' via stereotyped head slaps or tail slaps, when and where fishermen should throw their nets,"[26] writes lead author Fabio Daura-Jorge of the Federal University of Santa Catarina. The cooperation is helpful to both parties, he said. About 200 local artisanal fishermen are almost entirely reliant on the dolphins for catching their fish, according to Daura-Jorge.[26] The fishermen only fish with the assistance of cooperative dolphins, who are recognized and named.

Researchers found that one local group of about 20 dolphins works with the fishermen, while other local dolphins don't cooperate, finding other sources of food. The Daura-Jorge study found that the most helpful ones are also particularly cooperative and social with each other. Cooperative behaviour is passed down from mother dolphin to her calves through social learning, which is also how the trait is passed down by the fishermen: elders in the community teach the younger fishermen how to work with the dolphins.

The Journey Steps

Ultimately, the hero's journey is the Soul's search for Home—for wholeness. The hero (or Soul) must first separate through dualism in order to transform, then return to define its intrinsic truth in Unity.

Below I list twelve steps of water's and humanity's three-act Hero's Journey, adapted from Joseph Campbell:[9]

Act One: Separation
- The Ordinary World
- Call to Adventure & The Quest
- Refusal of the Call
- Meeting with the Mentor
- Crossing the Threshold

Act Two: Initiation & Transformation
- Tests, Allies & Enemies
- Approach to the Innermost Cave
- Ordeal (Abyss)
- Reward / Seizing the Sword (transformation and revelation)

Act Three: Return
- Road Block
- Resurrection / Atonement
- Return with Elixir

Act One—Separation

Act One of our story begins some 20,000 to 10,000 years ago, when agriculture was adopted by early civilizations in the Fertile Crescent in response to the latest of Earth's cycling ice ages.

It all starts with ice.

Ice on the planet has waxed and waned for millennia as small changes in the Earth's orbit influenced the amount of heat falling on different parts of the Earth's surface. Serbian scientist Milutin Milankovitch posited in the 1930s that three of Earth's orbital characteristics influence the planet's climate and associated glacial–interglacial ages. These included the tilt in the Earth's axis, the way the Earth wobbles on its axis and how close the Earth gets to the sun. Together, these rhythms, known as the Milankovitch cycles, induce an ice age every 22,000, 41,000 and 100,000 years.[27] During each of the past interglacial periods, the temperature steadily declined over a period of time. In our current interglacial period, the temperature should have begun to fall from its peak 7,000 years ago, and we should now be heading into a new ice age. That obviously hasn't happened. Geologist Iain Stewart boldly suggests that farming—which started around 11,000 years ago in the Fertile Crescent and spread across Europe and Asia by 7,000 years ago—may have prevented the next ice age.[7]

Photo 9.8: Tantalus Range in British Columbia, Canada.

Photo by Kevin Klassen

Twelve thousand years ago, when the planet's northern hemisphere was mostly covered by a vast ice sheet that "sucked" moisture from the planet, the Middle East's Fertile Crescent experienced a centuries-long drought. Climate change encouraged the hunting/gathering Natufians to embrace a different strategy to feed themselves: agriculture. By deciding not to chase food but to stay put and plant crops close to water, the Natufians ushered in the agricultural revolution—and with it, a change in our relationship with water. Rivers, our most reliable sources of water, became the magnets of major civilizations.

Stewart and other scientists posit that activities associated with agriculture interfered with the natural ice rhythms and kept the temperatures from falling, 7,000 years ago. "Fires were used to clear the forest for farmland, which increased the amount of carbon dioxide in the atmosphere,"[7] says Stewart. "We domesticated wild animals, which produced a lot of methane." Both carbon dioxide and methane are powerful greenhouse gases, capable of absorbing infrared radiation and trapping heat in the atmosphere. "Levels of carbon dioxide and methane are higher now than in the last 15 million years,"[7] Stewart adds.

The Ordinary World

"Water," writes Brian Fagan, "is one of the few cultural universals, inspiring a profound mingling of ritual and day-to-day use."[8] Beliefs and rituals with water underlie most stages of human life, from Christian baptism at birth to Hindu purification at death.

"The ancient Egyptians and the Maya believed that their worlds began in the still waters of the primordium," Fagan writes. "Bronze Age farmers on the shores of the North Sea three thousand years ago thought that their ancestors dwelled beneath the heaving waters of the ocean—the realm of the dead."[8]

Water was considered sacred by many cultures. The Egyptian sun god Ra cleansed himself in the sky-ocean before each day-excursion. Holy washings prevailed in many cultures, such as the Aztecs (and still do in many today, such as the Chinese and the Japanese). During ancient times we were divinely connected with Nature and water represented an important and powerful archetype; it was a time when we acknowledged water's power and life-giving agency. Water was not only revered as holy, with sacred wells and watercourses considered shrines and symbols of purification, but it represented creation and the matrix of life itself. Some ancient cultures considered springs to be inhabited

by water nymphs or other deities. Pagan rituals continued for centuries and were reflected in major pilgrimages to sacred water sites for curatives and general wellness. Historian Mircea Eliade writes that, "... water symbolizes the whole of potentiality; it is *fons et origo*, the source of all possible existence."[28] I talk more about this in Chapter 10, *Water Is Prayer*.

Physicist and environmental activist Vandana Shiva tells us that every river in India is sacred.[29] According to Hindu mythology the Ganges River originates in the heavens and is considered a sacred bridge to the divine. The Ganges is a place for crossing from one place to another. The Kumbh Mela is a great festival, centred on the Ganges, and celebrates creation. Hindus cast the ashes of their ancestors in the river to ensure their transition to the heavens. The Ganges, like many of the sacred rivers in India, is worshipped as a goddess and believed to cleanse and wash away spiritual and material impurities. According to Shiva, the Ganges "is saturated with antiseptic minerals that kill bacteria. Modern bacteriological research has confirmed that cholera germs die in Ganges water."[29]

The philosophy of *panpsychism*—that consciousness, mind and soul are universal features of all things—formed the ancient beliefs of Shinto, Taoist, Buddhist, Hindu, and Pagan religions. Advocated by philosophers such as Thales, Plato, and Spinoza, this belief reflects the Neoplatonic concept of the *anima mundi* or "World Soul." According to Plato, all things participate in the form of Being, which contains a psychic aspect of mind and soul.[30]

In the 17th century, philosopher Baruch Spinoza responded to Descartes' dualist theory of body and spirit as separate, with his book *Ethics*, which espoused a monist view that the two are the same. Spinoza advocated pantheism, an ancient belief that the Universe (or Nature) is identical with divinity and that everything composes an all-encompassing immanent God.[31] Ancient Hindu scriptures contained pantheistic concepts, such as "the unity of the world," in that the *Atman* (true self or human soul) is in fact indistinct from *Brahman* (the "unknown reality of everything").[32] Zhuangzi Zhou, a leading Taoist thinker in 4th century BC, described pantheistic thought this way: "Heaven and I were created together, and all things and I are one." According to Zhuangzi, "there is nowhere where [Tao] is not … there is not a single thing without Tao."[33]

Call to Adventure & The Quest

Around 5,500 BCE the Sahara began to dry. In response to the "call to adventure" by the herald of climate change, irrigation agriculture became well established by 4500 BCE in southern Mesopotamia and Egypt. By 3800 BCE, Southern Mesopotamia had become much drier. The rains failed and the rivers shrank and lakes dried. According to Fagan, climate change-induced shifts in monsoon patterns forced these growing societies to adopt more aggressive water management. "Summer no longer brought welcome rain to Mesopotamian farmers. Every village now relied more heavily on spring floods for irrigation water," writes Fagan.[8] Villagers, accustomed to a certain comfortable and familiar pattern found themselves changing the rules of engagement, and they subtly ushered in the first step toward commodification. Instead of moving with the rhythms of Nature, humanity now imposed its own rigid patterns, moulding Nature to our values and needs. With the perceived need to exploit came the real need to control and harness Nature and water.

Photo 9.9: A dory shop on the maritime shore of Lunenburg, Nova Scotia, Canada.

Photo by Nina Munteanu

Refusal of the Call

In some parts of the world, humanity remained self-limiting and in tune with Nature's rhythms and the water cycle.

Riane Eisler, author of *The Chalice & the Blade*, writes of the ancient Bronze Age culture of Minoan (later Minoan–Mycenean) Crete (1,000 to 1,500 BCE), which still revered the Goddess and lived a *gylanic life-model* (a social system based on equality of men and women in social and government practice).[34] Citing Nicolas Platon, an archaeologist who had excavated the island for over fifty years, Eisler writes of a society in which "the whole of life was pervaded by an ardent faith in the goddess Nature, the source of all creation and harmony."[34]

"In [ancient] Crete," writes Eisler, "for the last time in recorded history, a spirit of harmony between women and men as joyful and equal participants in life appears to pervade [in] a tradition that is unique in its 'delight in beauty, grace, and movement' and in its 'enjoyment of life and closeness to nature.'"[34] Despite the fact that they were surrounded by threats from an increasingly warlike and male-dominated world, Cretans remained an "exceptionally peace-loving people" and their art—which extoled the symbols of Nature, such as the serpent and butterfly, both symbols of transformation, rebirth and wisdom—did not idealize warfare. Cretans maintained "an ardent faith in the goddess Nature," writes Eisler. "This led to a love of peace, a horror of tyranny, and a respect for the law. Even among the ruling classes, personal ambition seems to have been unknown; nowhere do we find the name of an author attached to a work of art or a record of the deeds of a ruler."[34]

Cretan art reflected a society in which power was not equated with dominance, destruction and oppression. I think it is no coincidence that gender equality and harmony is linked to the pantheistic value of nature. The appreciation of beauty, grace and harmony is a "feminine" characteristic, one that ambitious warlike and highly competitive exploitive societies have no time to cultivate. Eisler notes that "a recognition of our oneness with all of nature" lay at the heart of both the Neolithic and Cretan worship of the Goddess.

In today's time, the Khasi people of Cherrapunji, in Megahalya, India—possibly the wettest place on Earth—have adapted to the rhythms of extreme abundance and scarcity in a monsoon ecosystem. The wet monsoon, bringing in over 1,000 mm of rain in a monsoon month, lasts only three months in the summer, averaging 12,000 mm of rain in a year. The rest of the year, the area faces drought. The people have adapted by using ground water during times of drought and living within the limits provided by their environment.

An example of their sustainable lifestyle with Nature is the living root bridges that the Cherrapunji have trained over the many criss-crossing swift-flowing rivers and streams of the Khasi Hills. The roots of the rubber tree (*Ficus elastica*) can run over a hundred feet long. They are very strong and actually gain strength as they age and grow, becoming fully functional as bridges in ten to fifteen years. Some ancient root bridges used daily by the people of the Cherrapunji villages may be well over 500 years old.

The First Nations people of North America continue to maintain a connected existence with Nature, recognizing and embracing Nature as a spirit and guide in their lives. The First Nations, Inuit and Métis people consider the natural world "home;" connecting with the Earth as their Mother and taking a position of respect, stewardship and gratitude.[35] Indigenous peoples consider themselves caretakers of "Mother Earth" and respect her gifts of water, air and fire. Over millennia, writes June Kaminsky, scholar of First Nations pedagogy, the First Nations and Inuit people developed intricate knowledge and understanding of the natural world. "First Nations and Inuit people see their relationship with each other and with the Earth as an interconnected web of life, which manifests as a complex ecosystem of relationships. Balance and holistic harmony are essential tenets of this knowledge and subsequent cultural practices. Embedded too is a keen belief in both adaptability and change, but change that further promotes balance and harmony, not change that creates distress, death, and the depletion of the Earth's populations and resources."[35]

Another North American example of a society living sustainably within the carrying capacity of its watershed is the town of Bolinas,

California, whose citizens have vowed to live sustainably within the carrying capacity of their watershed by stopping housing development when their limits were reached.[36]

Meeting the Mentor & Crossing the Threshold

New dialectics and philosophies emerged to fulfill a rising sense of "self," independent and separate from the Unity—and perceived shackles—of Nature. Patriarchal mentors were discovered and adopted by largely androcratic (male-ruled) societies whose mandate of jingoistic expansionism rejected cooperative pantheism for a more aggressive "Nature conquering" approach. In order to succeed in its perceived independence, humanity needed to separate from the "Unity" and cross the threshold into another world, "the special world" where different rules operated.

"Our struggle [and mandate] to control [water] has been behind the rise and fall of some of the greatest civilizations on Earth,"[7] says geologist Iain Stewart in the BBC documentary *How the Earth Changed History: Water*. Some societies successfully adapted to water's rhythms; others, like the ancient Khmer Empire of Angkor (Cambodia), epitomize societies that "conquered" water's rhythms to suit their needs and hubristic growth. The Khmer had adopted a dialectic and philosophy of duality and separation from Nature.

The Khmer dug reservoirs and an underground irrigation system to store water from the monsoon rains throughout the drought season. The water system spanned over 1200 square kilometres and connected the natural lake (Tonle Sap) to artificial reservoirs (*barays*) via a series of canals. In the 12th century, the Khmer built the "temple-mountain" Angkor Wat as a spiritual home for the Hindu god Vishnu.

Angkor flourished for six centuries and, undoubtedly as a result of the water-harnessing ingenuity of the Khmer, became the largest pre-industrial city in the world. However, the impact of water management to sustain a growing population, along with deforestation practices and other watershed alterations, eventually led to erosion that choked the system with sediment and rendered it unmanageable. By the 15th century, Angkor collapsed—a victim of its own success.

Scholars have speculated that the downfall of this elaborate water system and the commerce it generated led to the end of Angkor. While climate played a part, environmental issues caused by the Khmer themselves finally brought down the empire. By the 15th century, Angkor had outstripped its resources and tipped the movement of power toward Phnom Penh. Somehow, in their success, the Khmer empire had crossed the threshold from healthy adaptation to unsustainable expansionism. They achieved the fate of all great civilizations whose mandate is to grow unsustainably and conquer Nature—collapse.

"Instead of adapting our development to the available water supply of a region, we choose to force the water supply to 'adapt' to our desired locations,"[36] Malcolm McDowell tells us in the 2008 water documentary *Blue Gold*. For example, Mexico City is literally running out of water. Two-thirds of the capital's water use comes from groundwater, and for decades the city has been sinking as underground water pockets fill with air instead of water. Because the city sits on porous, spongy subsoil, the continuous water usage is sinking the city at a rate of 50 centimetres per year, write Maude Barlow and Tony Clarke in *Blue Gold*.[37]

Mexico City's reservoirs rank among the most contaminated supplies of any world capital. One in three homes have no access to running water. Recently, Barlow reported that the people of San Bartolo Ameyalco, Mexico, clashed with police in resisting a diversion of their volcanic natural spring well to satisfy the thirst of Mexico City's higher taxpaying population.[38]

"Conflicts over water are taking place all over the world," Iain Stewart tells us. "Israel and the Palestinians dispute access to the River Jordan; Egypt, Sudan, and Ethiopia quarrel over the waters of the Nile.

On the Indus River, India and Pakistan are in conflict over dams built over the river's tributaries."[7] We've constructed over fifty thousand dams on the planet, Helen Sarakinos, Dams Programs Manager of River Alliance of Wisconsin, informs us.[39]

I remember watching Roman Polanski's film *Chinatown* in 1974 and being struck by the premise and theme: the willingness of politicians and developers to murder for the right to bring water to the American southwest. The film drew inspiration from real life. In early twentieth-century California, Water Wars ensued when most of the water was surreptitiously siphoned off the Owens River to provide unlimited water to the Los Angeles basin. Owens valley farmers dynamited the aqueducts that took their water to Los Angeles, prompting the city to send in guards with guns to guard its infrastructure.[40]

Figure 9.10: Venice, Italy.

Photo by Nina Munteanu

Act Two—Initiation & Transformation

Mesopotamia's unchecked population growth responded to climate change with more aggressive water management. According to Fagan, "... an army of officials now supervised canal maintenance and harvests ... Inevitably, the scale of irrigation works grew and grew, with the Assyrians [from ~2500–600 BCE] and their small armies of prisoners of war, and with the Sassanians [Neo-Persian Empire: 224–651 AD] after them, who, like the Chinese emperors, transformed entire landscapes, sometimes with devastating ecological consequences ... Mesopotamia later became a salt-ridden wilderness after the Sassanians took up five times more land under irrigation than ever before in an insatiable quest for tax revenue and wealth. The result was promiscuous water usage and the ecological devastation of thousands of acres ... Viewed in retrospect, such failed projects offer a sobering example of what happens to cities, farmers, landscapes, and indeed entire societies when sustainability evaporates."[8]

Humanity had entered the Age of Commodification.

Commodification: "the process whereby goods and services which were formerly used for subsistence purposes are bought and sold in the market; within Marxist theory, this refers to the production of commodities for exchange (via the market) as opposed to direct use by the producer. It signals the conversion of use-values into exchange-values."

—*Encyclopedia.com*

While water harnessing associated with the agricultural revolution permitted humanity to flourish and expand, the Industrial Revolution truly birthed the age of commodification. Commodification—of land, water and even people—lay at the heart of a monumental paradigm shift that would irrevocably change the way we view and treat ourselves and our world. The Industrial Revolution of the mid 1700s to late 1800s—itself a function of a shifting philosophical hegemony during the Age of Enlightenment and the Scientific Revolution—precipitated the world's second increase in economic productivity. (The first, some 15,000 to 20,000 years before, during the Neolithic agricultural revolution, occurred when small communities abandoned their nomadic lifestyle to adopt animal husbandry and agriculture.) Development of steam power, turbine pumps, and the harnessing of fossil fuels (coal, oil and natural gas) helped to shift our capacity for productivity, particularly in agriculture and the resource industry. *Prior to industrialization*, communities relied on wave and wind power and solar energy for the production of food and goods. *Post-industrialization*, even the definition of productivity had changed.

Industrialization ultimately shifted our definition of ourselves. New dialectics and ideologies emerged to suit the changes in our worldview. It gave birth to urbanization and materialism, free-market capitalism, socialism and Marxism, utilitarianism and consumerism. The Industrial Revolution altered medicine and living standards. It contributed to and was in turn affected by a population explosion through increased longevity and more successful births.

Photo 9.11: Male mockingbird on a tree, Ontario, Canada.

Photo by Merridy Cox

A natural expansion of industrialized nations followed, accompanied by massive diversions, dam-building and aggressive mining of surface and groundwater. Over sixty percent of the world's wetlands (Nature's best water filtration system) have been destroyed over the past hundred years; with this, alongside freshwater depletion and pollution, humanity is currently mining groundwater faster than it can recharge.[36,37] Archaeologists studying the ancient city of Ubar (of the fabled Atlantis of the sands), in Southern Oman (Arabia), discovered that that city had sunk into the desert sands from groundwater pumping. Current examples of unsustainable and detrimental groundwater

Moving Waters

*From distant springs small
brooks emerge
fresh waters play, drink rain and
swell, connect in streams
tributaries join to make a river
in quiet flow and questing flight
a life.*

*Your river lives in all its streams
components, colours,
temperatures
blended, but not uniform
one flood of many waters.*

*My river is from different springs
as complex as yours
as interwoven yet inseparable
one stream's water from
another's
as calm where wide and flat, as
turbulent in willful flood
but in its own path.*

*Our rivers meet
they clash and turmoil, strands
mix but repel
too much from upstream, too
many parts, the parts are wrong
I am not yours to absorb, you
will not yield to my flow*

mining with devastating effects, such as sinkholes or entire watershed collapse, include Winter Park, Florida; San Joaquin Valley, California; and Mexico City, Mexico. "We now pump approximately 30 billion gallons of groundwater every day,"[38] says Robert Glennon, author of *Water Follies*. From the ingenious aqueducts of the Romans to the massive pipe-diversions of Mexico City or Los Angeles, humanity has found ways to divert massive amounts of water out of a given watershed. The Aral Sea, once half the size of England in the former Soviet Union, has dramatically reduced its volume by more than sixty percent over sixty years of intensive irrigation of the surrounding desert to grow crops. Satellite images taken by NASA in August 2014 revealed that, for the first time in modern history, the eastern basin of the Aral Sea had completely dried up.[41] The eastern basin is now called the Aralkum Desert.

Eric McLamb of the Ecology Global Network, writes that, "The Industrial Revolution marked a major turning point in Earth's ecology and humans' relationship with their environment."[42] We've witnessed devastating impacts to our environment as direct results of the Industrial Revolution: from Punch's first cartoon depicting a polluted Thames in 1858 to the Great London Smog of December 1952 (a hundred years later but just sixty-three years ago) that killed some 4,000 people.

Increased extraction of natural resources, land use, and waste generation has followed our increasing population. By the time Rachel Carson wrote *Silent Spring* in 1962, terms like "sustainable production" and "sustainable development" were being debated among ecologists, economists and social scientists. California suffers multi-year droughts and a greatly diminished water supply. Yet, users maintain a myopic air of entitlement without knowledge or consideration of sustainability. Farmers, for instance, continue to demand full allocations of irrigation water at heavily subsidized prices, illustrating how little people truly understand the functionality and ecological value—and limited sustainability—of their watershed.

Maude Barlow, Chairperson of the Council of Canadians, suggests that the latest step to global water commodification emerged in the 1980s. That was the era of Margaret Thatcher's water privatization in Great Britain, of a growing multi-nationalization of bottled water companies, and of the United Nation's growing view of water as a commodity. This commodification culminated in the Dublin Statement on Water and Sustainable Development on January 31, 1992, in which water was defined as an "economic good."[36,37]

The essential philosophy behind the idea of exploitation and commodification of Nature generally and water specifically is a worldview of separateness. It is a view that incorporates what we in the science fiction genre refer to as "the other." Nature is the alien. The unknown. The monster to be harnessed, controlled and exploited.

"When we see water, minerals, trees and so on as something less than sacred, as not having the qualities of self, then there is no alternative but to treat them in a utilitarian mode (i.e., to 'develop' them). The mindset of development is inherent to the way we see the world. Unless the narratives of ascent and separation change, any variant of development that we offer is unlikely to bear results much different from what we have seen already,"[43] concluded Charles Eisenstein, social philosopher and author of *The Ascent of Humanity*.

Tests, Allies, Enemies

Some philosophers and historians suggest that the Industrial Revolution was not the beginning, but the culmination of a shifting hegemony, spearheaded by the *Scientific Revolution*, which began in the late 1500s (with the Copernican revolution) and spread to the early 1800s. Under this emerging worldview of the *Age of Reason* (1650s to 1780s), Nature—and the Universe—wase viewed dispassionately as a mechanized entity to be studied objectively: dissected into its component

we are not one, my heat is cold
to you.

But finally, one day
my blue reflects your green,
your green takes on my hue
my warmth becomes your heat
and so we join, and move
together
integrated though not uniform
one river of our blended waters.

After the delta will be the end,
the silent end
no longer us nor any thing,
the cosmic all and nothing.

But before that, love, before!
we gently spread through mead-
ows, slow and tranquil
embracing love as flowers
we rage through canyons:
rough-walled, harsh, confining
that cannot hold us
our power together surges in
torrents
shouting love as passion
unheeding, headlong, explosive
— then calm again.

One river of all waters, we thrive
we shape the earth, we nurture,

we destroy
we are wild nature, alive and
free and primal
sweeping to the delta
to the end.

Published in Canadian Voices, Vol. 1 (Bookland Press, 2009) and The Courtneypark Connection 2013 (In Our Words Inc.)

parts to tease out the mysteries of "nature under constraint and vexed"[44] because "the nature of things betrays itself more readily under the vexations of art than in its natural freedom."[44]

Cultural historian Richard Tarnas in *The Passion of the Western Mind* traces a major paradigm shift in the western worldview from Copernicus' radical displacement of the human being with his model of the Universe and included the epistemologies of Kepler, Galileo and Newton, who described the Universe as a divine machine. This shift in cosmological perspective was expressed intellectually in Descartes' Cartesian premise, leading to the empiricisms of Locke, Berkeley and Hume and culminating in the epistemological crisis expressed by Kant.[45]

According to Alick Bartholomew, author of *The Spiritual Life of Water*, "the Enlightenment was a triumph of reason over authority and superstition. It brought about an immense advance in knowledge and developed the modern subjects of physics, chemistry, geology, and astronomy. It also helped sever our ties to the natural world and put an end to any pretence of being subservient to Nature." This inevitably led to a bias toward a more mechanistic worldview and a distrust of non-rational ways of knowing.[46]

"The new mentality and the new perception of the cosmos gave our Western civilization the features that are characteristic of the modern era,"[47] writes Fritjof Capra, author of *The Turning Point*. "They became the basis of the paradigm that has dominated our culture for the past 300 years and is now about to change."[47] Capra adds, "The man who realized the Cartesian dream and completed the scientific revolution was Isaac Newton, born in England in 1642, the year of Galileo's death. Newton developed a complete mathematical formulation of the mechanistic view of nature, and thus accomplished a great synthesis of the work of Copernicus and Keppler, Bacon, Galileo, and Descartes. Newtonian physics, the crowning achievement of the 17th-century science, provided a consistent mathematical theory of the world that remained the solid foundation of scientific thought well into the 20th

century."[47] Newtonian physics effectively secularized Nature and solidified the Cartesian division between spirit and matter.

Writer and professor of environmental history and ethics at UC Berkley Carolyn Merchant challenged the hegemony of mechanistic science as a marker of progress in her 1980 book *The Death of Nature: Women, Ecology, and the Scientific Revolution*.[48] Merchant implicated seventeenth-century science in the ecological crisis, the domination of Nature, and the devaluation of women. According to Merchant, scientists of the 1600s used metaphor, rhetoric, and myth to develop a new method of interrogating Nature. Their goal "was to use constraint and force to extract truths from Nature [as] part of a larger project to create a new method that would allow humanity to control and dominate the natural world."[49]

Of Nature, Sir Francis Bacon wrote in 1620: "she is either free ... or driven out of her ordinary course by the perverseness, insolence and forwardness of matter and violence of impediments, ... or she is put in constraint, moulded and made as it were new by art and the hand of man; as in things artificial ... nature takes orders from man and works under his authority."[44]

Photo 9.12: Birch forest in southern Ontario, Canada.

In 1696 Leibniz wrote about "the art of inquiry into nature itself and of putting it on the rack—the art of experiment which Lord Bacon began so ably."[50] Four years later, Jean Baptiste du Hamel, secretary of the Paris Academy of Sciences, wrote, "We discover the mysteries of nature much more easily when she is tortured [*torqueatur*] by fire or some other aids of art than when she proceeds along her own road."[51] It is not by chance that the rhetoric these scientists used resembles that used during the medieval witch-hunts and interrogations of women suspected as witches possessed.

In contrast to Leibniz and Hamel, Johann Wolfgang von Goethe complained that under scientific investigation "nature falls silent on the rack." He urged that, "phenomena must once and for all be removed from their gloomy empirical–mechanical–dogmatic torture chamber."[52]

Photo by Merridy Cox

The clockwork Universe theory, popular among deists during the Age of Enlightenment, compares the Universe to a mechanical clock, a perfect machine, with gears governed by the immutable and predictable laws of physics. This concept reflects an earlier postulation by John of Sacrobosco in his medieval text *On the Sphere of the World* in which he described the Universe as the *machina mundi* (machine of the world). He suggested that the eclipse of the sun at the crucifixion of Jesus was a disturbance of the order of that machine.[53] Both René Descartes and Thomas Hobbes conceptualized the bodies of humans and other animals as machines. Descartes denied thought to animals, although he admitted that they have life and sensation.[54]

Approach to the Innermost Cave

Photo 9.13: Waves along the Credit River, Ontario, Canada.

Photo by Nina Munteanu

Mathematician René Descartes (1596–1650), considered by many as the father of "modern" philosophy, described an ambitious—if not a rather androcentric and soulless—Hero's Journey for humanity. In 1637, Descartes prescribed in *Discourse on Method* a highly practical philosophy whose precepts yielded "knowledge, which is very useful in life."[54] He proclaimed that his methods would help humanity discover the basic mechanical principles of natural phenomena and then, like skilled craftsmen, intervene and put those principles to work. Use of technology would "thereby render ourselves, as it were, lords and possessors of nature." In that hubristic statement lay a celebration of a glorious destiny of entitlement, led by the rational and doubting spirit of the scientific method. Whereas Aristotle's philosophy sprang from the light of wonder, Descartes' methods were solidly based in the dark recesses of doubt. Descartes resolved: *"to reject as if absolutely false anything as to which I could imagine the least doubt, in order to see if I should not be left at the end believing something that was absolutely indubitable ... One will no longer have occasion to admire anything about what is seen,"*[53] he ended, some three hundred years before Rachel Carson wrote her book *The Sense of Wonder* in 1965.

Humanity "progressed from hunting and gathering, to agriculture, to industry, and now to the Information Age: from the biological to the mechanical to the purely mental, from the natural world to a manufactured world to a virtual world,"[55] writes philosopher and writer Charles Eisenstein. The resolution of that story is our complete mastery of our Universe, in which "we will conquer disease with genetic engineering and nanotechnology. We will conquer space. We will engineer body parts, synthesize food, expand our minds with computer add-ons." We will transcend our humanity, become transhumans and eventually achieve post-human status; and, to quote Descartes again, "overcome the enfeeblement of old age."[54]

In 1993, science fiction writer Vernor Vinge wrote, "Within thirty years, we will have the technological means to create superhuman intelligence. Shortly after, the human era will be ended."[56] Vinge was referring to the *technological singularity*. The technological singularity hypothesizes that, with the exponential progress of technological advancements—known as the "law of accelerating returns"—artificial intelligence will eventually exceed human intellectual capacity and control. This will radically change or even end civilization (as we know it), in an event called the *singularity*.

First used by Hungarian mathematician and physicist John von Neumann in 1958, the singularity is predicted by futurist Ray Kurzweil to occur by 2045.[57] Kurzweil suggests in his book *The Age of Spiritual Machines* that we will see "far greater transformations in the first two decades of the twenty-first century than we saw in the entire twentieth century."[58] In his book *The Singularity is Near*, Kurzweil predicts the rise of clouds of *nanobots* (nano-robots called foglets) and the development of Human Body 2.0 and 3.0, complete with nanotechnological prosthetics.[57] Described by Forbes as "the ultimate thinking machine," Kurzweil suggests that, by 2099, most humans will be transhuman.

Those "left behind," who still use native carbon-based neurons and remain unenhanced by neural implants, he calls *MOSH* (an acronym for Mostly Original Substrate Humans). How eager we are to "shuffle off this mortal coil! To become immortal. But at what cost?

Jaron Lanier, pioneer in the field of virtual reality and a partner architect at Microsoft Research suggests that, "what we are seeing is a new religion, expressed through an engineering culture ... What all this comes down to is that the very idea of artificial intelligence gives us the cover to avoid accountability."[59] According to Eisenstein, this narrative, with a worldview embodied in science, "says that we are separate individuals in an objective universe that lacks the qualities of *self*. Composed of generic particles and impersonal forces, the Universe is alien, purposeless and dead. We associate progress with an escalating domination of Nature, because we deny the Universe's inherent creative energy, sacredness and purpose."[43]

Ordeal (Abyss)

The Abrahamic religions—Judaism, Christianity and Islam—tell a creation story that begins with an all-knowing and all-powerful God. God, the patriarch, created humanity in *His* image; separate from Nature and destined to be "the lords and possessors of Nature."[54]

"Nature," according to Bacon, "takes orders from man and works under *his* authority."[44]

According to many sacred texts, humanity appears destined more to conquer, overcome, harness, harvest, compete and cull; rather than coexist, cooperate, co-evolve and synergize. This glorious destiny of a humanity that embraces the selfish gene of competitive evolution is what gifted us with great advances in medicine, technology, science and social organization. However, this false sense of entitlement also gave us prejudice, racism, eugenics, environmental pollution, and world strife.

"The modern self is a discrete and separate subject in a universe that is other. It is the economic man of Adam Smith; it is the skin-encapsulated ego of Alan Watts; it is the embodied soul of religion; it is the selfish gene of [Richard Dawkins],"[55] writes Charles Eisenstein, in *Orion Magazine*. "When we exclude the world from the self," Eisenstein adds, "the tiny, lonely identity that remains ... seeks to grow and connect through acquisition, building a realm of 'me and mine' to compensate for its lost 'beingness'." As those around us embrace this same "separateness," competition and an underlying anxiety feed this self-definition. Eisenstein suggests that "the defining diseases of our time—autism, AIDS, multiple sclerosis, fibromyalgia, asthma, arthritis, diabetes—are in whole or in part autoimmune diseases, the somatization of our self/other confusion."[43]

"Our essential current need as a species is to reorganize around a new culture and new institutions grounded in living-system values and design principles that bring us into alignment with nature and Creation's divine purpose,"[60] writes David Korten, author of *A New Story for a New Economy: To Find Our Human Place in a Living Universe*.

I mentioned the major paradigm shift in the western world, which began with the Copernican revolution of astronomy and cosmology and Newton's *Principia* published in 1687, which described the Universe as a divine machine,[61] leading to the Kant's expression of an epistemological schism.[45] Tarnas describes this evolution of our modern epistemological crisis with the example of the "double-bind," first brought forward by anthropologist and naturalist Gregory Bateson in *Steps to an Ecology of Mind* to describe an emotionally distressing dilemma in communication.[62] The distress follows when one receives two or more conflicting messages, which negate each other; Tarnas applied this example to describe the estrangement of our modern consciousness, "a threefold, mutually enforced prison of modern alienation." According to Tarnas, "the world revealed by modern science has been a world devoid of spiritual purpose, opaque, ruled by chance and necessity, [and] without intrinsic meaning."[45]

Tarnas applied Bateson's diagnosis to the larger modern condition with the following inevitable result: "Either inner or outer realities tend to be distorted: inner feelings are repressed and denied, as in apathy and psychic numbing, or they are inflated in compensation, as in narcissism and ego-centrism; or the outer world is slavishly submitted to as the only reality, or it is aggressively objectified and exploited. There is also the strategy of flight, through various forms of escapism: compulsive economic consumption, absorption in the mass media, faddism, cults, ideologies, nationalistic fervor, alcoholism, drug addiction."[41] He adds that when avoidance mechanisms cannot be sustained, what follows is, "anxiety, paranoia, chronic hostility, a feeling of helpless victimization, a tendency to suspect all meanings, and impulse toward self-negation, a sense of purposelessness and absurdity, a feeling of irresolvable inner contradiction, [and] a fragmenting of consciousness."[45] Many of these states describe some of the major ailments affecting our modern society.

According to Tarnas, the scientific method "has required explanations of phenomena that are concretely predictive, and therefore impersonal, mechanistic, and structural. To fulfill their purposes, these explanations of the universe have been systematically 'cleansed' of all spiritual and human qualities." Tarnas quotes Ernest Gellner, when he writes, "It was Kant's merit to see that this compulsion [for mechanistic impersonal explanations] is in us, not in things," and "it was Weber's to see that it is historically a specific kind of mind, not human mind as such, that is subject to this compulsion."[45]

In the nineteenth century Nietzsche told us that there are no facts, only interpretations. The premise behind this is that an unconscious part of the psyche exerts a decisive influence over our perception, cognition and behaviour—a notion that had been developing in Western thought for some time already. Essentially following Descartes and the post-Cartesian British empiricists, Freud (leaning on Darwinian precepts) recognized that the apparent reality of the objective world was unconsciously determined by the condition of the subject.

Photo 9.14: Small cascade in the Credit River, Ontario, Canada.

Photo by Nina Munteanu

Jung grasped what Freud could not. Perhaps because he was "more epistemologically sophisticated than Freud," suggests Tarnas; but also because he was less bound by nineteenth-century scientism (aka Darwinism), Jung discovered the full range of critical philosophical consequences offered by *depth psychology*. This led Jung to the discovery of universal archetypes. Where Freud had explored repressed thoughts and feelings in archetypal terms such as the *Id*, the *Superego*, *Eros* and *Thanatos*; Jung explored a richer multi-depth of archetypes representing the "primordial foundation of the psyche itself."[45] Jung's archetypes eventually evolved beyond the subject–object dichotomy, achieving something more like Platonic and Neoplatonic symbology.

In the 1980s, Stanislav Grof's psychoanalytic therapy in Europe and California, in which subjects reported profound experiences associated with birth trauma, strongly reflects Joseph Campbell's *Hero's Journey* stages of (1) *separation*, (2) *transformation*, and (3) *return*.

Grof's subjects reported moving: from (1) an initial condition of undifferentiated Unity with the maternal womb (*the ordinary world*); to a sudden fall and *separation* from that primal organismic Unity (*call to adventure*); to (2) a highly charged life-and-death struggle (*transformation*) accompanied by intense separation, duality and alienation; culminating in complete annihilation (*the abyss*); then followed immediately by (3) a sudden unexpected global liberation (*return*), both physical and spiritual, that overcame and fulfilled the intervening alienated state and restored the initial Unity, but on a new level that preserved the achievement of the whole trajectory.[45]

Tarnas writes that subjects who underwent the therapy commonly reported "experiencing a dramatic expansion of horizons, a radical change of perspective as to the nature of reality, a sense of sudden awakening, a feeling of being fundamentally reconnected to the universe, all accompanied by a profound sense of psychological healing and spiritual liberation."[45] These experiences were often accompanied by "memories" associated with "archetypal experiences of paradise, mystical union with nature or with the divine or with the Great Mother Goddess, dissolution of the ego in ecstatic unity with the universe, absorption in the transcendent One."[45] Tarnas notes that this archetypal dialectic was often experienced simultaneously on both an individual level and a collective level (humanity and Nature or personal and transpersonal).

"The story of ascent, the story of separation, and all the institutions built upon them are in a state of crisis,"[43] Eisenstein tells us. He adds that, "As the crisis intensifies, the core of the dominant culture will have an increasing need for new stories. These, we will discover, are not really new at all, but have been waiting for us in the corners of the world."

Seizing the Sword

Tarnas posits that the evolution of the Western mind has been driven by a "heroic impulse to forge an autonomous rational human self—a transforming self—by separating it from the primordial Unity with Nature."[45] Tarnas suggests that it began four millennia ago, with the great patriarchal nomadic conquests in the Mediterranean. These conquests embraced "the repression of undifferentiated unitary consciousness and the *participation mystique* with nature; a denial of the *anima mundi*, of the soul of the world, of the community of being, of the all-pervading, of mystery and ambiguity, of imagination, emotion, instinct, body, nature, woman."[45]

This "heroic impulse" to leave "the fold" on adventure was reflected in the rejection of pre-Hellenic matrifocal mythologies in favour of rationalist philosophy; the Judaeo-Christian denial of the Great Mother Goddess; and Enlightenment's objectivist science in modern Europe that extolled the self-aware ego separate from an alienated Nature.

Of course, all separation stirs a yearning for reunion. And a return.

Act Three — Return

In the opening of my 2012 historical fantasy, *The Last Summoner*, the main character—Lady Vivianne Schoen, the Baroness of Grunwald—dreams of rescue by a shining knight from her terrible fate of marriage to a stranger, a misogynist and brutal mercenary in her father's guard. She learns that there is no knight coming to rescue her; that ultimately she must be that knight. That she is that knight … that her dream and vision of that knight was really of herself.[63]

We have sold ourselves on the story that science—like the ultimate reality show—tells us the best story, because it tells the truth as "story" never could. But the story science has been telling us for several hundreds of years was and still is based on the assumption of a reality independent of humans and our interference: a material universe constructed of parts to be objectively and independently examined to study a whole. A universe that we could study without actually being part of it.

Quantum physics changed all that. Physicists discovered that the universe is made of energy waves and every moment of our human reality is a wave function collapsed from probability by a conscious observer (see my discussion of Schrödinger's cat and quantum entanglement in the author's *Preface*). This means that our world is a product of our consciousness. Realities aren't fixed but ever-changing creations we bring forth, both individually and collectively through our beliefs and actions. It's more like a storytelling universe that we iteratively express rather than a stable physical entity in which we grope our way through. "The universe looks more and more like a great thought rather than a great machine,"[64] says British physicist James Jeans.

"The new view, revealing a conscious Universe and a living Earth in which we are co-creators, takes us out of fatalistic victimhood to becoming consciously active agents of our destiny. It lifts the fog of

"We may be seeing the beginnings of the reintegration of our culture, a new possibility of the unity of consciousness. If so, it will not be on the basis of any new orthodoxy, either religious or scientific … It will recognize that in both scientific and religious culture all we have finally are symbols, but that there is an enormous difference between the dead letter and the living word."

—Robert Bellah, Beyond Belief

our self-image as consumers of stuff, giving us awesome rights and responsibilities to live out our full co-creative humanity,"[2] writes Elisabet Sahtouris.

"Our rigid, narrow self/other distinction is coming to an end, victim of its own premise," writes Eisenstein. "The separate self can be maintained only temporarily, and at great cost. We have maintained it a long time, and built a civilization upon it that seeks the conquest of nature and human nature. The present convergence of crises has laid bare the futility of that goal. It portends the end of civilization as we know it, and the instauration of a new state of human beingness defined by a more fluid, more inclusive sense of self. This convergence of crises is a birth crisis, propelling us from an old world, an old self, into a new … When we recognize that nature is itself dynamic, creative and alive, then we need no longer transcend it, but participate in it more fully."[43]

According to Tarnas, this is already occurring in the tremendous emergence of the feminine in our culture, in the widespread acceptance of feminine values by both men and women: in the increasing sense of Unity with the planet and Nature and our growing sense of participation and belonging: "Jung prophesied that an epochal shift would take place in the contemporary psyche; a shift that would reconcile the two great polarities, engender a union of opposites (a *hieros gamos* or sacred marriage) between the long-dominant but now alienated masculine and the long-suppressed but now ascending feminine."[45]

During the same time that Darwin was writing his *Origin of Species*, several 19th century writers and philosophers were embracing pantheism. Writers and philosophers such as William Wordsworth, Johann Gottlieb Fichte and Georg Wilhelm Friedrich Hegel, Walt Whitman, Ralph Waldo Emerson and Henry David Thoreau believed and wrote about a Universe of participation and a Nature that includes humanity.

Road Block

"The Western environmentalist might admire the sustainable water use practices of a traditional villager and wish they be preserved, but is likely to see the ceremonies around water as a kind of superfluous add-on to concrete conservation practices,"[43] Eisenstein writes. "He might oppose the privatization of water, the drawdown of aquifers for industrial purposes, the pollution of rivers and lakes. But does he go so far as to say, 'We must do these things because water is a living, sacred being that must be respected?' Or does the instrumental reason come first, the utilitarian concern about what will happen [to us] if we waste and pollute water?"

When James Lovelock and Lynn Margulis first proposed the Gaia Hypothesis, the scientific community all but ridiculed it. Margulis herself endured over twenty years of censure from the scientific community on her theory of *endosymbiosis* (that the eukaryotic cell arose from the symbiotic cooperation of single-celled organisms), which at its root suggested a world driven much more by cooperation than competition, as was currently promulgated.

"It must be deeply understood that the term 'evolution,' which is not used by Charles Darwin—he called the process 'descent with modification'—is Anglo-Saxon. It is very much a British–American 'take' on the history of life, traditionally limited to Anglophones,"[64] said biologist Lynn Margulis in an interview with *Scoop News* in 2009. "Most English-speaking scientists think in hushed hagiographic terms when they mention Charles Darwin, comparable to English thought about physics before Einstein, when Newton was the only game in town. It's a very English nationalist phenomenon, especially as Darwin was later interpreted."[65]

I spoke earlier (under "Refusal of the Call") of Riane Eisler's account of the ancient Bronze Age culture of Minoan Crete, a society that embraced a gylanic life-model within an increasingly warlike androcratic world. Eisler notes that a "recognition of our oneness with all of nature"[61] lay at the heart of both the Neolithic and Cretan worship of the Goddess. She adds, "Increasingly, the work of modern ecologists indicate that this earlier quality of mind, in our time often associated with some types of Eastern spirituality, was far advanced beyond today's environmentally destructive ideology. In fact, it foreshadows new scientific theories that all the living matter of earth, together with the atmosphere, oceans, and soil and the universe forms one complex and inter-connected 'life' system."[34] Quite fittingly, Lovelock and Margulis called this the Gaia Hypothesis—Gaia being one of the ancient Greek names of the Goddess.

Eisler provides examples of sociobiologists who draw on nineteenth-century Darwinism by citing insect societies to support their *androcratic* (social and political rule by men; patriarchy) theories. We are still looking to adopt a cultural revolution that embraces a partnership society heralded by new and renewed symbology, language and myth.[34]

Photo 9.15: West coast rainforest stream, Vancouver Island, British Columbia, Canada.

Photo by Kevin Klassen

Resurrection / Atonement

Although the Cartesian–Kantian perspective has dominated our modern Western philosophy since the 1600s, a very different perspective also gained ground in the 1700s, starting with Spinoza's espousal of ancient pantheism and Goethe's study of natural forms. It developed in new directions by Schiller, Schelling, Hegel, Coleridge, Emerson, and most recently by Rudolf Steiner,[45] the Austrian philosopher and artist of the late 1800s, who developed anthroposophical medicine and Waldorf education. Steiner's biodynamic agriculture included use of the vortex principle to simulate the action of mountain streams, preferably while exposed to the sun.

Steiner shared with Goethe, Schiller and the others "a fundamental conviction that the relation of the human mind to the world [is] ultimately not dualistic but participatory,"[45] says Tarnas, who adds, "these subjective principles are in fact an expression of the world's own being, and that the human mind is ultimately the organ of the world's own process of self-revelation." In this view, Nature is not a separate, independent self-contained reality to be 'objectively' examined by humanity from without; rather, "Nature's unfolding truth emerges only with the active participation of the human mind."[45] It is something that comes into being through the very act of human cognition—the entangled mind.

"The collective psyche seems to be in the grip of a powerful archetypal dynamic in which the long-alienated modern mind is breaking through, out of the contractions of its birth process, out of what Blake called its 'mind-forg'd manacles' to rediscover its intimate relationship with nature and the larger cosmos,"[45] writes Tarnas. He further suggests that we are now witnessing the culmination of a long meta-trajectory of human evolution that began with the *participation mystique*. A trajectory that gave rise to the birth of philosophy from the mythological consciousness in ancient Greece through the classical, medieval, and modern eras to our own postmodern age. A trajectory that is now poised to return us, changed and wiser, Home and to Wholeness.

Tarnas, and others, acknowledge that the epistemological and philosophical evolution of humanity—which has dictated our relationship with Nature generally, and water specifically—has been up to now overwhelmingly a masculine phenomenon. Western thought and worldview was created and canonized by men and naturally dominated by the male perspective. From the choice of a masculine gender to describe humanity (e.g., *l'homme, l'uomo, chelovek, der Mensch,* man) to the heroic stories we tell ourselves, the Western tradition has embraced the questing masculine hero. A hero, in Tarnas' words, is "a Promethean biological and metaphysical rebel who has constantly sought freedom and progress for himself, and who has thus constantly striven to differentiate himself from and control the matrix out of which he emerged."[45] This transformative stage is not only characteristic, contends Tarnas; it is essential to humanity's journey Home.

Return with the Elixir

In the September 2009 Peace Summit in Vancouver B.C., the Dalai Lama shared that "the world will be saved by the western woman."[66] This "call to adventure" by His Holiness reflects the Hero's Journey steps suggested by Richard Tarnas in the epilogue of his book *The Passion of the Western Mind*: "the driving impulse of the West's masculine consciousness has been its dialectical quest not only to realize itself, to forge its own autonomy, but also, finally, to recover its connection with the whole, to come to terms with the great feminine principle in life … to reunite with the mystery of life, of nature, of soul."[45]

According to Tarnas, the great challenge—and the truly heroic aspect of our journey—is for "the masculine [in all of us] to overcome its hubris and one-sidedness, to own its unconscious shadow, to choose to enter into a fundamentally new relationship of mutuality with the feminine in all its forms. The feminine then becomes not that which must be controlled, denied, and explained, but rather fully acknowledged, respected, and responded to for itself. It is recognized: not the objectified "other," but rather source, goal, and immanent presence."[45]

Poised and ready, rising from its previous dualistic perception, the soul finds Home in Wholeness, and returns to the intrinsic truth of the world. The world realizes itself within and through the human mind, projecting a fractal vision of a holonomic Universe. Part of this realization is our greater connection—to each other and to all things—with an emerging sense of values of integrity and compassion. This has always been the Dalai Lama's belief; that compassion and love are our source, vehicle and destiny. "I believe that the purpose of life is to be happy,"[66] says His Holiness.

In Act Two, I mentioned how, prior to industrialization, communities had relied on wave and wind power and solar energy for the production of food and goods. We are now returning to these pursuits—not so much out of need, but out of choice, by choosing a dialectic and worldview that promotes Nature participating.

Photo 9.16: Author stands on a bridge in the west coast rainforest of British Columbia.

Photo by Herb Klassen

In Act Three, cooperative creative, artisanal enterprises and the involvement of communities have all emerged with renewed meaning and vigour.

As part of what quantum physics is revealing about our Universe, a renewed interest in *pantheism* (the belief that the Universe is identical with divinity) is emerging: from 19th and 20th century writers and philosophers, such as Wordsworth, Fichte and Hegel, Whitman, Emerson, Thoreau and even Einstein. They are the basis of the current World Pantheist Movement.

Many pantheists have furthered the initial belief (that the Universe is identical with divinity) to forward the view that everything is *alive*, including the entire Universe, and that everything has a soul or spirit.[67,68] The World Pantheist Movement, founded in 1975, returns humanity to some of the early worship and respect for Nature in what has been described as *dark green religion*, with a focus on environmental ethics.[69]

Holism—that systems and their properties are better viewed as wholes, rather than a collection of parts—includes the notion that functioning of the whole cannot be fully understood by the collective functioning of the parts. The growing Holism movement (considered a form of anti-reductionism) and associated *systems thinking* (which encompasses chaos and complexity theories) are reflected in the *science of ecology*, which studies the relationships encompassed by the natural world. Holism forms the basis of Hegel's "substance universal," of Köhler's gestalt psychology, of John Muir's conservationism, of Schumpeter's theory of economics, and of Bohm's Implicate Order. The agricultural science of permaculture and organic farming use a holistic approach, as do many alternative healing approaches, such as acupuncture and energy healing.

The emerging science of consciousness and the "hard problem of consciousness" (e.g., why we have phenomenal experiences and how sensations acquire characteristics, such as colours and tastes)—a term introduced by cognitive scientist David Chalmers—has fired a growing worldview that the entire Universe is alive and possesses a cosmic consciousness.

Some see the world as a still photograph; they see us standing in chaos and destruction; I prefer to see the world in motion; I see us walking toward a new paradigm, in the act of embracing an ancient wisdom. And it is heartening to witness fractal pieces of the same resonance reflected in all aspects of our societies and life: from an active adoption of the slow food movement, artisanal community creative, alternative and complimentary medicines and wellness practices, to respecting environmental footprints and embracing our ancient practice of using the musical note A tuned to 432 Hz.

As for water, water is water. From when the dinosaurs quenched their thirst in the pre-Cambrian swamps to the crystal pools of our new cities, water has been with us. It will continue to be water: flowing, transporting and depositing; filling; scouring; destroying and creating; transforming, invigorating and giving life.

Water—always changing—will never change.

"An alder leaf, loosened by wind, is drifting out with the tide. As it drifts, it bumps into the slender leg of a great blue heron staring intently through the rippled surface, then drifts on. The heron raises one leg out of the water and replaces it, a single step. As I watch I, too, am drawn into the spread of silence. Slowly, a bank of cloud approaches, slipping its bulged and billowing texture over the earth, folding the heron and the alder trees and my gazing body into the depths of a vast breathing being, enfolding us all within a common flesh, a common story now bursting with rain."

—David Abram

ACT ONE: SEPARATION. *A shift in self-view in relation to Nature and "home"; when humanity separated the concepts and study of "economy" and "ecology."*	
1. Ordinary World	Early humanity revered water as sacred: it was the well-spring of all life and all powerful—determining life and death. Humanity followed the rhythms and patterns of water.
2. Call to Adventure	Ancient climate change heralds humanity's bold stray from the simple path to realize its intelligence, power, and independence. Matriarchal and galanic worldviews were usurped by patriarchal and androcentric dialectics as humanity considered itself separate from Nature and able to control and command Her.
3. Refusal of the Call	Some remained on the "simple" and cooperative path with Nature and the rhythms and patterns of water. They were considered "backward" or "simple" by many progressives
4. Meeting with the Mentor	The Mentor—a shape-shifter representing a dualistic patriarchal dialectic and hegemony—helps humanity cross into the Industrial Age. The mentor includes the scientific revolution, the Copernican revolution and the post-Copernican Double Bind.
5. Crossing the Threshold	The intellectual teleology of reductionism was based on a perception of reality that separated mind from heart, religion from science, and ultimately, humanity from Nature and its "Wholeness."

Table 9.1: The Twelve-Step Hero's Journey of Water and Humanity (after Joseph Campbell)

Table 9.1: The Twelve-Step Hero's Journey of Water and Humanity (after Joseph Campbell)

ACT TWO: INITIATION & TRANSFORMATION. *A shift in view towards commodification, with a more complete separation between "ecology" and "economy."*	
6. Tests, Allies, Enemies	Industrial nations expand, birthing urbanization and materialism, free-market capitalism, socialism and Marxism, utilitarianism and consumerism. The Industrial Revolution increased living standards, medicine, technology and life-expectancy. We built dams and mined surface and groundwater to accommodate our great cities and agriculture. Darwin's "survival of the fittest" is a model of the western worldview.
7. Approach to the Innermost Cave	Over 60% of the world's wetlands are destroyed. Air, water and soil pollution increase worldwide. Inland seas shrink and rivers don't reach their mouths, from overuse. Major droughts occur, due as much to over-population and over-exploitation as to climate change. Water wars begin in earnest
8. Ordeal (Abyss)	Rachel Carson writes *Silent Spring*. Terms such as "sustainable production" and "sustainable development" are debated among ecologists, economists and social scientists. Climate change is blamed for everything.
9. Reward/Seizing the Sword (Transformation and Revelation)	Movements extolling the Mother Goddess and Sacred Feminine Wisdom emerge in all societies. "Feminism" emerges as well. Slow-grow and local food movements begin. We experiment with organic foods, artisanal enterprises, creative cooperatives, syndicalism and other alternative economic movements to capitalism.

ACT THREE: RETURN. *A return toward self-respect and respect of all things; a return to wholeness and "Home" through integration of "ecology" and "economy", and a reconciliation of paradoxical opposites comprising the Whole: of masculine and feminine, of yin and yang, and so forth.*	
10. Road Block	Mainstream science, policy makers and established patriarchies quell and disparage alternative medicine and wellness practices. Feminism is misinterpreted with hostility. Larger corporations bully smaller independent cooperatives. Discoveries and theories of quantum physics are sidelined by the Second World War.
11. Resurrection/ Atonement	Significance of quantum physics is embraced by the world. The Dalai Lama announces the "The Western Woman will save the world." Alternative movements emerge and create emerging philosophies. Ancient wisdom is rediscovered and shared.
12. Return with the Elixir	Small independent (Indie) enterprises flourish in all sectors from publishing and the arts, to food, beer, and wellness products; and practices of individual expression and creativity are celebrated. Artisanal and naturally grown or family-run products are sought after by enlightened communities. Epistemological, philosophical and sociological worldviews embrace the significance of quantum physics.

Adapted from Joseph Campbell's 12-step Hero's Journey

Water is Story

Story meanders through varied landscape; cutting jagged rock and stirring fertile soils to release their messages; then joining in the great sea of the plenum. Story springs from the depths, bubbling forth with fresh bracing news of a new land.
Story is water.

References

1. Emoto, Masaru. 2001. "The Hidden Messages in Water." *Atria Books*. 159 pp.
2. Sahtouris, Elisabet. 2014. "Ecosophy: Nature's Guide to a Better World." *Kosmos*, Spring/Summer 2014: 4–9.
3. Ball, Philip. 2000. "H2O: A Biography of Water." *Phoenix*. London, UK. 387 pp.
4. Wetzel, Robert. 2001. "Limnology." 3rd edition. *Academic Press*. 1006 pp.
5. Round, F.E. 1984. "The Ecology of Algae." *Cambridge University Press*. 664 pp.
6. Vannote, R. L., G. W. Minshall, K. W. Cummings, J. R. Sedell, and C. E. Cushing. 1980. "The River Continuum Concept."*Canadian Journal of Fisheries and Aquatic Sciences* 37: 130–137.
6. Schubel, Jerry. 1994. "Coastal Pollution and Waste Management." In: Environmental Science in the Coastal Zone: Issues for Further Research, Chapter 9: 124–143. *National Academies Press*.
7. Stewart, Iain. 2010. Host in: "How the Earth Changed History: Water." BBC TV Mini-Series.
8. Fagan, Brian. 2010. "Elixir, a History of Water and Humankind." *Bloomsbury Press*. New York, NY. 384 pp.
9. Campbell, Joseph. 1949. "A Hero with a Thousand Faces". *Pantheon Books*. 432 pp.
10. Pearson, Carol S. 1998. "The Hero Within: Six Archetypes We Live." *Harper*, San Francisco. 3rd Edition. 368 pp.
11. Campbell, Joseph, Bill Moyers. 1991. "The Power of Myth." *Anchor*. 293 pp.
12. Pearson, Carol S. 1986. "The Hero Within: Six Archetypes We Live By". *Harper & Row*. 368 pp.
13. Cameron, Julia. 2002. "The Artist's Way." *Tarcher*. 272 pp.
14. Margulis, Lynn. 1981. "Symbiosis in Cell Evolution: Microbial Communities in the Archean and Proterozoic Eons." *W.H. Freeman & Co Ltd*. New York, NY. 419 pp.

15. Mazur, Suzan. 2010. "The Altenberg 16: An Exposé of the Evolution Industry" (Chapter 18: 'Lynn Margulis: Intimacy of Strangers and Natural Selection'). *North Atlantic Books*, Berkeley, California. 376 pp.

16. Margulis, Lynn and Dorion Sagan. 1986. Margulis, Lynn and Dorion Sagan. 1986. "Microcosmos: Four Billion Years of Microbial Evolution". *Summit Books*, NY. 301 pp.

17. Ryan, Frank. 1998. "Virus X: Tracking the New Killer Plagues." *Back Bay Books*. 448 pp.

18. Libby, Eric and William C. Ratcliff. 2014. "Ratcheting the Evolution of Multicellularity." *Science* 24 October: 426 – 427.

19. MacArthur, R and E.O. Wilson. 1967. "The Theory of Island Biogeography" (2001 reprint). Princeton University Press. 224pp.

20. Pianka, E.R. 1970. "On r and K selection." *American Naturalist* 104(940): 592–597

21. Harden, Garrett. 1968. "The Tragedy of the Commons". *Science* 162 (3859): 1259-1248.

22. Ruche, Alain. 2014. "International Cultural Engagement. Part One: Are We at the Tipping Point?" *Kosmos*, Spring/Summer Issue: 55–59.

23. We Day. 2015. Online: http://www.weday.com

24. Grossmeier, Greg. 2013. "Case Studies/Cory Doctorow." Creative Commons Corporation, Wiki online: https://wiki.creativecommons.org/wiki/Case_Studies/Cory_Doctorow

25. Manning, Aubrey. 2008. "Animal Magic: Why Species Give Each Other a Helping Hand (or Flipper)!" *The Daily Mail*, March 13. Online: http://www.dailymail.co.uk/news/article-533571/Animal-magic-Why-species-helping-hand-flipper.html

26. Daura-Jorge, Fabio, M. Cantor, S.N. Ingram, D. Lusseau, and P.C. Simoes-Lopes. 2012. "The Structure of a Bottlenose Dolphin Society Is Coupled to a Unique Foraging Cooperation with Artisanal Fishermen." *Biol. Lett.* 8: 702–705.

27. Gosnell, Mariana.2007. "Ice: The Nature, the History and the Uses of an Astonishing Substance." *University of Chicago Press*. 576 pp.

28. Eliade, Mircea. 1958. "Patterns in Comparative Religion." *Cambridge University Press*. 484 pp.

29. Shiva, Vandana. 2002. "Water Wars: Privatization, Pollution and Profit." *Between the Lines*, Toronto. 156 pp.

30. Plato. 360 BCE. "Timaeus." Translated by Benjamin Jowett. MIT Classics.

31. Picton, James Allanson. 1905. "Pantheism: Its Story and Significance." *Archibald Constable & Co., Ltd.*, Chicago. 96 pp.

32. Geisler, Norman and William D. Watkins. 2003. "Worlds Apart: A Handbook on World Views." 2nd edition. *Wipf and Stock Publishers*. 308 pp.

33. Fung, Yu-lan. 1937. "A History of Chinese Philosophy." Volume 1. Translated by Derk Bodde. *Henri Vetch*. Peiping.

34. Eisler, Riane. 1988. "The Chalice and the Blade: Our History, Our Future." *Harper*, San Francisco. 261 pp.

35. Kaminski, June. 2013. "Theory: Learning with the Natural World". *First Nations Pedagogy*. Online: http://firstnationspedagogy.com/earth.html

36. Bozzo, Sam. 2008. "Blue Gold," a film based on the book by Maude Barlow and Tony Clarke and narrated by Malcolm McDowell. Purple Turtle Films. 90 min. Online: www.bluegold-worldwaterwars.com

37. Barlow, Maude and Tony Clarke. 2005. "Blue Gold." *New Pr*. 304 pp.

38. Patterson, Brent. 2014. "Mexico City Residents Clash with Police." Online: http://canadians.org/blog mexico-city-residents-clash-police-over-water

39. Sarakinos, Helen. 2008. In: "Blue Gold," a film based on the book by Maude Barlow and Tony Clarke, and narrated by Malcolm McDowell. *Purple Turtle Films*. 90 min. Online: www.bluegold-worldwaterwars.com

40. Reisner, Marc. 1993. "Cadillac Desert." *Penguin Books*. 582 pp.

41. Liston, Enjoli. 2014. "Satellite Images Show Aral Sea Basin 'Completely Dried'." *The Guardian*, London. October 1, 2014.

42. McLamb, Eric. 2011. "The Ecological Impact of the Industrial Revolution." September 18. *Ecology Global Network*. Online: http://www.ecology.com/2011/09/18/ecological-impact-industrial-revolution/

43. Eisenstein, Charles. 2014. "Development in the Ecological Age." *Kosmos*, spring/summer: 74–79.

44. Bacon, Sir Francis. 1620. *"Distributio Operis, Instauratio Magna and Novum Organum."* Translated into English by Robert Ellis. In James Spedding's "The Works of Francis Bacon" (1858). *Longmans & Co.* 519 pp.

45. Tarnas, Richard. 1993. "The Passion of the Western Mind: Understanding the Ideas that Have Shaped Our World View." *Ballantine Books.* 560 pp.

46. Bartholomew, Alick. 2010. "The Spiritual Life of Water: Its Power and Purpose." *Park Street Press.* Rochester, Vermont. 368 pp.

47. Capra, F.1982. "The Turning Point: Science, Society, and the Rising Culture." *Simon & Shuster*, NY. 464 pp.

48. Merchant, Carolyn. 1980. "The Death of Nature: Women, Ecology, and the Scientific Revolution." *Harperone.* 384 pp.

49. Merchant, Carolyn. 2006. "The Scientific Revolution and the Death of Nature." *Focus—ISIS*, 97: 3. Online: http://nature.berkeley.edu/departments/espm/env-hist/articles/84.pdf

50. Leibniz, Gotfried Wilhelm. 1696. "Rice III: Mathematischer, Naturwissenschaftlicher und Technischer Briefwechsel." Berlin. In: "Philosophical Papers and Letters", ed. Leroy E. Loemker. *Chicago University Press.* 1956. Volume 2.

51. du Hamel, Jean Baptiste. 1701. "Regiae Scientiarum Academia Historia." 2nd ed. Paris.

52. von Goethe, Johann Wolfgang. 1907. In: "Maximen und Reflexionen: Nach den Handshriften des Goethe und Schiller." Archives herausgegeben von Max Hecker (Weimar: Goethe–Gesellschaft, 1907).

53. de Sacrobosco, Johannes. 1230. De Sphaera Mundi (On the Sphere of the World), quoted in Edward Grant, A Source book in Medieval Science. Cambridge: *Harvard Univ. Press* 1974. 465 pp.

54. Descartes, Rene. 1637 (1960). "A Discourse on Method and Meditations" Laurence J. Lafleur (trans). The Liberal Arts Press, NY.

55. Eisenstein, Charles. 2008. "Down with Descartes." *Orion Magazines, Point of View*, May. Online: https://orionmagazine.org/article/down-with-descartes/

56. Vinge, Vernor. 1993. "The Coming Technological Singularity: How to

Survive in the Post-Human Era." Vision–21: Interdisciplinary Science and Engineering in the Era of Cyberspace, G.A. Landis (ed.) *NASA Publication* CP–10129, 11–22.

57. Kurzweil, Ray. 2006. "The Singularity Is Near". *Penguin Books*. 672 pp.

58. Kurzweil, Ray. 2000. "The Age of Spiritual Machines: When Computers Exceed Human Intelligence." *Penguin Books*. 400 pp.

59. Lanier, Jaron. 2010. "The First Church of Robotics." The New York Times. Online: http://www.nytimes.com/2010/08/09/opinion/09lanier.html?_r=1

60. Korten, David. 2014. "A New Story for a New Economy." *Yes* Magazine, March 19. Online: http://www.yesmagazine.org/happiness/a-new-story-for-a-new-economy; http://www.yesmagazine.org/pdf/kortennewstory.pdf

61. Newton, Isaac. 1687 (1999). "Philosophiæ Naturalis Principia Mathematica." I. Bernard Cohen and Anne Whitman (trans). *University of California Press*. 991 pp.

62. Bateson, Gregory. 1987. "Steps in the Ecology of Mind." *Jason Aronson Inc.* Co. London. 512 pp.

63. Munteanu, Nina. 2012. "The Last Summoner." *Starfire World Syndicate*. 406 pp.

64. Jeans, James. 1930. "The Mysterious Universe." *Cambridge University Press*, UK. 163 pp.

65. Margulis, Lynn. 2009. "Lynn Margulis: Intimacy of Stangers & Natural Selection." Interview with Suzan Mazur. Scoop, March 16. Online: http://www.scoop.co.nz/stories/HL0903/S00194/lynn-margulis-intimacy-of-strangers-natural-selection.htm

66. Gyatso, Tenzin (14th Dalai Lama). 2015. "Compassion and the Individual." Online: http://www.dalailama.com/messages/compassion

67. Seager, William and Sean Allen-Hermanson. 2012. "Panpsychism," In Edward N. Zalta (ed). *The Stanford Encyclopedia of Philosophy*. Winter edition Stanford.edu archives.

68. Haught, John F. 1990. "What Is Religion?: An Introduction." *Paulist Press*. 288 pp.

69. Levine, Michael. 1994. "Pantheism: A Non-Theistic Concept of
    Deity." *Psychology Press.*
69. Abram, David. 1997. "The spell of the sensuous: Perception and lan-
    guage in a more than human world". *Vintage Books*, NY. 352 pp.

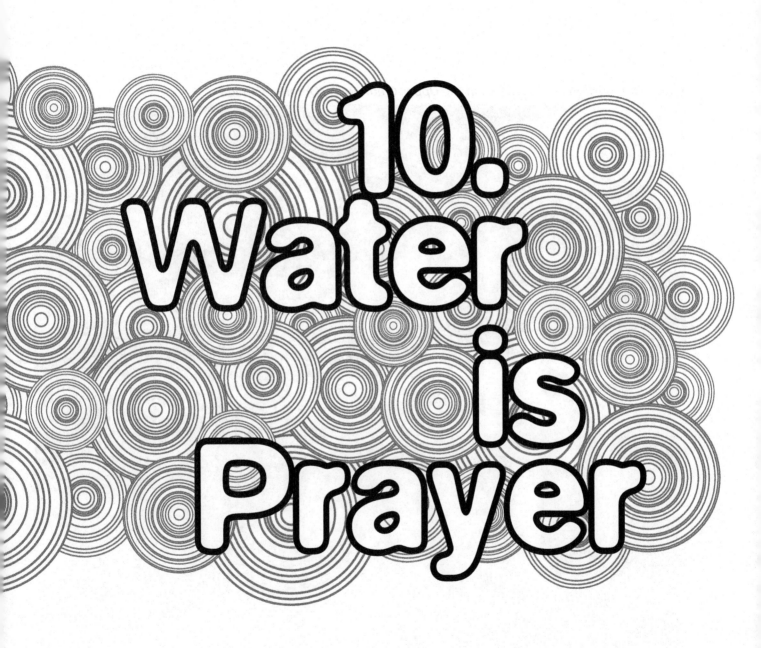

10.
Water is Prayer

Photo 10.1: Surfing rapids pattern in the Upper Credit River, Ontario, Canada.

Photo by Merridy Cox

"In every drop of water dwells a deity whom indeed we all serve"

—Viktor Schauberger

I grew up with prayer. My father was Romanian Orthodox and my mother Roman Catholic. We prayed before every meal and at night before going to bed.

It was over an hour's drive to Montreal, where the Romanian Orthodox Cathedral was located; so we didn't go that often. I remember attending mass at Easter, one of the most important religious celebrations for Romanians. On Easter Day, called *Paştele*, which was usually celebrated a week after the other Christian Churches, I remember knocking painted eggs with my family. There was definitely an art to "winning" the bout without your egg cracking. It's believed that people who knock each other's eggs will see each other again after death. If that's true, I'm certainly seeing all my family again! I remember also looking forward to eating *Pască*, a form of *cozonac* (a yeasty egg bread).

The feast of Epiphany of the Romanian Orthodox Church commemorates the baptism of Jesus in the Jordan River. The ceremony is long, solemn and—of course—involves water.

The priest first makes his way to the centre of the nave where a vessel with clean water sits. The deacon reads from Isaiah, excerpted here:

... The desert of Jordan shall blossom abundantly ... and my people shall see the glory of the Lord, and the excellency of our God ... He

will come and save us ... for in the wilderness shall waters break out, and streams in the desert ...

A heart without faith in God and His Grace is like a desert. Now with His Spirit the desert shall rejoice. The redeemed shall obtain song and joy in His companionship. Every one that thirsteth, come ye to the waters, and he that hath no money ... Seek ye the Lord, and when ye have found him call ye upon him ... and return ye unto the Lord, and he will have mercy.

The priest prays: "We beseech Thee, sprinkle upon us Thine unworthy servants purifying water which is the gift of Thy compassion ...' He asks the Holy Spirit to sanctify the water: 'give sanctification, blessing, cleansing, and health to all those touched, anointed, and partaking thereof." After the blessing, he then immerses the sacred cross upright in the water and raises it with a prayer. After the service, the faithful receives sanctified water and takes it home and reverently drinks of it and sprinkles it around his home and field.[1]

When I was very young, the priest came to our house several times and blessed it with water, sprinkling it here and there. At the time I had no concept of the significance, but I understood that water was important.

In most of the world's religions prayers are recited before a meal or to consecrate the food during a major religious holiday. It turns out that the vibrational frequency of prayers and prayerful chants uttered in any language is generally 8–10 Hertz, which is the alpha rhythm of the brain during relaxation and meditation. It also corresponds to the oscillations of the Earth's magnetic field (i.e., the natural resonance frequency range known as Schumann Resonance), which I talk about in Chapter 7.

I think it no coincidence that the vibrational frequency of prayer or deep meditative intention (both sacred acts) resonates with the "heart" frequency of the Earth. Just as most life contains the same proportion of water as what exists on the Earth. We reflect each other through fractal relationships of self-similarity.

Frequency appears to play a major role in how we both receive and connect through prayer and intention. Experiments using a superconducting quantum interference device (SQUID) magnetometer provided evidence for shifts in the magnetic field emitted by practitioners performing Therapeutic Touch (TT).[2] In a subsequent study, the biomagnetic component of a TT practitioner showed a field with a variable frequency also around 8–10 Hz. The studies suggest that a frequency band of 8–10 Hz is associated with human biofield (energy) emissions during this therapeutic intervention.[3]

The power of prayer can be real and palpable. Several years ago, at a wellness conference in Chicago, I participated in a group meditation. Our leader, David Wilcock, prepared us as we focused our prayers on a particular issue. Then the room went utterly silent as several hundred minds, hearts and souls meditated and prayed in unison. I felt my body tingle with energy and witnessed blazing purple and blue colours in my mind's eye as I sat, eyes closed, among a hundred others bent in prayer. While we didn't "move the Earth," I was moved. And perhaps that was enough.

Who am I to say our concerted prayer didn't exert an effect? What is effect and how do we measure its success? A decade ago, a young girl, a good friend of my best friend's daughter, suffered a deep depression about her performance in high school and her self-image. She developed anorexia and was hospitalized. I felt somehow drawn in. I'd briefly met the young girl, who had shown great vitality, joy and intelligence. She was also Romanian, like me; part of my "tribe." So, I prayed daily; not *for her*—but *to her*. I sent her my intention: *you are beautiful and intelligent and love is all around you, ready to envelope you with joy. You will find your joy again.* She fully recovered. Not because of me. But who am I to say? ...

"Perhaps scientists will tell us sometime what prayer is," says Metropolitan Smolensky Kirill of the Russian Orthodox Church. "Perhaps scientists will tell us sometime what happens with human nature under the influence of divine grace," he adds. "The Holy Scripture contains these marvellous words: nothing shall be impossible to him who believes."[4]

Photo 10.2: View of the Matterhorn with ski hut in foreground, Zermatt, Switzerland.

Photo by Nina Munteanu

Perennial Philosophy & The Maharishi Effect

"We are not humans trying to be spiritual. We are spiritual beings trying to be human."

—Jacquelyn Small

In 1960, Maharishi Mahesh Yogi predicted that if, within a population, one percent practised Transcendental Meditation (TM) (within the 4–10 Hz frequency), the quality of life in that whole population would improve. The impact of group meditation, now called "The Maharishi Effect," is described as a phase transition to a more harmonious state of life, "as measured by decreased crime, violence, accidents, and illness,"[5] in addition to improvements in economic conditions and other social indicators of wellness. In the past several decades, scientists have documented this transformation of society at the city, state and national levels, and culminating at the global level.[5,6,7,8,9,10]

In 1988, Orme-Johnson and his colleagues reported in the *Journal of Conflict Resolution* an improved quality of life in the Middle East and a reduced armed conflict, correlated with an increase in individuals practicing TM.[8] Several years later, in 1994, Orme-Johnson and colleagues reported a reduction in crime by sixteen percent when one percent of the community in Washington D.C. practiced TM.[11] The study results were reported with a high level of statistical significance ($p \leq 0.0008$). Several studies in other cities also demonstrated the same phenomenon with high significance.[12,13]

According to Orme-Johnson, the proportion of TM practitioners (i.e., one percent of the population) is so small that beneficial interactions of the participants with other members of society are not able to account for the effects. Instead, writes Orme-Johnson, "the results indicate a field effect, in which an influence of coherence produced by the

participants radiates throughout society."[5] Researchers theorize that the effect arises through wave coherence in the *collective consciousness* (of the unified field that connects the diverse forces and particles) of a community or of the world. Quantum physicist John Hagelin describes it this way: "The influence of the meditating group travels through an underlying field—in the same way that you can hear a live radio program broadcast from the other side of the world. In the one case, the electromagnetic field links the radio station and your radio. In the other example, the field of consciousness links the meditator to the rest of the population. Waves of coherence from the peace-creating group spread throughout the field of consciousness, producing a beneficial and measurable influence throughout society."[14]

The notion that we interact directly at a distance through an underlying common field of consciousness has been expressed since ancient times. More recently, Aldous Huxley, in 1945, used the term *perennial philosophy* to describe the persistence of a universal system of thought and a collective consciousness, such as Fechner's "transcendental basis of perception," Émile Durkheim's "conscious collective," and Jung's "collective unconscious."[15,16,17,18,19] Jung saw the *collective unconscious* as a "reservoir of experience of our species"[19] or a reservoir of humanity's collective experience, which embodies archetypal patterns that guide our individual psyche toward integration and self-actualization. These common patterns, Jung argued, can be found all around us, in art, literature, cultural artefacts, symbols and heralds; they are manifested and expressed through dreams, intuition and social roles. Mythologist and scholar Joseph Campbell suggested that individuals actualized specific universal patterns (through archetypes), defining their unique roles in society.[20] Ultimately, archetypes of the collective unconscious can be viewed as structures of consciousness.

These iterations of a unified field of consciousness were expressed by Plato two thousand years ago. Plato held that abstract Forms (or ideas)—not the material world of change we know and sense—pos-

Photo 10.3: Close up view of cascade in Upper Credit River, Ontario, Canada.

Photo by Nina Munteanu

sess the highest and most fundamental reality. According to Plato, the Forms are blueprints from which all created beings are shaped. They are "structures of consciousness" or "Ideas" of the great original intelligence.[21] Plato's *theory of Form* with its "hidden order" led to an epistemology based on sacred geometry that included what became known as the *Platonic solids* (as the fundamental components of the physical universe). This ultimately led him to a "Theory of Everything" within a unified fractal cosmology. I talk more about this in Chapter 8.

Orme-Johnson shares that the Maharishi theory of collective consciousness reflects quantum physics in positing that transcendental consciousness operates in a *self-referral* state in which "the observer, observation, and observed relationship collapses into the observer becoming the direct object of observation."[5]

British physicist James Jeans, who first proposed that matter is continuously created in the Universe, shared his insight in 1932 on the evolution of the scientific worldview of the universe: "Thirty years ago, we thought, or assumed that we were heading towards an ultimate reality of a mechanical kind ... Into this wholly mechanical world ... life had stumbled by accident ... Today there is a wide measure of agreement ... that the universe begins to look more like a great thought than a great machine. Mind no longer appears as an accidental intruder into the realm of matter; we are beginning to suspect that we ought rather to hail it as the creator and governor of the realm of matter—not of course our individual minds, but the mind in which the atoms of which our individual minds have grown exist."[22] He adds that when we pass beyond space and time, we may form ingredients of a single continuous stream of life, just like light and electricity.[22] Just like water. So, it is perhaps that we are "carrying on separate existences in space and time while, in the deeper reality beyond space and time, we may all be members of one body."[23] In the concluding page of his book *Mind, Matter, and Quantum Mechanics*, physicist H.P. Stapp called quantum particles and their interactions more "idea-like" than "matter-like."[24] Erwin Schrödinger,

best known for the Schrödinger equation in quantum theory, suggested that "Mind has erected the objective outside world … out of its own stuff. The reason why our … thinking ego is met nowhere within our scientific world picture can easily be indicated in seven words: because it is itself that world picture."[25] Current neuroscience recognizes that perceptions of shape, colour and texture, are subjectively experienced.[26]

Orme-Johnson concludes from this that, "the apparent stability of the observed world and the high degree of agreement that is achieved between observers is because the most fundamental level of consciousness where perception is constructed, transcendental consciousness, is universal and eternally non-changing, infinitely stable."[5]

We honour all holy water
Which stills the thirst of the
earth, all the holy water
And all the plants, which the
Creator made.
For all are holy!

We honour the Waters of life,
And all that is water on earth.
Still, flowing and springing
water
The ever flowing springs
Blessed raindrops
We devote ourselves to the holy
waters
Which have created the law.

A flood of love springs forth
From the hidden places beneath
the earth.

—Writings of the Essenes

Figure 10.4: Looking upstream at the Limmat River from the Zurichsee Brucke, Zurich, Swizterland.

Photo by Nina Munteanu

The Power of "Mind"

"Whoever believes in me, as Scripture has said, rivers of living water will flow from within them."

—*John 7: 38–39*

When I was in Grade seven, we had a mid-term science test and for some reason, I decided—jokingly—to tell everyone that I'd scored 100% on the test. I knew I'd done well, but truly hadn't thought I'd done that well. Or had I? When the tests came back, I had indeed scored a 100%. I was stunned. It was the only perfect score of all of us tested. And it was the only time I'd scored a perfect mark in a major test. What had prompted me to make that cocky statement? Had I "tapped into" the *greater knowledge* or had I "created it" through *intention*? Or was it more *collaboration* between me and the whole? I have experienced many incidents—like the example of my personal prayer for the young high school student—of what some might call coincidence, but which I suggest is divine collaboration. It is moments like these when all the aspects of the Universe seem to be acting in a synchronous coherence to create a collective pattern of "good."

Masaru Emoto writes in his book *The Secret Life of Water*, that the intention of Shinto prayers (referred to as *norito*) is to create vibration, which forms a link to the sacred.[25] Emoto tells us that the Shinto prayer is not a prayer to the One and Only, but a prayer to myriad holy beings: types of consciousness and life forms currently beyond our limited ability to sense. Materials scientist Rustum Roy shares that, "intention may be imprinted on the water; it is … like prayer."[26]

According to Russian scientist Konstantin Korotkov and others, prayer creates a harmonic structure in water—a large component of most food—that resonates with the intention.[6] Korotkov wisely suggests that, "we can take some purely practical advice from this: to sit down at the table in a very good mood and under no circumstances to

dine with cruel or aggressive-minded people, because this will have a direct destructive effect on our health."[27]

"A person who is thinking negative thoughts is polluting his own water," says Austrian researcher Allois Gruber. He adds that, "If [a person] approaches the water with good thoughts, blesses it and says thank you to it—the quality of the water will improve and will have a positive effect on a person and his body."[28]

Gerbert Klima, professor of the Institute of Nuclear Physics, in Vienna Austria asserts that, "Not a single scientist who is familiar with systems theory doubts [the power of thought to enact change]. It is entirely a question of waiting for a moment when the system is in a state of instability. In a phase of instability, the motion of thought alone is sufficient for the system to start to change."[29]

Israeli Rabbi Adin Steinsaltz shares of his own experience: "I do not always see it; when my own mistake or sin comes back to me in another guise ... whatever it is that I did wrong returns to me, not as punishment but as a result."[30]

Figure 10.5: The "Varanasiganga", the Holy Ganges River, India.

Photo by Babasteve, Wikimedia Commons

Sacred Water, Holy Water

"Everything that lives is holy."
—William Blake

"From our worldly entrance in a burst of amniotic fluid to the ritual washing of the dead (*taharah* in Judaism; *ghusl al-mayyit* in Islam), water flows through our lives, scribing a line between sacred and profane, life and death," writes *National Geographic* editor-at-large Cathy Newman in the 2010 Water Issue of *The National Geographic*. "We are doused, dunked, dipped, sprinkled—and blessings flow, deep and wide as the River Jordan of scripture, wondrous as the spring at Lourdes, cathartic as tears."[31]

The Egyptian sun god Ra cleansed himself in the sky-ocean before his daily excursions. This is reminiscent of the ubiquitous holy washings of most cultures on Earth. "From the droplets in a baptismal font to the scattering of ashes on a holy river, water blesses our lives,"[8] says Newman. According to historian Mircea Eliade, waters "are spring and origin, the reservoir of all the possibilities of existence; they precede every form and support every creation."[32]

Babylonians believed the world was created by the joining of fresh and salt water. Pima Indians proclaimed that Mother Earth was impregnated by a drop of water.[31] In the Hindu Vedas, ancient teachings written in Sanskrit, water is called *matritamah*, which means "most maternal." According to the Vedas, the waters of life bring humankind the life force.

Worshippers in Hindu temples participate in a ritual bathing using a kalash, a pot symbolizing the "source of life," which contains holy water. The water is sprinkled on worshippers' heads after *puja* (simple ritual worship). A *kamya* worship involves a pilgrimage to a holy site. One of these is the holy pilgrimage to bathe in the Ganges River. Each year the Ganges River receives hundreds of thousands of pilgrims, who wish to bathe in its sacred waters during the *Kumbh Mela* (named after the mythical water pot). "The celebration of the Kumbh is a celebration of creation,"[33] Indian scholar Vandana Shiva tells us. Water plays a vital role in Balinese life. They call their Hindu religion *Agama Tirtha*: "The Religion of the Holy Water." *Tirtha* is Sanskrit for "holy" or "cleanse." Water for the Balinese contains mysterious potential, has the power to make all life grow and flourish, and is a medium for spiritual regeneration. Holy water initiates and completes every ceremony of gratitude to Dewi Danu, Goddess of lakes, waters, fertility and prosperity. The Balinese created the *subak* irrigation system to maintain the harmonious relationship between human, Nature and God, protecting and honouring the sacred water. The *subaks* on Bali follow a natural sinuous path within an ecological management system that includes planting cycles and division of water resources.[34]

Rain making rituals are universal, even in normally well-watered places, writes Jungian analyst and psychiatrist Anthony Stevens, author of *Ariadne's Clue*. Considered a fertilizing agent that descends from Heaven, rain was commonly equated with the divine semen, which bore fruit; it was the *heirosgamos* between Heaven and Earth, archetypes of male and female. The ancient Egyptians worshipped a sky goddess, Nut, and celebrated rainfall as "milk" descending from her breasts to give fertility to all life.

Intangible, beautiful and mysterious, rainbows, like rain, provided a bridge between Heaven and Earth and known by various terms; the Norse called it Byfrost; it is Buddha's staircase; Muslim mystics paint the rainbow in an image of a godhead. Others associate it with the mystic serpent, representing power and regeneration.[35] In the Judeo-Christian tradition, the rainbow appeared to Noah as a covenant or promise.

Hasidic Jews immerse themselves before Rosh Hashanah in pools that serve as *mikvehs* (bodies of water used for spiritual cleansing).

Photo 10.6: Boaters on the "Varanasiganga", the Holy Ganges River, India.

Photo by Babasteve, Wikimedia Commons

While most forms of impurity are considered nullified through immersion in any natural collection of water, some impurities require *zav* or "living water", such as spring water or groundwater from a well.

Muslims throughout the world perform *wudu*, a washing ritual (ablutions) before their prayers in a mosque. "Cleanliness is half of faith," Muhammad told his followers. Hundreds of millions of Muslims turn to Mecca to pray five times daily. Mount Arafat, where Mohammed gave his last sermon, overlooks Mecca. The Shrine of the Black Stone houses a small temple and a cupola that covers a sacred well, *Zemzem*.

The Christian church celebrates the sacrament of holy baptism with blessed water. Jesus bent to wash the feet of his disciples, as would a servant. In churches, holy water is sprinkled on the faithful during ceremonies to help purify the soul. Many early Christian churches were constructed near pagan sacred wells. The Celtic church used them for baptism and, later, the Roman church incorporated them inside a building with a font. Several old churches contain a crypt or grotto that opens into a subterranean spring; these places are guarded and cherished as the innermost sanctum of the sacred enclosure.[36]

Mircea Eliade writes: "immersion in water symbolizes a return to the pre-formal, a total regeneration, a new birth, for immersion means dissolution of forms, a reintegration into the formlessness of pre-existence; and emerging from the water is a repetition of the act of creation in which form was first expressed … Water purifies and regenerates because it nullifies the past, and restores—even if only for a moment—the integrity of the dawn of things."[32]

Thunder and lightning—a potent blending of fire and water—figure as important symbols of god: power and intent. Wielding his hammer (*Mjöllnir* or Lightning), the Norse warrior god Thor defended the *Aesir* gods and their fortress, *Asgard*. To the ancient Greeks, Zeus was a thunder god and ruled Olympus. In the Vedas, Indra, god of the thunderbolt, brought rain to the fields and ensured fertility to all life forms. He wielded a *vajra* (a lightning thunderbolt). Like the Ouroboros it-

self, lightning and thunder encompass the polarity of creative destruction: from the angry catastrophic storms, floods and fires to the gentle nurturing of all life's well-being and growth. "The idea of illumination from Heaven, the divine logos piercing the darkness, is a symbol of enlightenment and sudden intellectual insight,"[36] writes Stevens.

Water destroys and creates. Water confuses and clarifies. Water cleans. Water heals.

Japan's Sacred Water

The Japanese Shinto ritual *misogi shuho* is commonly celebrated at a sacred waterfall and involves washing the whole body. This purification ritual celebrates the communion among worshipper, waterfall, and the creative life force of the Universe.[31] Shinto shrines contain a water bowl decorated with sacred images. Upon entering the shrine, priests wash their hands and clean out their mouths, enacting an ancient ritual of purifying the spirit and body before worship. Shintoists also believe that departed spirits return to rivers and streams on their way "home."[37]

In gratitude for the many blessings of water, the Shinto have dedicated many shrines to water deities, such as *Suijin* (a water deity) and *Ryujin*, a water dragon *kami* (spirit), associated with the sea. The water kami is a guardian of fishermen and oversees fertility, motherhood and easy childbirth.[38] Offerings are made with hope for pure and unpolluted water. When I went to Japan in 2012 with my friend Kumiko, we visited Tsukiji Fish Market in Tokyo, where the Tsukiji Suijin Shrine is conveniently located to watch over the fishers.[39]

The Matsuo-taisha Shrine, in Kyoto's Arashiyama district, is one of the oldest shrines in Japan, and is dedicated to the deity of water. The Hata clan, who founded it in the year 701, brought sake-brewing techniques from the continent, and spring water for sake is still drawn from the *Kame-no-ido* or Turtle Well. The Kibune Shrine is located north of

Photo 10.7: Early morning tuna auction at Tsukiji Fish Market in Tokyo, Japan.

Photo by Nina Munteanu

Kyoto at the source of the Kibune River, where, according to tradition, the mother of Emperor Jimmu sailed up the stream in a stone boat. The shrine was associated with rain rituals, and today people float fortune slips on the water hoping to tell one's fate.[39]

My Japanese friend Kumiko took me to a local spa to bathe in the mineral-rich waters of an *onsen*, or hot spring. Japan is volcanically active with thousands of *onsen* scattered throughout it. *Onsen* water is said to promote wellness, due to its mineral content and source water; these include chronic skin disease, diabetes, constipation, and general aches and pains.[40] The Japanese word for Universe, *Ukiyo*, also means "the floating world." Their ancient word *umi*, which means "ocean" also relates to the concept of birth. The Japanese word for water is *mizu*. Kumi told me that a dead fetus is called "mizuko" (water child).

Given that Japan is an island nation, it is not surprising that water is such an important feature in their culture.

England's Sacred Water & Glastonbury's Water Ceremony

Surrounded by peat moors and grasslands and overlooked by the Tor (a conical hill), the village of Glastonbury in Somerset, England, has existed since Neolithic times. The town and the Tor tease with myth and legend about Joseph of Arimathea, the Holy Grail, King Arthur, Lady of the Lake and Excalibur. The damp moorland in the area can apparently promote a visual effect known as *Fata Morgana* (derived from the sorceress Morgan le Fay)—a kind of birefringence, due to a steep thermal inversion that results in mirages.[41]

The French poet Robert de Boron introduced the legend of Joseph of Arimathea coming to Avalon (i.e., Glastonbury) after the crucifixion, carrying the Holy Grail. He buried the chalice with the blood of Christ near the Tor, which now causes the reddish water of the artesian

spring (groundwater under positive pressure) at Glastonbury. In 2001, the site was designated a World Peace Garden.

The Chalice Well is also called the Red Spring because of the red hue of the natural spring water, which deposits iron oxides. Archaeological evidence suggests that the well has been in almost constant use for over two thousand years and flows constantly.[42] The spring water is believed to possess healing qualities and is considered holy. The Well is often interpreted as a symbol of the divine feminine. The *vesica piscis* (associated with sacred geometry and the *flower of life*) forms the shape of the wrought iron design on the well cover.

Nowadays, on July 25, a water ceremony amidst the ancient yew trees in the peaceful garden—complete with *vesica piscis* pools and Steiner-inspired flowforms—is conducted by an Avalon Goddess priestess, who gives thanks for the blessings of water and emphasizes the need to protect it from pollution. Water brought from other spiritual places is added to the well, and those gathered pray for purity and meditate on its life-sustaining nature.[39]

The idea for a water ceremony was the initiative of Japanese researcher Masaru Emoto. Every July 25 (the World Day of Love and Thanks to Water), water ceremonies are held internationally, in accordance with his belief that human consciousness affects the structure of water. Emoto's simple prayer is: "Water we love you, water we love you, water we love you; water we thank you, water we thank you, water we thank you; water we respect you, water we respect you, water we respect you."[39]

Canada's Sacred Water & the Water Ceremony in Mississauga, Ontario

Only weeks before writing this chapter, I attended a water ceremony, presided over by the Reverend Fiona Heath, at the Unitarian Congregation in Mississauga, Ontario, Canada. My friend Betty, who

Photo 10.8: The chalice well cover with design dusplaying the vesica piscis *at Glastonbury, England.*

Wikimedia

knew I was writing a book on water, suggested that I attend. I knew right away that I was in a special place and would experience something special, when I saw the church grounds as we drove up to the parking lot. The church had naturalized their property and returned the grounds to its native growth, complete with a swale, berm and water garden to protect the water. Reverend Fiona Heath of the Mississauga Congregation of the Unitarian Universalist Association, later told me that they also use a bio-filter septic system and have banned bottled water from the building.[43] The ministry had even placed signage to explain the ecosystem.

As Reverend Heath writes in her blog article *Sacred Water*, the Unitarian Universalists (UUs) acknowledge the "interdependence of life on this planet, and seek a healthy, respectful relationship with water. Our ecological sensibility is in harmony with other, ancient traditions, from India to the First Nations on this continent."[44]

The Water Ceremony, sometimes called Water Communion, is a recent tradition in the UU community. It started in East Lansing, Michigan in 1980, when Carolyn McDade (author of *Spirit of Life*) and Lucile Shuck Longview were asked to create a ritual for the Women and Religion Conference there. "They wanted their service to speak to the worship needs of women, which some felt had not been widely included in UU life," Reverend Fiona told me. "They focused on Nature and community. This 'celebration of connectedness,' as McDade called it, empowered women instead of calling them to serve others. The water symbolized the birth waters, the cycles of moon, tides and women, and all the waters of this small blue planet."[43] The conference generated great interest and now most Unitarian congregations hold this ceremony in September, to welcome in the congregation from the life-bustle of summer.

The ceremony, on September 13th, 2015, was appropriately called "Flowing Waters." We were ushered into the celebration with several songs devoted to celebrating the sacred Beauty of Nature. Reverend

Fiona spoke of the importance of water in our lives and its healing connection to everyone. Pamela Smith-Loeters read a touching Sufi poem called "Story for All Ages," which you can read in Chapter 12, *Water Is Joy*. We were then called upon to come forward with some water that we had brought with us (from a place special to each of us), pour it into the water chalice, and then share our story of how our spirit was nourished this past summer. I brought rainwater from a recent storm and gave my thanks for the rains. Following a group meditation of thanks and good intentions for the water, we then followed Reverend Fiona as she took the chalice of blended waters out to the berm and returned the water to the earth with a prayer of gratitude. A small portion was kept to begin the water ceremony next year.

Figure 10.9: The Chalice Well seven bowls of flowing sacred spring water, displaying vesica piscis *pools and Steiner-inspired flowforms at Glastonbury, England.*

Photo by Spmiler, Wikimedia Commons

Holy Water, Blessed Water

"If you knew the gift of God and who it is that asks you for a drink, you would have asked him, and he would have given you living water."

—John 4:10

Photo 10.10: Holy water container (stoup) at the Church of Santa Maria degli Angeli, Rome, Italy.

Photo by Mattes, Wikimedia Commons

According to the Roman Catholic, Eastern and Oriental Orthodox, and Anglican churches *holy water* is water that has been blessed by a member of the clergy and is used as a sacrament, recalling baptism. It is prepared through a ritual of consecration. Both the Orthodox and Catholic churches keep some holy water in a font or stoup, usually at the entrance of the church. Catholics typically bless themselves upon entering the church (by dipping their fingers and making the sign of the cross). The Orthodox may or may not bless themselves with holy water when they enter a church; however, they will often take it home to drink and cook with. Holy water is used in baptisms and originates from the significant baptism of Jesus by John the Baptist (see below).

Holy water is also sprinkled on the congregation during Roman Catholic mass (called aspersion) or during a particular event in the Orthodox Church; I remember being sprinkled with holy water on Palm Sundays.

Clergy prepare holy water in several ways, depending on how it will be used. The holy water found in fonts and stoups is meant for blessings and aspersions and preserved with a small amount of salt. *Chrism* (anointing oil) is added to baptismal holy water; water used to consecrate a church includes a small amount of wine, salt and ashes. Easter water is distributed on Easter Sunday and meant to be used at home.

Sikhs use holy water (*amrita*) in their baptism ceremony, called *Amrit Sanchar*, and the Shia Islam "healing water" is commonly to be drunk. In the tradition of the *Twelver Shi'a*, dust from sacred locations (e.g., the holy city of Karbala in Iraq) is dissolved in water that is later drunk for curative purposes. Since the 13th century, the *Ismaili* of South Asia drink water blessed by the *Imam* (an Islamic leader of a mosque).

The Hindus consider the Ganges a holy river and bathe in its waters during the Kumbh Mela (see more below). In the *Theravada* tradition, Buddhists place their blessed water into a pot for a *Paritrana* (deliverance) ceremony. This purifying "lustral water" is created by the burning and extinction of a candle above the water, which represents the four elements (earth, fire, air and water), and is shared with others.

William Marks, author of *The Holy Order of Water*, tells us that in Genesis 7:11, "the Hebrew term *Mayanot Tehom Raba* translates to 'the fountains of the great deep,' which burst forth at the same time that the 'windows of heaven' were opened at the beginning of Noah's flood." Marks adds that the Hebrew word for 'deep' is *tehom*, which comes from the word *Tiamat*, the name of the ancient goddess of the heavenly waters and the waters of the deep. The connection to the goddess was eventually lost but the term *tehom raba* continued to refer to flowing water from the ground. According to Marks, the ancient writings implied that the Tigris and Euphrates rivers "flowed from the eye of the goddess Tiamat", which correlates with these rivers emerging from large springs in the foothills of the Zagros Mountains along the border of Iraq, Iran, and Turkey.[37]

Photo 10.11: The Jordan River, seen from the baptism complex, 5 miles north of the Dead Sea in Jordan.

Marks adds that Christ was called the fountain of life. "Theologians did not hesitate to identify this water with Christ,"[35] says Marks. He quotes Clement of Alexandria's *Discourse on the Holy Theophany*, who wrote of water "that not only is it 'the natural source of life,' but it was also a spiritual element without which the life of the soul cannot exist. In fact, this water is none other than 'Christ, the maker of all,' who came down as the rain and was known as a spring (John 4:14, KJV), diffused himself as a river (John 7:38, KJV), and was baptized in the Jordan. Christ is the 'boundless River that makes glad the city of God ...' (Psalms 46:4, KJV), the illimitable Spring that bears life to all men and has no end, who is present everywhere and absent nowhere, who is incomprehensible to angels and invisible to human beings."[37]

Photo by B. Crawford, Wikimedia Commons

Sacred Lakes, Springs & "Lines"

"I must live near a lake. Without water, I thought, nobody could live at all."

—*Carl Jung*

In Chapter 1, I mention that Lake Baikal is called "the Sacred Sea", due to its life-giving properties, diverse biology and extreme clarity, not to mention its Prussian blue colour.

In another part of the world, Mount Kailash rises some 22,000 feet above sea level in the far western region of Tibet and is a destination for holy pilgrimage. Lake Mansarovar, located on that holy mountain, personifies purity in Hinduism, and is source to four of Asia's greatest rivers: the Indus, Sutlej, Brahmaputra and Karnali. The almost circular meltwater-fed lake is a stunning cobalt blue colour and considered sacred by Buddhists, Hindus and Jainists, whose origin myths all involve the holy water of Mount Kailash. According to Hindu mythology, Lake Mansarovar is a personification of purity, and one who drinks water from this chilly lake will go to the Abode of Lord Shiva after death. The sycophant is believed to be cleansed of all his sins committed over even a hundred lifetimes. Mount Kailash is commonly referred to as the centre of the Universe in eastern religious scriptures.

The healing water of Lourdes, a water grotto in southern France, is world-renowned and attracts six million pilgrims a year. The water flows from a spring in the Grotto of Massabielle in the Sanctuary of Our Lady of Lourdes. The location of the spring was described to Bernadette Soubirous by an apparition of *Our Lady of Lourdes* (Blessed Virgin Mary), in 1958. Since then, Lourdes has become a major Marian pilgrimage site and pilgrims follow the Virgin Mary's instruction to "drink at the spring and bathe in it." While not formally encouraged by the Roman Catholic Church, Lourdes water became a focus of devotion to the Virgin Mary.[45] Many have testified to its curative properties;

the Lourdes authorities provide it free of charge to any petitioner.

The Orthodox Church considers the spring at Pochaev Lavra in the Ukraine and the spring of the *Theotokos* (Mother of God Incarnate) in Constantinople to contain holy water with miraculous properties.

William Marks writes of the system of "holy lines", called *ceques*, by which the ancient Incan Empire linked water features to human-made and natural holy places. The Inca believed that they received, by right of birth, the underground water from their ancestors who resided within the earth.[37]

Incan *ceques* may be similar to *ley lines*, hypothetical alignments of places of geographical interest, such as ancient monuments and mega-liths. Amateur archaeologist Alfred Watkins first brought them to attention through his 1921 book *The Old Straight Track*, which discussed the ancient (pre-Roman, Neolithic) straight trackways in the British landscape. These alignments have evolved into new significance for mystics and meta-physicists through the "planetary energetic grid theory." Proposed by Chris Bird, this theory was based on icosahedron (one of the Platonic solids) research by Ivan P. Sanderson and later by Bethe Hagens and William S. Becker, who drew their inspiration from systems theorist Buckminster Fuller's geodesic domes.[46,47] The energy grids are composed of icosahedral lines that join various interesting points (Earth energy nodes at each vertex) to form a matrix. The nodes occur at some of the strongest power places on the planet, including Giza, Lake Baikal, Dragon's Triangle in Japan, Ankor Wat, Nazka (Peru), Axum (Ethiopia) and Sarawak (Borneo). Many ley-markers or "nodes" are associated with springs and underground water sources.[37] These may currently manifest above ground in various ways as moats, ponds, fords and wells.

The Chinese art of *feng shui*, which translates to "wind and water," also means "*that which cannot be seen and cannot be grasped.*" Essentially, a philosophical art form of harmonizing a person with their surrounding environment, it relates to one of the Five Arts of Chinese Metaphysics called *Xiang* (i.e., the study of forms and interpreting nature).

Those who practice feng shui determine the flow of *lung-mei* ("dragon currents") and arrange one's abode to conform to these currents. Determining factors include local features such as water bodies, but also the position of the stars and cardinal directions. Feng shui considers *Qi* (chi) energy, yin and yang polarity and the *bagua* (eight trigrams).[48] The eight trigrams, used in Taoist cosmology, represent eight concepts of the fundamental principles of reality and have correspondences in astronomy, astrology, geography, geomancy, anatomy, and family.[49] According to Guo Pu, the *Qi* (chi or life force) "rides the wind and scatters, but is retained when it encounters water."[48] In modern feng shui, the water element is considered flowing and truth-seeking, replicating the flow of *Qi* energy. Water is "reflective" on many levels, from its mirroring polish to its archetype—the philosopher, who helps explain the mysteries of the world.[50]

Figure 10.12: Lourdes Basilica and the Town of Lourdes, France.

Figure 10.1: Micrograph of a dried water drop from Lourdes, France, potentised with Ignatia, *from* Welt im Tropfen *("World in a Drop", page 39.*

Berndt Kroplin, Institute for Statistic and Dynamics of Aerospace Structures, University of Stuttgart

Photo by Milorad Pavlek, Wikimedia Commons

Sacred Rivers

According to Hindu mythology, the Ganges River, India's holiest river, originates in the heavens. The *Kumbh Mela* is a fifty-five-day festival of life that occurs in Allahabad, where the Ganges, Saraswati and Yamumuna Rivers meet. It is the largest bathing ritual in the world and named after the mythological water pot of life. *Sadhus* (holy practitioners) cover themselves with ash and then bathe in the river nude. Cremation is an important part of the Hindu faith and many will have their cremated ashes scattered over this holy river.

"In India, every river is sacred,"[33] writes Indian scholar Vandana Shiva. "Rivers are seen as extensions and partial manifestations of divine gods." According to Rigvedic cosmology, Shiva tells us, life is associated with the release of heavenly waters by Indra, the god of rain. Shiva tells the story of how Indra defeated Vrtra, the demon of chaos who had withheld and hoarded the waters, releasing the heavenly waters that rushed to earth and allowed life to spring forth.

The Mekong River, considered the "mother of waters" receives offerings from Laotians during *Boun Pi Mai Lao*, their New Year's celebration. Citizens remove Buddha images from the temples in order to clean them with scented water, and then take to the streets to douse one another—an act of cleansing and purification in anticipation of the end of the dry season.

The River Jordan is significant to Jews, Christians and Muslims as the site where the Israelites crossed into the Promised Land. It is the site of several miracles mentioned in the Bible. Jesus of Nazareth was baptized by John the Baptist in the Jordan.

According to the Orthodox Church, which celebrates this event in the *Feast of Theophany* (celebrating the "manifestation of God," when God revealed his divine presence), John's baptising was "a baptism of

"Anyone who drinks the water that I shall give will never thirst again: the water that I shall give will turn into a spring within them, welling up to eternal life."

—John 4:14

repentance, and the people came to have their sins washed away by the water. Since Jesus had no sin, but was God incarnate, his baptism had the effect not of washing away Jesus' sins, but of blessing the water, making it holy—and with it all of creation, so that it may be used fully for its original created purpose to be an instrument of life."[51]

Where the River Jordan empties into the sea, the salty water there becomes fresh: "Swarms of living creatures will live wherever the river flows ... Fruit trees of all kinds will grow on both banks of the river. Their leaves will not wither, nor will their fruit fail. Every month they will bear fruit, because the water from the sanctuary flows to them. Their fruit will serve for food and their leaves for healing."[52]

The apostle John saw the River Jordan in his vision of the end times and the New Jerusalem: "Then the angel showed me the river of the water of life, as clear as crystal, flowing from the throne of God and of the Lamb down the middle of the great street of the city. On each side of the river stood the tree of life, bearing twelve crops of fruit, yielding its fruit every month. And the leaves of the tree are for the healing of the nations."[53]

Photo 10.14: Grapes on the vine in Niagara-On-The-Lake, Ontario, Canada.

Photo by Nina Munteanu

Figure 10.13: Vineyard in Niagara-On-The-Lake, on the fertile Niagara escarpment of the Niagara River, Ontario, Canada.

Photo by Nina Munteanu

Healing Water

In Wetaskiwin, Alberta, Canada, Elder John Crier with the Samson Cree Nation performed *The Spirit of the Water Ceremony* four times before moving on to other communities, who asked him to do the same. Four is a power symbol in Aboriginal Culture. The ceremony includes the celebration of the Four Sacred Elements: earth, air, water, and fire.[54]

Maskwacis Elder Roy Louis told reporter Christina Martens of the *Wetaskiwin Times* in 2015 that Aboriginal ceremonies had been banned by the government in 1885. But Louis wanted to revive the water ceremony in the Battle River. "I wanted to have the water blessed. You have to have good water to have a good life."[54] He felt it was important to have the river taken care of and asked Elder John Crier to perform the water ceremony.

In the early spring of 2002 in Superior, Wisconsin, in the time of the Bear Moon (when Black Bear cubs are generally born), the Ojibwa held a Water Ceremony for the first time in 150 years. Thirteen grandmothers participated.[55]

"Traditionally, in most cultures, the women are considered the keepers of the water,"[54] the article in *Mazina'igan, a Chronicle of the Lake Superior Ojibwa* says. "We have the connection and the ways and the ceremonies to bless and purify our waters as well as the waters that make up seventy percent of our physical bodies. We are the keepers of the water because we are more in tune with the natural cycles."

The ceremony is simple; women gather in a circle playing birch bark clapper sticks and singing the water ceremony song. The ceremony best occurs at the thirteenth moon (February/March) and at a new moon. The song is sung one time for each of the seven directions: east, south, west, north, above, below, and within. The Ojibwa article exhorts women from all over the world to, "Go and sing at lakes and rivers, wells

"When we are born, it is water that comes first. Birth is sacred and so is the water."
—George Brertton, Cree Elder, Saddle Lake First Nation

Re-Wilding the Sacred

Lake of sand, so grand
Teardrops to fill the gap
One by one bring life back

Vision lost to pain
Green grass much to gain
The stream dulls the flowers
Fear of all loss, cowers

Bring forth much play
Where all children will stay
Let us all have a say
Tomorrow brings hope, pray

Re-wilding: let the waters run
down
Re-wilding: let the sunshine
come
Re-wilding: all will come around
Time for some real fun

Let the healing begin
Back to the original sin
Take a bite, fly a kite
Run wild, run free

Rain rain come today
Much grass to grow
Many waters to flow
Colourful flowers no gray

Bring back the sacred
Bring back the sacred
The naked   the waters
the flowers   the frogs
the spirit   the faith
Integrate, meditate, levitate
Re-wild the sacred

Re-Wilding the Sacred ©2014
L.C. Di Marco, B.A., M.E.S.

and oceans and at the kitchen sink … We are living in the days of the great purification of the Earth. We have the choice to sit by helplessly watching the events take place or to be active participants in easing her passage. It can be as simple as singing a song at a river bank, putting our hands over a bowl of water for our children's consumption, giving thanks and blessing the water that goes into our morning coffee, or picking up the garbage at the beach."[55]

The ceremony was held again in 2003, and this time two to three thousand women from all around the world sang the purifying song for water at the same hour. The following year over nine thousand women participated. Eagle feathers were distributed to spiritual elders and healers around the world.[54]

Gladyce Wahlendyasa, an Ojibwa member of the Sault Ste. Marie Chippewa Tribe, told those at the Environment Film Festival of the Lac Courte Orilles Ojibwa Community College, "Water is the gift of life. Water is sacred. Water is alive and guided by spirits. Water is the transporter of other energies. Sing to the water to resonate vibrational healing. Give thanks to the water in ceremony. Water assists us in power. Give offerings to the water spirits. Give tobacco ties for water ceremony. Do a water ceremony around the New Moon. Water spirit is feminine. Water ceremony is fluid."[56]

Living with a Thankful Heart

In his book *The Secret Life of Water*, scientist and philosopher Masaru Emoto suggests that the reason we continually search for happiness is because we have a link to unlimited existence. But, he warns, most of us make the serious mistake of setting up conditions for happiness based on riches and fame, momentary pleasures, and things that are limited and always changing.[25]

According to Emoto, "water crystals are just one aspect or face of the universe. Water changes its appearance at will, as it attempts to speak to us concerning the formation of the cosmos. It is in itself a temporary world formed within a severe environment."[25] He described the structure of water crystals according to three properties: frequency, resonance, and similarity.

Emoto suggested that we speak to water every day:

Water, we love you.

We thank you.

We respect you.

"Whoever is thirsty, let him come; and whoever wishes, let him take the free gift of the water of life."
—***Revelations 22:17***

Water's Healing Melody

Traditional Eastern medicine has been based for many centuries on the vibrations and resonance of the body's water content. An experienced physician conducts energy scans of the body based on pulse, makes a diagnosis and prescribes treatment. "We do not heal with water," says Tibetan doctor Ogun Bolson, "because a person, a human, is water. The person simply reads the mantras or prayers in order to correct the bad water he has inside."[57]

"Water teaches us how to live," says Emoto. It teaches us "how to forgive, how to believe. If you open your ears to the possibilities in life, you may just be able to hear the sound of the pure water that flows through your body even now. It is the sound of your life—a melody of healing." He adds that, "The human body is ... a universe of its own. Our bodies consist of some 60 trillion cells, each carrying out its specialized responsibility while simultaneously harmonizing with other cells in a wonderful way to make us who we are. The organs, nerves, and cells of the body have their own unique frequency. The body is like a grand orchestra consisting of the harmonization of various sounds."[25]

I recall being shown by Canadian scientist David Suzuki how the normal heart beats in a symphony of "chaos," with a kind of playful cadence. Suzuki showed that in people suffering from heart problems, their heart had taken on a monotonic structured beat, a kind of "deadbeat" sound.[58] "The apparent regularity of the heartbeat conceals abundant variability, and contrary to common intuition, the more healthy the heart, the more variable the beat," says biochemist Mae Wan Ho. She adds that, "The most exciting discovery about the healthy heartbeat is the rich mathematical structure underlying the apparent variability

that distinguishes it from arbitrary randomness; in much the way that music can be distinguished from noise."[59]

The heart dances a rhythmic symphony like a swirling brook—at once turbulent and ordered.

Prayer ripples out in circular waves of coherence from its source and back. Gestalt self-actualization. Prayer is a rainbow, revealing the reflected soul. Prayer scours, cleanses, refreshes and renews in a cycle of creation and connection.

Prayer is water.

Photo 10.15: Boathouse on the South Shore of Nova Scotia, near Peggy's Cove, Canada.

Photo by Nina Munteanu

References

1. Mastrantonis, Rev. George. 1996. "The Feast of Epiphany: The Feast of Lights." Greek Orthodox Archdiocese of America. Online: http://www.goarch.org/ourfaith/ourfaith8383/

2. Seto, A.., C. Kusaka, S. Nakazato, WR Huang, T. Hisamitsu, C. Takeshige. 1992. "Detection of Extraordinary Large Bio-Magnetic Field Strength from Human Hand." *Acupuncture Electrother Res Int J.* 17:75.

3. Zimmerman J. 1989. "Laying-on-of-hands and Therapeutic Touch: a Testable Theory, BEMI Currents." *J Bio-Electro-Magnet Ins.* 2:8.

4. Smolensky Kirill, Metropolitan. 2006. In: "Water, the Great Mystery." Julie Perkul and Anastasiya Popova, directors. *Intention Media.* 87 min.

5. Orme-Johnson, David. 2006. "Societal Effects." Truth About TM. Online: http://www.truthabouttm.org/truth/SocietalEffects/Rationale-Research/index.cfm#summary

6. Dillbeck, M.C., G. Landrith and D.W. Orme-Johnson. 1981. "The Transcendental Meditation Program and Crime Rate Change in a Sample of Forty-eight Cities." *Crime and Justice* 4: 26–45.

7. Dillbeck, M.C., C.B. Banus, C. Polanzi & G. Landrith. 1988. "Test of a Field Model of Consciousness and Social Change: The Transcendental Meditation and TM-Sidhi Program and Decreased Urban Crime." *Journal of Mind and Behavior* 9: 457–486.

8. Orme-Johnson, D.W.; C.N. Alexander, C.N., J.L. Davies, H.M. Chandler and W.E. Larimore. 1988. "International Peace Project in the Middle East: The Effect of the Maharishi Technology of the Unified Field." *Journal of Conflict Resolution* 32(4): 776–812.

9. Cavanaugh, K.L. and K.D. King. 1988. "Simultaneous Transfer Function Analysis of Okun's Misery Index: Improvements in the Economic Quality of Life Through Maharishi's Vedic Science and Technology of Consciousness." In: *Proceedings of the American Statistical Association, Business and Economic Statistics Section*: 491–496.

10. Davies, J. L. and C. N. Alexander. 2005. "Alleviating Political Violence

Through Reducing Collective Tension: Impact Assessment Analysis of The Lebanon War." *Journal of Social Behavior and Personality* 17: 285–338.

11. Hagelin, J., D.W. Orme-Johnson, M. Rainforth, K.L. Cavanaugh, and C.N. Alexander. 1994. "The Effects of the National Demonstration Project to Reduce Violent Crime and Improve Governmental Effectiveness in Washington, D.C.: Interim Report." *Institute of Science, Technology and Public Policy Technical Report* 94: 1.

12. Hagelin, John. 2006. In: "Peace from the Quantum Level." Interview. YouTube video online: https://www.youtube.com/watch?v=TsvEkPNitdQ

13. Hagelin, John. 2009. "Can Group Meditation Bring World Peace? Quantum Physicist, John Hagelin Explains." YouTube video online: https://www.youtube.com/watch?v=yVFa6Wtuxu8

14. Hagelin, John. 2009. "A Scientific Introduction to Transcendental Meditation by Dr. John Hagelin." YouTube video online: https://www.youtube.com/watch?v=TfIqvZLlZz8

15. Sheer, J. 1994. "On Mystical Experiences as Empirical Support for the Perennial Philosophy." *Journal of the American Academy of Religion* 62(2): 319–342.

16. Bohm, David. 1980. "Wholeness and the Implicate Order." *Routledge*, UK. 284 pp.

17. James, William. 1909. "A Pluralistic Universe." Volume 4. Eds. Burkhardt F., F. Bowers. *Harvard University Press*.

18. Durkheim, Émile. 1893 (1997). "Division of Labour in Society." Trans. W. D. Halls, *Free Press*, NY. 262 pp.

19. Jung, C.G. 1916 (1953). "The Structure of the Unconscious." Collected Works vol. 7: 437–507.

20. Campbell, Joseph. 1949. "A Hero with a Thousand Faces." *Pantheon Books*, NY. 432 pp.

21. Plato. 360 BCE (1921). "Thaetetus" and "Sophist." Harold North Fowler (trans.). Jeffrey Henderson (ed). Loeb Classical Library. *Harvard University Press*. 480 pp.

22. Jeans, James. 1930. "The Mysterious Universe." *Cambridge University Press*, UK. 163 pp.

23. Dossey, L. 1989. "Recovering the Soul." *Bantam Books*, NY. 336 pp.

24. Stapp, Henry. 1993. "Mind, Matter and Quantum Mechanics." *Springer-Verlag*, NY. 248 pp.

25. Emoto, Masaru. 2005. "The Secret Life of Water." *Atria Books*. 178 pp.

26. Roy, Rustum. 2006. In: "Water: the Great Mystery." Interview. Julie Perkul and Anastasiya Popova, directors. *Intention Media*. 87 min.

27. Korotkov, Konstantin. 2006. In: "Water, the Great Mystery." Julie Perkul and Anastasiya Popova, directors. *Intention Media*. 87 min.

28. Gruber, Allois. 2006. In: "Water, the Great Mystery." Julie Perkul and Anastasiya Popova, directors. *Intention Media*. 87 min.

29. Klima, Gerbert. 2006. In: "Water, the Great Mystery." Julie Perkul and Anastasiya Popova, directors. *Intention Media*. 87 min.

30. Steinsaltz, Adin. 2006. In: "Water, the Great Mystery." Julie Perkul and Anastasiya Popova, directors. *Intention Media*. 87 min.

31. Newman, Cathy. 2010. "Sacred Waters." National Geographic, Water Issue. *National Geographic*. April, 2010.

32. Eliade, Mircea. 1996. "Patterns in Comparative Religion." *Bison Books*. 484 pp.

33. Shiva, Vandana. 2002. "Water Wars: Privatization, Pollution and Profit." *India Research Press*. 160 pp.

34. Bali Advertiser. 2012. "Bali Hindu: The Religion of the Holy Water." *Bali Advertiser*. Online: http://www.baliadvertiser.biz/articles/feature/2012/holy_water.html

35. Stevens, Anthony. 2001. "Ariadne's Clue: A Guide to the Symbols of Humankind." *Princeton University Press*. 480 pp.

36. Freeman, Mara. 2015. "Sacred Waters—Holy Wells." The Order of Bards, Ovats & Druids. Online: http://www.druidry.org/library/sacred-waters-holy-wells

37. Marks, William. 2001. "The Holy Order of Water." *Bell Pond Books*. 256 pp.

38. Schumacher, Mark. "Sujin." Online: http://www.onmarkproductions. com/html/suijin.html

39. Dougill, John. 2012. "Pagan Connections (3) Sacred Water." *Green Shinto*. Online: http://www.greenshinto.com/wp/2012/07/26/ pagan-connections-3-springs-and-wells/

40. Masamiito. 2003. "Getting into Hot Water for Health." *The Japan Times*. May 25. Online: http://search.japantimes.co.jp/community/2003/05/25/ community/getting-into-hot-water-for-health/#.Vhhrzktgrlx

41. Young, Andrew. 2012. "An Introduction to Mirages." San Diego State University. Online: http://www-rohan.sdsu.edu/Ăaty/mirages/ mirintro.html

42. Chalice Well Trust. 1975. "Chalice Well, Glastonbury, Somerset, England: A Short History." Glastonbury: *Chalice Well Trust*. Page 10.

43. Heath, Fiona. 2015. Personal Communication. E-mail, September 30, 2015.

44. Heath, Fiona. 2015. "Sacred Water." The Empty Chalice. Online: http://emptychalice.com/2015/09/12/sacred-water/

45. Harris, Ruth. 1999. "Lourdes: Body and Spirit in the Secular Age." *Penguin Books*. 496 pp.

46. Bird, Chris. 1975. "Planetary Grid." *New Age Journal* 5: 36–41.

47. Hagens, Bethe. 1984. "The Becker-Hagens Grid." *Biblioteca pleyades*. Online: http://www.bibliotecapleyades.net/mapas_ocultotierra/ esp_mapa_ocultotierra_12.htm

48. Pu, Guo. 2001. "The Zangshu Book of Burial." Translated by Stephen L. Field. Online: http://fengshuigate.com/zangshu.html

49. Tsuei, Wei. 1989. "Roots of Chinese Culture and Medicine." *Chinese Culture Books Co*. 130 pp.

50. Anonymous. 2014. "The Water Element: Feng Shui Shapes & Colors, Part 5." *Open Spaces Feng Shui*. Online: http://openspacesfengshui.com/ feng-shui-tips/2014/12/water-element-feng-shui-shapes-colors-part-5/

51. St. Mary's Holy Assumption Russian Orthodox Church. 2015. "Holy Water Miracle." *St. Mary's Holy Assumption Russian Orthodox Church*, Stamford, CT. Online: http://stmaryofstamford.org/holywater.html

52. Ezekiel 47: 8–9. *The Holy Bible*, King James Version.

53. Revelation 22: 1–2. *The Holy Bible*, King James Version.

54. Martens, Christina. 2015. "Celebrating the Spirit of the Water." *Wetaskiwin Times*, June 10, 2015. Online: http://www.wetaskiwintimes.com/2015/06/10/celebrating-the-spirit-of-the-water-2

55. Anonymous. 2007/2008. "Nibi Wabo a Woman's Water Song." *Mazina'igan, a Chronicle of the Lake Superior Ojibwa*. Winter 2007/2008 issue. p. 20.

56. Whitedeer, Tonya. 2010. "Water Ceremonies." *The Sisterhood of the Planetary Water Rites*. Online: http://www.waterblessings.org/ceremonies_general.html

57. Bolson, Ogun. 2006. In: "Water: the Great Mystery." Julie Perkul and Anastaysia Popova, directors. *Intention Media*. 87 min.

58. Suzuki, David. 2003. "The Matrix of Life." A Sacred Balance: Rediscovering Our Place in Nature, Part 4. *Bullfrog Films*. 214 min.

59. Ho, Mae Wan. 2007. "Physics of Organism & Applications: The Heartbeat of Health." *Institute of Science in Society* 25/07/07. Online: http://www.i-sis.org.uk/HeartbeatofHealth.php

11. Water is Wisdom

"Water does not resist. Water flows. When you plunge your hand into it, all you feel is a caress. Water is not a solid wall, it will not stop you. But water always goes where it wants to go, and nothing in the end can stand against it. Water is patient. Dripping water wears away a stone. Remember that, my child. Remember you are half water. If you can't go through an obstacle, go around it. Water does."

—Margaret Atwood, *The Penelopiad*

Photo 11.1: Flow patterns of a cascade in the Credit River, Ontario.

Photo by Nina Munteanu

Quantum Wisdom

"The natural world," Alick Bartholomew, author of *The Spiritual Life of Water*, tells us, "is essentially an indivisible unity, but our present culture is [currently] condemned to apprehend it from two different directions, through our senses (perception) or through our minds (concepts). A child simply observes and marvels, but as our rational minds develop, we are taught to interpret what we see, usually through other peoples' ideas, in order to 'make sense' of our sensory experience. Both are forms of reality, but unless we are able to bring the two aspects together in a meaningful way, the world will present nothing but incomprehensible riddles to us."[1]

The worldviews between classic science and quantum science diverge in significant ways. The Newtonian model of classic science is mechanistic and applies a *reductionist approach*, investigating the parts of a whole to determine separate and overall functionality. For instance, in classic science an organism may be described as being controlled by a brain and its nervous system with energy applied according to the second law of thermodynamics; the neo-Darwinian model would add a competitive random nature to life systems functions. Quantum theory applies a *holistic approach* to describe the whole as an inter-communication of all its parts. The quantum approach acknowledges cooperation and reciprocity, local freedom and cohesion as part of an indivisible whole. According to the late physicist David Bohm, quantum theory embraces as primary the role of wholeness and process, linked to movement.[2,3] According to Bohm, everything is in what he calls *universal flux* (a state of process or becoming), a dynamic wholeness-in-motion in which everything moves together in an interconnected process: "undivided wholeness in flowing movement."[3]

"I think we are beginning to perceive nature in Earth in exactly the opposite way we viewed it in classical physics. We no longer conceive of nature as a passive object ... I see us as nearer to a Taoist view, in which we are embedded in a universe that is not foreign to us"
—**Ilya Prigogine**

Photo 11.2: David Bohm, American theoretical physicist.

Wikimedia

A student of Einstein, Bohm created the *Holomovement concept* as part of his critique of the mechanistic assumptions behind much of modern physics and biology: "each relatively autonomous and stable structure is to be understood, not as something independently and permanently existent, but rather as a product that has been formed in the whole flowing movement and that will ultimately dissolve back into this movement. How it forms and maintains itself, then, depends on its place–function within the whole."[3]

Movement gives shape to all forms, and structure gives order to movement, says Bohm. In other words, information contributes fundamentally to or "informs" substance. Bohm suggested that "a deeper and more extensive inner movement creates, maintains, and ultimately dissolves structure."[3] Wheels within wheels in a fractal arrangement, wherein electrons have a mind-like quality.[2] A wise friend once explained it this way: if you were a finger of a hand, you might in your limited perspective see yourself as separate from all the other fingers; yet you are connected to them all through the hand—whose connection to you as well you may not recognize. The hand, in turn, is connected to a greater moving whole, the torso, and so on.

Photo 11.3: Old barn under fresh snow on the road from Lunenburg to Wolfville, Nova Scotia, Canada.

Photo by Nina Munteanu

Geneticist Mae-Wan Ho compared the mechanistic view of matter to studying dead matter and the holistic view to studying "the living fabric of life."[4]

Physicist Fritjof Capra wrote in his book *The Tau of Physics*: "Quantum theory reveals a basic oneness of the universe ... As we penetrate into matter, Nature does not show us any isolated 'basic building blocks,' but rather appears as a complicated web of relations among the various parts of the whole ... The human observer constitutes the final link in the chain of observational processes, and the properties of any atomic object can be understood only in terms of the object's interaction with the observer."[5]

Bohm proposed that creation is aware of itself and its oneness in "continuous creation." He proposed that space is filled with the dynamic energy he called "etheric or universal flux," with flow being at the basis of everything. Bohm posited a *holographic model* of the universe.[3] He saw the universe as a vast undivided and coherent whole, which he called "implicate or implied," and contended that everything in the everyday material reality—explicit, manifest—contained all the information of the implicate order; essentially, every part has the information of the whole.[2] This harkens to the concept of *fractals* and recursive self-similarity, which I discuss in Chapters 3, 6 and 8: the tendency of things to self-repeat from one level and reveal coherence.

Biophysicist Mae-Wan Ho writes that "*quantum coherence* is a paradoxical state of wholeness that is anything but uniform. It is infinitely diverse and … maximizes both local freedom and global cohesion. The quantum-coherent organism … is a domain of coherent energy storage that accumulates no waste or entropy within, because it mobilizes energy most efficiently and rapidly to grow and develop and reproduce."[6]

That water behaves coherently, like a self-organized fractal organism, is a concept that remains unaccepted by most scientists. However, Ho and other scientists such as Voeikov and Del Guidice suggest that water's quantum characteristics (e.g., water stores information, self-organizes, self-purifies, and demonstrates properties of an organism) reflect its two states (low density and high density), which toggle within a stable non-equilibrium. These energy dynamics of water defy the second law of thermodynamics.[6,7]

Photo 11.4: Fresh snow on trees on the road from Lunenburg to Wolfville, Nova Scotia, Canada.

Natural systems work like wheels within wheels. This image is mentioned in the Judeo-Christian bible and Hindu scriptures: like fractals within the constant flux of stable chaos. Ho aptly calls this totality of Nature's activities "quantum jazz."[6]

Water does quantum jazz so very well.

"When I discovered that water was the key to my experience in life, everything else started to connect, like pieces of a jigsaw puzzle,"[1] says Bartholomew in the introduction to his book *The Spiritual Life of Water*. This astonishing admission reflects my own experience in writing this book, which I discuss in *Afterthoughts*.

Photo by Nina Munteanu

"It is difficult to understand the importance of water through a rational process," Bartholomew concludes. "When we use our imagination and our intuition, the meaning starts to unfold. It is an exciting path that may illuminate your own vision about the meaning of life."[1] In 1959, philosopher of science Karl Popper wrote, "There is no such thing as a logical method of having new ideas, or a logical reconstruction of this process … Every discovery contains an irrational element or a creative intuition."[8]

Intuitive naturalist Viktor Schauberger wrote, "the majority believe that everything hard to comprehend must be very profound. This is incorrect. What is hard to understand is what is immature, unclear, and often false. The highest wisdom is simple and passes through the brain directly into the heart."[9]

Water is the question. And the answer.

Photo 11.5: Boat in the snow at the Lunenburg dory shop, Nova Scotia, Canada.

Photo by Nina Munteanu

Fractals, Synchronicity & the Unexpected Universe

The mysterious alchemist Hermes Trismegistus (perhaps the Egyptian priest Thoth), provided the following principle of correspondence: "As above, so below; as within, so without; as the Universe, so the soul." That is, the microcosm reflects the macrocosm. This in essence describes a fractal Universe. A Universe of recapitulation. And connection.

Water's restless spirit is a quantum trait. Water is ever-changing, constructing and deconstructing, opening and closing, chaotic and stable. Water is "compliant, mobile, tasteless,"[10] reflecting the qualities of its surroundings. Water is clear, invisible, paradoxical, anomalous. Ordered. Chaotic. Playful. Dark and flowing. Destroying the status quo and creating opportunity through rhythm.

Water inspires. It is the herald of change. Inspiration catalyzes movement and creates unexpected opportunities. All artists know that a routine, predictable life provides little opportunity or creative spark.

Just as rhythmic turbulence in water creates opportunity for the environment, so rhythm and turbulence brings opportunity for the creative soul. Often through a disaster or calamity. In her book *The Artist's Way* Julia Cameron gives the example of writer May Sarton's experience after a painful loss. Upon entering her empty house, "I was stopped at the threshold of my study by a ray on a Korean chrysanthemum, lighting it up like a spotlight, deep red petals and Chinese yellow center … Seeing it was like getting a transfusion of autumn light."[11] Sarton's

"Do I contradict myself? Very well, then I contradict myself; I am large—I contain multitudes."
—Walt Whitman

use of the word *transfusion* was no accident, writes Cameron. In the act of paying attention, Sarton opened to creativity and her healing began. "The reward for attention is always healing, ... connection,"[11] and transcendence. I talk more about this in the section on evolution below. Carl Jung adds that "the creation of something new is not accomplished by the intellect but by the play instinct acting from inner necessity. The creative mind plays with the objects it loves."[11]

Water is like an unruly child, playful, disorderly and ultimately wise.

The late Nobel Laureate chemist Ilya Prigogine suggested that disorder creates simultaneously stable and unstable oscillating systems in a spiral form that leads to order.[1] This allows the emergence of what I call *stable chaos*—a kind of dynamic equilibrium of stable change that embraces paradox. Prigogine tells us that this oscillation of dynamic *homeostasis* (stability) increases complexity and energy levels. His position reflects the notion of a two-state complex, as discussed by Ho and Voiekov & Del Guidice (see Chapter 2), with the vortex serving as both vehicle and window between different qualities of energy.

Photo 11.6: Ocean pebbles on Hirtle Beach, Nova Scotia, Canada.

Recent evidence suggests that black holes are vortex gateways that link different parts of a universe or universes. Physicist Nikodem Poplawski published findings in 2010 that suggested that *black holes*, instead of harbouring space–time singularities, were tunnels for spiralling matter falling into them between universes in a multiverse. According to Poplawski's equations, the matter that black holes absorb and apparently destroy is actually expelled and provides the building blocks for galaxies, stars, and planets in another reality.[12] "Like part of a cosmic Russian doll, our Universe may be nested inside a black hole that is itself part of a larger universe,"[12] wrote Ker Than in the *National Geographic News*. The still-controversial *dark flow* describes a non-random movement possible in galaxy clusters, suggesting that the clusters are being tugged on by the gravity of something lurking beyond our known Universe. Astrophysicist Alexander Kashlinsky and his colleagues at the Goddard Space Flight Center in Maryland tracked the coherent "dark flow" that extends out at least 2.5 billion light-years from Earth and strongly hints at our Universe as part of something larger: a fractal multiverse.[13,14,15]

It is noteworthy that scientific pursuit and discovery reflect prevailing worldviews—it makes sense. We see what we are ready to see, and not sooner.

In Chapter 7, I talk about multiple and synchronous discoveries: serendipitous discoveries, sudden epiphanies and bursts of genius. Had the scientists tapped into something greater than themselves, something that all were connected to? *The Field* perhaps? Or merely coincidence?

Carl Jung created the concept of *synchronicity* in the 1920s to describe events such as "meaningful coincidences," if they occurred with no apparent causal relationship, yet were meaningfully related. In other words, events connected by meaning need not have an explanation through causality.[16] Jung's causality vs. meaning reflects Bohm's *substance* vs. *form* argument (see above).[2,3] By describing a governing dynamic that underlies the whole of human experience, synchronicity confirmed Jung's concept of *archetypes* (underlying form in universal patterns and images in the minds of individuals) within the *collective unconscious* (structures of the unconscious mind shared by humanity, populated by instincts and archetypes). The fractal whole.

Jung gives an interesting example of synchronicity in his book:

"My example concerns a young woman patient who, in spite of efforts made on both sides, proved to be psychologically inaccessible. The difficulty lay in the fact that she always knew better about everything. Her excellent education had provided her with a weapon ideally suited to this purpose, namely a highly polished Cartesian rationalism with an impeccably 'geometrical' idea of reality. After several fruitless attempts to sweeten her rationalism with a somewhat more human understanding, I had to confine myself to the hope that something unexpected and irrational would turn up, something that would burst the intellectual retort into which she had sealed herself. Well, I was sitting opposite her

Photo 11.7: Carl Gustav Jung, Swiss psychiatrist and psychotherapist who founded analytical psychology.

Wikimedia

one day, with my back to the window, listening to her flow of rhetoric. She had an impressive dream the night before, in which someone had given her a golden scarab—a costly piece of jewellery. While she was still telling me this dream, I heard something behind me gently tapping on the window. I turned round and saw that it was a fairly large flying insect that was knocking against the window-pane from outside in the obvious effort to get into the dark room. This seemed to me very strange. I opened the window immediately and caught the insect in the air as it flew in. It was a scarabaeid beetle, or common rose-chafer (*Cetoniaaurata*), whose gold-green colour most nearly resembles that of a golden scarab. I handed the beetle to my patient with the words, 'Here is your scarab.' This experience punctured the desired hole in her rationalism and broke the ice of her intellectual resistance. The treatment could now be continued with satisfactory results."[17]

In his book *Thirty Years That Shook Physics—the Story of Quantum Theory*, George Gamow discusses a term he whimsically called the *Pauli effect* to describe a mysterious phenomenon surrounding the theoretical physicist Wolfgang Pauli. "It is well known that theoretical physicists cannot handle experimental equipment," Gamow shares. "It breaks whenever they touch it. Pauli was such a good theoretical physicist that something usually broke in the lab whenever he merely stepped across the threshold."[17]

Jung embraced the parallels between synchronicity, relativity theory and quantum mechanics.[18] Jung believed that life was not a series of random events, but rather an expression of a deeper order, which he and theoretical physicist Wolfgang Pauli called *Unus mundus*. His suggestion—that we are embedded in a framework or whole and are, at the same time, the focus of that whole—was later described by David Bohm in his work with quantum theory (see previous section).

"So above, so below."

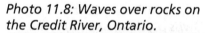

Photo 11.8: Waves over rocks on the Credit River, Ontario.

Photo by Nina Munteanu

Body Consciousness

Years ago, I was visiting my good friends Anne and Bob in the Lower Fraser Valley in British Columbia. They owned a small ranch and Anne invited me to ride with her in the local forest near their property. I gladly agreed and looked forward later to one of Anne's gourmet meals. Although not an experienced equestrian, I somehow coaxed my horse into a gallop and was exalting in the thrill of speeding through the trees when we rounded a corner—and I saw a rogue tree in the middle of the path. I leaned left but the horse swerved right, not getting my message. Locked in a frozen moment, I realized that my body and my head were rushing headlong for the tree. Time deconstructed and slowed to a dream. A carillon of men and women's voices burst into my mind, urging me to move my head. "Not your time yet," they sang. I twitched my head aside in time to avoid cracking it open and only grazed it, letting my shoulder take the brunt of the hit. It knocked me right off my galloping horse, and I was winded by the fall. It all happened within a fraction of a second. When I sat up, I paid little heed to the sharp pain in my shoulder and general ache of my body; I was totally enraptured by the voices that had saved my life. We all have our guardians. What shape they take, and the ironic path they lead us in, can often surprise us.

What really saved me? What—who—were those "voices" that called to me, as if from a different dimension? Anne, who had been riding close behind me, had heard nothing—except the thunk of my head and shoulder against the tree and the hard thump of my ensuing fall.

On Gerald Pollack's out-on-a-limb diagram, I'm heading to the outer branches when I suggest that something was definitely communicating with me. Something beyond my recognized world. Were the choral voices angels? *An intervention of grace*? Did my brain conjure

"A discovery is said to be an accident meeting a prepared mind."

—Albert Szent-Gyorgyi

voices in its panicked state? Was it "water" acting as a doorway to other dimensional beings and/or other aspects of me? Were the trees talking to me? Was it all these? Had I simply tapped into "all of me"?

According to Bohm, we carry within us pieces of our whole and the pieces, in turn, make up a whole. We are fractal beings of self-organized frequency, oscillating between form and formlessness, determining our reality through intention—through consciousness. We are a community, living in a community. If our bodies are a holographic projection of our consciousness, as some believe, and at the same time the sum total of our beliefs about ourselves, then we define our human energy field as part of our relationship with the flowing whole. I talk about aspects of this, including exterior mind, non-local phenomena, and morphic resonance and fields in Chapter 4.

Albert Einstein shared his wisdom in this advice, "A human being is a part of a whole, called by us the universe, a part limited in time and space. He experiences himself, his thoughts and feelings as something separated from the rest … a kind of optical delusion of his consciousness. This delusion is a kind of prison for us, restricting us to our personal desires and to affection for a few persons nearest to us. Our task must be to free ourselves from this prison by widening our circle of compassion to embrace all living creatures and the whole of nature in its beauty."[19]

Those who practice Theosophy postulate a hierarchy of consciousness from lower to higher frequencies, encompassing domains or dimensions and each separated by a "veil" that keeps the higher dimension inaccessible. In other words, the higher frequency is aware of the lower frequencies, but the lower is not aware of or cannot understand the higher. Intuition and inspiration act as doorways for glimpsing higher dimensions of consciousness.

Collagen, a connective tissue that dominates multicellular animals, is made up of a crystalline matrix of proteins embedded in water.[1] Tests by scientists led by Gary Fullerton at Texas University suggest that water

associated with collagen demonstrates quantum order[20] and therefore the potential for a process called *jump-conduction of protons.* According to biochemist Mae Wan Ho, this process enables water to become superconductive and therefore makes possible instant communication among different parts of the body—faster than nerve impulses to the brain and back—toward a kind of "body consciousness."[21] This reflects the body's impeccable coordination and synchronicity that is currently insufficiently explained using the model of brain and nervous system communication. It explains how we operate as a coherent whole.

Research by Cleve Backster and others, while ignored or condemned by mainstream science (mainly due to the lack of repeatability and predictability of the experiments), suggests a kind of intelligence at the cellular level and a non-local communication (most likely through water).[1] Physicist Basil Hiley called the world "basically organic" and suggested—though somewhat whimsically—that even "an electron may have a proto-consciousness."[22]

"For a person to feel in *bliss*," writes clinical herbalist Terry Willard, "they have to have a high level of coherence. We could say this is a feeling of oneness, but it is much more than that. It is not only oneness within one's self; it is a feeling of being in the 'flow' with a greater whole. This concept has been around for many millennia, as reflected in the ancient Taoist term *wu wei.* (*Wu wei* can be translated into 'being in the flow' or 'knowing when to act and when not to act.') Another way of saying this is to 'do' without 'doing.' Just like a tree grows without thinking it is now time to grow."[23] Willard adds, "The more coherence we have, the more we can be in the flow (*wu wei*) of the fractal relationship of our galaxy … Create coherence and you are automatically in the flow."[23]

The same concept is evident in the Vedas, scriptures from India about five thousand years old.

Photo 11.9: Shed on the Atlantic Ocean with ice at Blue Rocks, Nova Scotia, Canada.

Photo by Nina Munteanu

The Heartbeat of an Intelligent Earth

"Water is peaceful and extends its beneficent action throughout Nature, not even disdaining those gloomy depths which the vulgar look upon with horror, for water works much as God does."

—Lao Tzu

Photo 11.10: Johann Wolfgang von Goethe, writer statesman and polymath.

Wikimedia

German poet and polymath Johann Wolfgang von Goethe believed, as did Johannes Kepler, that the Earth was an intelligent organism.[1] Goethe and Kepler are joined by others such as Plutarch, Leonardo da Vinci, and later by Steiner, Lovelock and Bohm in embracing the concept of Earth "evolving as part of a rising consciousness in the cosmos."[1]

Bringing in his artistic appreciation of all things, Goethe's experiential science, known as *phenomenology of nature*, provided a conceptual method to enter into a dialogue with Nature. Goethean science touched on concepts later developed in ecology, evolutionary science, and quantum mechanics. Goethe's intuitive science provided the seeds of what is currently called *deep ecology*, an ecology-based and intuitive-based worldview that advocates the inherent value of the natural world, whether connected to human utility or not, and one that encompasses the concepts of *holism* (grasping the authentic whole rather than a collection of parts, given that no parts are independent of the whole) and ecological consciousness—with both forming a Unity.[24]

Goethe called water "the ground of all being." His reference to "being" encompassed more than visible life. It was also the ground of Bohm's Implicate Order (see "Water & the Consciousness Whole" below).

Heavily influenced by Goethe, Rudolf Steiner, an inspired polymath, postulated that water was a conveyor of "cosmic intelligence" or "consciousness." Steiner suggested that water's role was to transfer information to the individual parts of the web of life (such as, organisms) for their growth, development and connectedness to the *flowing whole* (that is, the planet's biosphere patterns and rhythms within the cosmic whole).[25]

Water, according to Steiner, "self-regulates" and "self-evolves" from instincts of wholeness. This thinking reflects the Implicate Order of Nobel Laureate David Bohm. Flow scientist Theodor Schwenk, inspired by both Steiner and Goethe, describes water as Nature's central organ, its "heart," mediating and balancing the energy transfer between organisms.[25]

"The flow of water has much to teach us,"[26] writes Masaru Emoto. "The act of living is the act of flowing. It's almost as if the water within your body has a desire to flow. In the same way, your soul must also flow. When your soul is allowed to flow, you feel a burden lifted ... If you have been offended, forgive the offender ... forgive yourself ... Forgiveness opens up the path for you to naturally and freely flow toward your future."[26]

The Buddha wrote that all things are in flux and nothing is permanent. "All life flows with the flow of water."

Water is circulation.

Photo 11.11: Atlantic surf on Hirtle Beach, Nova Scotia, Canada.

A Purposeful Evolution in a Holistic & Holographic Universe

In his book *The Spiritual Life of Water*, Alick Bartholomew described how quantum physicists observed that *quanta* (tiny subatomic particles that sometimes defied Newtonian laws of space and time) behaved like vibrant, continually changing subtle energy rather than matter. This resonated with the Hindu concept of *akasha*, "an etheric substratum from which all matter was created, as well as the traditions of many other early civilizations."[1]

In his book *Earth Under Fire*, physicist and systems theorist Paul LaViolette resurrects the concept of "ether" to suggest that tremendous (galactic) energy discharges (caused by galactic super waves from massive explosions at the galactic core) comprise part of an ongoing process of the creation of matter from the etheric flux, which invisibly pervades the universe.[27] The idea of "continuous creation," which reflects ancient Hindu metaphysics, contravenes the Big Bang Theory. Recent findings, suggesting that black holes are not singularities but possible gateways to continuous creation and the concept of "dark flow," are challenging some of the classic ideas of creation, including the Big Bang Theory.[12,13,14,15] The Michelson–Morley experiments of 1887 disputed the concept of ether, but they based their conclusions on viewing ether as another physical dimension, rather than a precursor to energy itself. Current science, ironically, utilizes a version of ether to explain the propagation of radio and television waves and other phenomena. The late physicist David Bohm foresaw a new worldview emerging in

the Western world focused on "wholeness and process [context-dependent] rather than analysis into parts and esthetic constituents." His work and quantum theory may also have given the concept of "ether" a new place in a unified holistic universe with "the notion that the universe is an indivisible whole rather than separately interacting constituents."[2]

In Chapter 9, I discuss the three stages of water and humanity (Separation, Transformation, Return) in a co-evolutionary "Hero's Journey" from ancient times to the present. Just as I teach my writing students about experiencing their own "Hero's Journey" through life's adventures, water teaches us about change and opportunity through its own transformative stages. Turbulence transforms water into something more complex with a higher order. The key is movement and the transformative change that goes along with it. When you "go with the flow" you are showing faith in the wisdom of Nature and water. This isn't the same as blind faith; it is faith through *seeing*.

"Perhaps humanity's purpose at this time may be to initiate healing and a raising of consciousness in the soul of our planet," writes Bartholomew. "Earth has its own sense of purpose, which may have contributed to, or even determined, the environmental upheavals that have led to evolutionary changes. Earth, however, required water to transmit the new information necessary for creating new species and optimizing conditions for a flowering of biological life-forms."[1]

Photo 11.12: Mallards swimming on Toogood Pond, Unionville, Ontario, Canada.

Bartholomew discusses how each burst of a new life form was accompanied by higher complexity and diversity. "The greater evolutionary advances always seemed to follow cataclysm of some kind." He saw this form of evolution as "spontaneous steps emerging out of a catastrophic situation initiated by Earth herself in the process of her evolution … We might call it 'purposeful evolution'."[1]

Philosophers of all great civilizations have long recognized that change results only from the "failure" of the status quo, followed by learning and transcending. Bartholomew says it this way: "Order must be preceded by chaos." As I have mentioned in several preceding chap-

Photo by Nina Munteanu

ters, but particularly in Chapter 9, the long road of humanity's journey has been punctuated by calamity. I earlier noted that, in the Chinese *I Ching*, the hexagram for "crisis" also represents "opportunity." This is because when we are in *stasis* (which represents lack of movement), we do not recognize our path; perspective only comes with movement. In this way, calamity, initially seen as disaster, may be viewed as unexpected opportunity for creative change—the creative destruction I talk about in Chapter 6. The unpredictable nature of water provides the opportunity to teach and learn.

"It is the restlessness of water that gives living systems the ability to become ever more complex ... As the driver of evolution, water is a model for our own striving," writes Bartholomew. "Water is emotional," says Dr. Alexander Zehnder, Scientific Director of the Alberta Water Research Institute. "You cannot explain water; you have to feel water."[51]

Water is a herald.

Geneticist Mae-Wan Ho equates *organic coherence* with the notion of consciousness: "Quantum coherent organisms invariably become entangled with one another. A quantum world is a world of universal mutual entanglement, the prerequisite for universal love and ethics. Because we are all entangled, and each being is implicit in every other, the best way to benefit oneself is to benefit the other. That's why we can really love our neighbour as ourselves. It is heartfelt and sincere. We are ethical and care about our neighbours and all of creation, because they are literally as dear to us as our own self."[6]

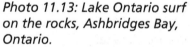

Photo 11.13: Lake Ontario surf on the rocks, Ashbridges Bay, Ontario.

Photo by Merridy Cox

The Complexity of Nature & the Tau of Water

Though incredibly elegant, Nature is not simple, or "simple-minded"; Gaia has a complex agenda that reflects an infinite set of scales or levels.

Scale is something you can't see or easily measure and assess if you are in it. Scale is like hindsight. *Perspective* is another matter, and often connected to scale. According to research at the University of Bristol, a major extinction event (and climate change) at the end of the Permian period (about 250 million years ago) killed over 90 percent of life on Earth, including insects, plants, marine animals, amphibians, and reptiles. Ecosystems were destroyed worldwide—this was the nearest that life came to being completely wiped out. It apparently took 30 million years for ecosystems to fully recover, according to the Bristol study.

The systems of Gaia are complex, from the tiniest cell to the complex planet itself. Weather, for instance, is a chaotic system that displays a fractal structure and a range of chaotic behaviour on many scales. Temperature, air pressure, wind speed and humidity are all sensitive to initial conditions and interrelated. In his book *Complexity: The Emerging Science at the Edge of Order and Chaos*, Mitchel Waldrop quotes Brian Arthur, professor at Stanford University: "The complex approach is total Taoist. In Taoism there is no inherent order. 'The world starts with one, and the one become two and the two become many, and the many lead to myriad things.' The universe in Taoism is perceived as vast, amorphous, and ever changing. You can never nail it down. The elements always stay the same, yet they are always arranging themselves. So, it's like a kaleidoscope: the world is a matter of patterns that

"Nothing is softer or more flexible than water, yet nothing can resist it."

—Lao Tzu

change, that partly repeat, but never quite repeat, that are always new and different."[28]

Western scientists are just beginning to appreciate this through the application of complexity theory and chaos theory, something the Eastern world and indigenous peoples have known since ancient times: to show humility before Nature; respect the richness and diversity of life, now it generates complexity from simplicity, and the need to understand the whole to understand the part. To live your life with integrity.

Photo 11.14: West coast rainforest stream on Vancouver Island, British Columbia, Canada.

Photo by Kevin Klassen

Water & the Consciousness Whole

During the early 1980s Bohm developed his *theory of Implicate Order* to explain the bizarre behaviour of subatomic particles—behaviour that quantum physicists have not been able to explain. Basically, two subatomic particles that have once interacted can instantaneously "respond to each other's motions thousands of years later when they are light-years apart."[3] This sort of particle interconnectedness requires superluminal signalling, which is faster than the speed of light. This odd phenomenon is called the *EPR effect*, named after the Einstein, Podolsky, and Rosen thought experiment.

Bohm believes that the bizarre behaviour of subatomic particles might be caused by unobserved subquantum forces and particles. Indeed, the apparent weirdness might be produced by hidden means that pose no conflict with ordinary ideas of causality and reality. Bohm believes that this "hiddenness" may reflect a deeper dimension of reality. He maintains that space and time might actually be derived from an even deeper level of objective reality. This reality he calls the *Implicate Order*.[2,3] Within the Implicate Order everything is connected; and, in theory, any individual element could reveal information about every other element in the universe.

For Bohm, *consciousness* "involves awareness, attention, perception, acts of understanding, and perhaps yet more."[3] He describes consciousness as a "series of moments," one giving rise to the next and switching places—being implicate or explicate. Consciousness is a feedback process that results in a growing understanding. "Bohm conceives of consciousness as more than information and the brain; rather it is information that enters into consciousness,"[29] writes David Story in *Science and Nonduality*. Bohm considers us an "intrinsic feature of the universe, which would be incomplete, in some fundamental sense," if we did not exist.

Bohm believes that individuals participate in the whole and consequently give it meaning. Because of human participation, the "Implicate Order is getting to know itself better."[3]

"Bohm also senses a new development,"[29] writes Story. "The individual is in total contact with the Implicate Order, the individual is part of the whole of mankind, and s/he is the 'focus for something beyond humankind.' Using the analogy of the transformation of the atom ultimately into a power and chain reaction, Bohm believes that the individual who uses inner energy and intelligence can transform [hu]mankind. The collectivity of individuals have reached the 'principle of the consciousness of [hu]mankind, but they have not quite the 'energy to reach the whole, to put it all on fire.'"[29]

Bohm believes that enlightened individuals who form trusting relationships with one another can generate the power to ignite the whole consciousness of the world. In the depths of the Implicate Order there is a "consciousness, deep down—of the whole of humankind."[2] Bohm argues that each individual is responsible for contributing to building this *collective consciousness*. "There's nothing else to do," says Bohm. "There is no other way out. That is absolutely what has to be done and nothing else can work."[2]

Bohm also believes that the individual will eventually be fulfilled upon the completion of cosmic *noogenesis* (emergence of intelligent life forms). Referring to all the elements of the cosmos, including human beings, as projections of an ultimate totality, Bohm notes that as a "human being takes part in the process of this totality, he is fundamentally changed in the very activity in which his aim is to change that reality, which is the content of his consciousness."[3]

Native Science & Quantum Science

The Native North Americans—encompassing Aboriginal, First Nations, Métis and Inuit peoples—embrace a *Native paradigm* based on a Native worldview. According to Harvard scholar Dr. Leroy Little Bear, the Native paradigm is founded on the concepts of, "constant motion and flux, existence consisting of energy waves, interrelationships, all things being animate, sacred space/landscape, trickster energy, renewal, and all things being imbued with spirit."[30] The Native paradigm embraces archetype in its worldview and lore. For instance, the Trickster archetype is revealed through chaos or flux. Trickster shape shifts, at once culture hero, clown, teacher and giver of gifts. Trickster embraces all the notions of Native paradigm, moving in harmony with constant flux, crossing boundaries of time, space and place, transforming from one state of being to another, while remaining interconnected with all the beings of Mother Earth.[31]

Photo 11.15: Cormorant stretches its wings on the rocky shore of Lake Ontario, Canada.

Photo by Merridy Cox

Several scholars agree that the basic principles of quantum physics are central to the Native North American worldview and its science,[30,31,32] one in which no parts stand alone in fragmentation or segmentation, but live and breathe—like fractals—as part of a whole. "It is not that the whole is greater than the sum of its parts; the part enfolds the Whole; everything and everyone becomes the whole."[32]

The foundation of "Native science" arises from a pantheistic world-view. According to *Native scientist* Gregory Cajete, Native science encompasses metaphysics and philosophy, art, architecture, practical technologies and agriculture; in addition to ritual and ceremony. Native science focuses on the importance of astronomy, farming, plant domestication, plant medicine, animal husbandry, hunting, fishing, metallurgy, and geology. Native science also concerns itself with studies related to plants, animals, and natural phenomena. Ultimately, Native science embraces spirituality, community, creativity, and technologies that sustain environments and support essential aspects of human life.[30]

Canadian scientists David Suzuki and Peter Knudtson confirm that Indigenous science has been ignored, yet has valuable insights to offer: "Native spiritual and ecological knowledge has intrinsic value and worth, regardless of its resonances with or 'confirmation' by modern Western scientific values. As most Native authorities would be quick to point out, it is quite capable of existing on its own merits and adapting itself over to meet modern needs."[33]

In 1956, a collection of essays by Benjamin Lee Whorf was released that explored Indigenous languages. Entitled *Language, Thought and Reality*, the essays discussed—among other things—Whorf's discovery that, for the Hopi, space and time were inter-relational. Newtonian time disappears and space is altered, so that "it is no longer the homogenous and instantaneous timeless space of our supposed intuition or of classical Newtonian mechanics."[34] For instance, instead of three notions of time—past, present and future—Hopi time operates out of "the manifested and/or the manifesting." The Hopi live in a state of being where time and space are fused, not fragmented. The *manifested* (also called the objective) includes both past and present, "all that is known without differentiation." The *manifesting* (the subjective) includes future events, the mind, the heart and all of creation.[31,34]

The idea of probability (or potential) lives in the language of Indigenous peoples. "The movement, the process is embedded in the language,"[35] writes Dr. Nancy Maryboy, founder of the Indigenous Education Institute in Florida. "It is, what I might say, *verbocentric*. Everything in the universe is in *constant motion*. It has been said that the Navajo language has more than 200,000 ways to say 'go'. Much in the Navajo language is full of potentiality, that which can be. It's only when it is translated into English that the potentiality is left behind."[35] David Peat, University of Liverpool theoretical physicist, adds that, "English, and for that matter French, German, Italian, and the other

European languages, are noun-orientated. They are employed to divide the world into physical objects (nouns), and thinking into separate concepts (nouns). Many Native American languages do not work this way. They are verb-based."[36]

"If you think predominantly within the notions of movement and process, as reflected in Native languages, then the outcome of your reality will be different and relationship then becomes the methodology for navigating the world,"[31] says Canadian scholar Elizabeth Ferguson. She suggests that Western noun-based language creates fragmentation, classification and objectification. Joseph Rael, Native American writer and artist agrees. "If you dropped the nouns and the pronouns in the English language and just used verbs you'd begin to see the world the way the Tiwa-speaking see it—a flow, with everything in motion and in relationship to everything else."[37] David Peat adds that, "the Mic Maq [Mi'kmaq] language is in itself a world of sounds that echoes and reflects the vibrations of the physical world. While the surface world of objects and material things can easily be identified by the eye, it is the ear that must deal with the more subtle levels of flux, transformation, and reality behind appearances."[36]

Photo 11.16: West coast rainforest stream, British Columbia, Canada.

Begay and Maryboy argue that "Native American languages, such as Navajo [Diné], have the ability to express complex and holistic ideas, but they go much further than that. In their very essence, they are themselves complex, polysynthetic and at the same time holistic, containing elements of process, relationship and wholeness in virtually every utterance."[38] Physicist David Bohm pointed out how the subject–verb–object structure of modern languages implies that all action arises in a separate subject, creating separate entities that are fixed and static in their nature.[2,3]

"Spoken words are constantly creating our universes because we are essences of perpetuity," writes Joseph Rael. "Everything on the earth, since the beginning of time, has been and is being created by the sounds of words as they are spoken."[40] To this Ferguson adds that "you must al-

Photo by Nina Munteanu

ways be aware of what you are saying or thinking—for … you are manifesting your reality. It's about a reciprocal relationship with universal vibration, since sound is a vibration that creates alliances with the natural flow of universal energy … It is intention expressed through language that is the catalyst for the manifesting reality, the principle being that what you put out there (energy, inceptive) will return to you (energy, expective). Time and space in the sense of past, present and future are irrelevant, what matters is relationship in the moment. So, what works on a material, physical level also works on a universal, vibrational level, and these concepts are embedded in a language that embraces process, movement, respect and reciprocity."[31]

Ferguson holds that the Native American language may provide the key to another way of being and may offer crucial insights into the quantum world—perhaps even "open the door to that elusive paradigm shift." David Bohm reflects this notion by suggesting the creation of a language that embraces aspects of Native American language with an emphasis on verb-based communication. Such communication would be "in harmony with the unbroken, flowing movement of existence as a whole."[3]

"If everything is forever moving and changing, one has to look at the whole to discern developing patterns,"[41] writes University of California, Berkeley scholar Amethyst First Rider. "For instance, the cosmic cycles are a part of the constant motion but have a regular pattern resulting in reoccurrence, like seasons and migrations of animals. Constant motion, as it manifests itself in cyclical or repetitive patterns, emphasizes processes".[41]

"*Spirit* is the 'glue' that binds flux together,"[31] writes Ferguson. Spirit is energy. "In Native science there is then an inclusive definition of *being alive*. Everything is viewed as having energy and its own unique intelligence and creative process,"[30] writes Cajete. Spirit permeates all things with a life-force. "A stone has its own form of animation and unique energy," argues Cajete. "The rock may vibrate at a much slower

pace than [living things], making it appear as an inert object,"[30] adds Little Bear, who goes on to say that, "The modern description leaves out so much—it leaves out the sacredness, the livingness and the soul of the world. And it does get troublesome when scientists tell us, often with a voice of authority, that the part they leave out is really not there."[30] Native science observes that all things are energy and imbued with a unique intelligence and creative process—including plants, animals and microorganisms, but also inanimate entities such as rocks, mountains, and rivers.[30]

Milton M.R. Freeman, at the University of Alberta, discussed the difference between the scientist's approach to knowing what is happening and that of the "tradition-based resource user" (or indigenous person). Freeman suggested that the key difference was epistemological: "the scientist is concerned with causality, with understanding an essentially linear process of cause and effect ... but the forager lives in a world, not of linear causal events, but of constantly reforming multi-dimensional interacting cycles, where nothing is simply a cause or an effect, but all factors are influences impacting other elements of the system-as-a-whole. Linear approaches to analysis cannot be applied to cyclical systems, and ... ecosystems are in fact complex cycles of recirculating energy matter, and relationships. Nowhere does the Cartesian model of modern science fail so completely and utterly as in trying to explain the workings of natural ecosystems."

For the Native American, time is circular and attached to the rhythms of the moment, writes Evan T. Pritchard, a Mi'kmaq and professor at Marist College in New York. "There is no word for time in the Micmac language, nor in most Algonquin tongues."[43] Time is expressed in waiting for the right moment; the right time to pick the sweetgrass, pollinate the corn or perform a ceremony. In Native paradigm (as with quantum physics) time can move forward or backward.

Enter the Trickster, the chaos creator. The Indigenous worldview subscribes to the notion that it is up to us to establish order from chaos,

Photo 11.17: The LaHave River icing over, near Bridgewater, Nova Scotia, Canada.

Photo by Nina Munteanu

which is partially done by the observation of cycles, rhythms and patterns. According to Ferguson, the Trickster facilitates the process of establishing order out of the flux of disorder. The Trickster always brings gifts coming from a high degree of order. "One might say that the notion of disorder is a matter of perspective."[31] According to Michael Talbot, author of *Mysticism and the New Physics*, it occurred to physicist David Bohm that what we may perceive as disorder isn't disorder at all. "Perhaps their order is of such an 'indefinitely high degree' that they only appear to us as random."[44]

"The cosmos is in a constant state of readjustment in an effort to maintain balance. Trickster acts as a catalyst to maintain order, coming from a highly-ordered state of perfection and creativity, manifesting as chaos, but ultimately creating balance,"[31] says Ferguson. "Creation stories speak of emergence: emergence from the earth; emergence from the sky; or emergence from a song—a vibration materialized. Navigating alternative dimensions is normal in Native America. It is from these dimensions that knowledge is sought and applied."[31]

"All of the things in our life have power, and how we use them and take care of them strengthens or limits their power for us. In the traditional way, everything has life spirit in and around it and should be treated with caution and respect, and perhaps awe ... A single blade of ...sweetgrass, *umptseegooabee*, puts you in touch with the spirit of sweetgrass everywhere, just as much as a whole armful would. It is all one spirit."[43]

Native Americans have always believed in an interconnected whole.

Bohm "believed that dividing the universe up into living and non-living things also has no meaning," writes Talbot. "Animate and inanimate matter are inseparably interwoven, and life, too, is enfolded throughout the totality of the universe. Even a rock is in some way alive, says Bohm, for life and intelligence are present not only in all of matter, but in 'energy,' 'space,' 'time,' the fabric of the entire universe, and everything else we abstract out of the Holomovement and mistakenly view

Photo 11.18: Water flow patterns among the reeds of the Upper Credit River, ON, Canada.

Photo by Nina Munteanu

as separate things. The idea that consciousness and life (and indeed all things) are ensembles enfolded throughout the universe has an equally dazzling flip side. Just as every portion of a hologram contains the image of a whole, every portion of the universe enfolds the whole."[44]

Physicist Fritjof Capra adds that "whereas in classical mechanics the properties and behavior of the parts determine those of the whole, the situation is reversed in quantum mechanics; it is the whole that determines the behavior of the parts."[45]

"In Native paradigm, *renewal* is integral to the art of existence,"[31] writes Ferguson. "Renewal [through ceremony] is a way of complementing and cementing relationships and compacts with the universe. Ceremony is intention, and intention attracts outcome through relationship." Ferguson contends that quantum physics acts as a bridge, linking ancient understanding and Western science. "Quantum physicists are proving the notions of interconnectedness, animate, constant flux, trickster and observer-created reality."

Photo 11.19: Marshy stream winds its way along the road from Lunenburg to Wolfville, Nova Scotia, Canada.

Photo by Nina Munteanu

Theosophy & the Epic of Gilgamesh

Like water, Theosophy soaks up and reflects a body of knowledge that has been taught since early times, often in myth, symbolic legend, allegory, and hieroglyph. One example is the *Epic of Gilgamesh*, an allegorical journey of the soul told in the cuneiform tablets of early Mesopotamia.

According to Toronto poet and Theosophist Joan Sutcliffe, the first fundamental proposition of theosophical teachings is that "there is one ultimate basic source from which everything has sprung, from universes and galaxies to the human, … plant, mineral and atoms … It's almost a misnomer to say everything has sprung from the source, because at the very deepest level we are that source, as is everything else. It's like an outpouring into manifestation, yet the thing that was outpoured from is still present. Eventually everything returns to the source, and rests in a period of inactivity until the next outpouring."[46]

Helena Petrovna Blavatsky, originator of Theosophy, uses the metaphor of *The Great Breath* to express the ceaseless movement of continual coming into being, growing, maturing, dying and coming again.[47] This embraces quantum theory and David Bohm's Implicate Order and Holomovement. Reflecting the Hindu philosophy of cycles within cycles in a multiverse that always has been, always will be, but in a perpetual state of flux, Blavatsky describes the process of cycles as a whole mysterious field of searching in itself. She describes an ethereal consciousness, of being on a "mythic journey" described by Joseph Campbell as "the hero with a thousand faces."[48]

It is the greater all-encompassing journey that Nobel Laureate George Wald referred to when he said:

"Surely this is a great part of our dignity ... that we can know, and that through us matter can know itself; that beginning with protons and electrons, out of the womb of time and the vastness of space, we can begin to understand; that organized as in us, the hydrogen, the carbon, the nitrogen, the oxygen, those 16 to 21 elements, the water, the sunlight—all, having become us, can begin to understand what they are, and how they came to be."[49]

According to Hindu scriptures, the birth of the universe (Brahma) is followed by the life of the universe (Vishnu) and the destruction of the universe (Shiva), which brings in Brahma energy in a never-ending cycle of "creative–destruction" and shifting polar forces. Like the cosmic Great Breath (*Maha Vishnu*) described by Blavatsky.

Blavatsky opens her book *The Secret Doctrine* with passages from the Stanzas of Dzyan, ancient scriptures from Tibetan esoteric writings. She writes of the "daytime" manifestation of the Universe, known as *Manvantara*, followed by the "night" period of dormancy, known as *Pralaya*:

"Could we have a better symbol of this than in the deciduous tree? One fascinating aspect of the life of this tree is that at the time that it is shedding its leaves, the cells within the branchlets are those which will form the new leaves in the following spring. So, the life of the tree is carried over from one season to the next. What a lesson we have from Nature! As we reincarnate, the karmic seeds are already prepared at the time of death, and will be carried over into the next incarnation. We cannot escape the Karma of our past lives for we are the sum-total of all that we have been through during a long series of incarnations. We are what we have made ourselves to be, just as we are now building for our own future."[47]

Photo 11.20: Paper birch tree in southern Ontario forest, Canada.

Photo by Merridy Cox

Water Ethics & the Nbi Mnidowug

"There's some deeper water ethic that we need and the closest I see to that water ethic is what I see in older Native people."
—Dr. David Schindler

"In the Holy Scripture, water is more than simply a physical substance," says Metropolitan Kirill, Patriarch of the Russian Orthodox Church. "It is a certain concept, and that concept is connected in a special way with the idea of life … It is absolutely no accident that the opening lines of the Bible mention water, where it talks about the creation of the world, of life, and of man; it has to do with water, first and foremost."[50]

Water is sacred in Aboriginal cultures and considered a sacred gift. "It is in our stories, it is in our ceremonies and it gives us life,"[51] the narrator for *Water, the Sacred Relationship* tells us. "The cyclical nature of life is the fundamental understanding of Indigenous cultures around the world … and embedded in our philosophy." Fittingly, the Cree worldview is represented by a spiral with levels of relationship that run from the individual and family up through the clan, nation, environment and finally cosmos. *Wahkotowin* (the "doctrine of relationships"), based on respect for all that is sacred, is the stuff that gives the spiral its structure.

The Aboriginal people express their truths through story.

"In Blackfoot, we're sky people," Amethyst First Rider writes. "And so much of our knowledge comes from the stars. So, in putting up our teepees, the top part of our teepee is the star people and that connection with the sky people; the middle of the teepee is this Earth relationship; and at the bottom of our teepee are the underground beings or the water beings. Encompassed in that is all of the universe relationships in our sacred geometry: the rocks, the earth we sit on, our altar—it's all about non-locality. But the most important thing, it's holy; and it reminds us when we enter that we're entering into holiness, and it's just a reflection of what's bigger in the world."[52]

Isaac Murdoch, a native Ojibwa from the Serpent River on the northern shore of Lake Huron in Ontario, Canada, tells us that the Anishinaabe people have long believed that water has a spirit. This spirit, he contends, needs to be respected and protected.[53]

The Serpent River First Nation community lives by the Serpent River where it empties into Lake Huron, one of Canada's Great Lakes and the fifth largest lake in the world. The basin of Lake Huron lies on the Precambrian Shield of rolling wind-swept hills of mixed forest. Well known for its arresting northern beauty, the North Channel and Georgian Bay shorelines were immortalized by several Group of Seven painters and also, most notably, by Tom Thomson.

Near the river mouth, smooth granite rocks rise out of the water like the roof of a drowned house. Two undulating serpents emerge, facing each other. Created by lines of exposed grey rock beneath the dry, black moss and lichen, the two 150-foot-long serpents rise vertically from the water with their tails submerged and metre-long horns taper back from the tops of their heads.

The *Mishi Genebek* (Great Serpent) is black with two to four legs and part of the *Nbi Mnidowug* (water spirits) that inhabit the lake and river. The Anishinaabek hold a close and respectful relationship with the Serpent. An Ojibwa legend (common in Lake Nippising, Lake of the Woods, Sarnia, and Sheshegwaning) tells how people were turned into black snakes for disturbing the *Nbi Mnidowug*. In the spring, the women make offering bundles to the serpent. These consist of a willow raft with tobacco, ribbons and other nice things, which they send down the river as payment to the Great Serpent for being able to travel in its waters. Murdoch gives the following account of a man, accidentally left behind from his party and stranded on John Island (*Shkodeying*) and how the serpent helped him:

"Day after day no one came back to get him and he became very lonely and wondered when and how he was going to get back. In the afternoon, he decided to have a nap on the beach and had a dream. In

Figure 11.1: The Jack Pine *painted in 1917 by Tom Thompson.*

The National Gallery of Canada, Ottawa

his dream he saw a little snake on the beach wiggling in the sand. He asked the snake to help him. The snake grew bigger and bigger. It had horns and little feet. In his dream the serpent told him to get on his back and that he would take him back to the main land. So he did. In his dream he was taken to the mainland, and when he woke up he was on the main land near the big point." A petroglyph commemorates the location, now called Serpent Point.[53]

Murdoch writes of an elaborate system of "serpent tunnels through all of the north shore of Lake Huron—highways of the water *mnidoog* (spirit or entity)."[53] Murdoch writes about the two small lakes on John Island, forbidden to the Ojibwa. "They say that in one of those lakes, a loon would swim down and come up in the other lake," Murdoch writes. "A serpent tunnel connects the two lakes."

In 2001, The Institute for Exploration discovered many submerged sinkholes and pockmarks on Lake Huron's lakebed. Over 8,000 years ago, Lake Huron's limestone bedrock lay exposed following the last glacier maximum. A reaction between limestone and acidic water dissolved passages in the limestone to create sinkholes, caves and underground drainage systems, and *karst formations* (landscape formed from the dissolution of soluble rocks). Rocks of karst limestone and marble occur throughout the Canadian Precambrian Shield, with the most widespread surface karst being small solution pits, grooves and runnels, collectively called *karren*. Individual karren are rarely longer or deeper than ten metres, but often occur in dense clusters dissecting large areas and referred to as limestone pavement. Manitoulin Island is known for this feature.[54]

Coastal karren occur along many of the Great Lakes shores, creating mazes and stream caves.[55] The sinkholes and passages along Lake Huron's lakebed are currently seeping groundwater to the bottom of the lake, providing a unique habitat for aquatic life.[56] Exotic extreme life that thrives in these sinkholes include brilliant purple mats of cyanobacteria (related to microbes found at the bottom of permanently ice-covered

Illustration 11.1: Karst formations in soluble rocks such as limestone, showing underground drainage systems, sinkholes and caves. A) sinking stream; B) fissures and sink holes; C) shafts; D) dry caves; E) wet cave and underground stream; F) limestone.

Illustration by Kerste Voute

lakes in Antarctica).[57] "These are almost primordial Earth conditions, with high sulphur and low oxygen, like in the ancient oceans that covered the Earth three billion years ago," ecologist Bopaiah Biddanda of Michigan's Grand Valley State University told CBC News.[58]

Murdoch writes that some Anishinaabe people have begun to regard land [and water] in the *zhaaganaash* (English people) way. "We don't own the land or have title to it," writes Murdoch. "Rather, we belong to her. Our lands were traditionally occupied by our *doodemag* (clan) and spirit helpers, and we shared it. Why should we as humans have any right to claim it as our own? We are Anishinaabeg and our worldview is different," says Murdoch. "Our richness is the heartbeat of the land. Our wealth is the watersheds. We will die without them; they are truly our lifelines and should be treasured because our lives still depend on it ... We must focus on rebuilding the unity we once needed to survive in the bush."[53]

"Knowledge about who we are and our place in the world is earned through ceremony. A fasting ceremony teaches us not only about sacrifice but about our relationship with water," the narrator of *Water, The Sacred Relationship* tells us. "As Aboriginal people, when we seek knowledge, we offer protocol. It is an act of respect, acknowledging that in order for learning to occur there must be a relationship between the learner and the teacher."[51]

Narcisse Blood, Blackfoot Studies Professor at Red Crow College, Alberta, shares: "For the Blackfoot ... in ceremony it is very realistic to honor and acknowledge what gives us life ... It is in our ceremonies, it is in our language, it is in our stories that we need to be wisely aware of not just what we see, but what we don't see ... that ultimately our journey of knowledge-seeking is to be wisely aware of where you are and who you are."[51]

For generations, the relationship between Aboriginal people and the rest of North America has been damaged. Can water be the common ground that begins to reconcile this relationship?

"The sacred relationship is essentially a trust relationship," Dr. Patti La Boucane-Benson shares. "It's a connecting relationship with the water, and to do that we have to have a sacred relationship with each other." Dr. David Schindler, professor of ecology at the University of Alberta, believes that the natural meeting ground for Western science and Indigenous science lies in the naturalist field. "Most aboriginal people are good naturalists and it's a very powerful tool … it isn't all about more sensitive instruments or powerful computers."[51]

"If we don't teach our children and grandchildren how to respect the environment, how to respect those spirits, what kind of a world is that going to be?" asks Fred Campiou, Cree Elder of the Driftpile First Nation. "We always hear this term growing up: 'what kind of world are we going to leave for our children?' I ask: 'what kind of a child are we going to leave for the world?'"[51]

Photo 11.21: Soowahlie First Nation students participate in a stream clean up of Sweltzer Creek, which flows into Cultus Lake in British Columbia, Canada.

Photo by Nina Munteanu

Go with the Flow

The nightmare began vaguely with me and my family in a restaurant in some unrecognizable part of town … it was midday and we were watching an alarming news release about linked turbulent weather patterns all over the globe. The tension that emanated from everyone was palpable, as though I could feel the tension of every person on the planet. I noticed that the sky looked queer, strange. It had grown dark like a deep sea storm and I noticed the clouds flaming with crimson. Drawn by curiosity mixed with dread, I slipped outside to get a better look and walked up the hill a bit to see beyond the building. What I saw was spectacular at first then terrifying: the flame-rimmed clouds were racing across the sky at breakneck speed and against them in gold ochre shades I could make out the silhouettes of the continents, as though the burning sun had flung them up there (okay, so this is a dream, folks!) … As I stared up, dumbfounded, at the clouds speeding across the dark sky, I suddenly realized with gut-sickening alarm that it wasn't so much the clouds racing across the sky as the planet speeding up! I could actually feel its rotation speeding up! I could feel the centrifugal pull of its motion unbalancing me. When I awoke, a dark heaviness and foreboding clung to me that I found hard to shake. It stayed with me the rest of the day.

I'd experienced the nightmare in 2008, during an interesting time in my life journey: I didn't realize it at the time but I was poised to change my life significantly. The dream reminded me of the 1982 movie, Koyaanisqatsi. Directed by Godfrey Reggio with cinematography by Ron Fricke, the film is a time-lapse rushing flow of cities and natural landscapes to the hypnotic music of minimalist composer Philip Glass. The visual tone poem uses no dialogue or narration to depict our relationship with nature and technology. Its compelling imagery and hyp-

"Nothing in the world is softer and more yielding than water; yet it wears down the hard and strong and none can overcome it; though anyone can conquer it. That which is yielding conquers the strong. And the soft overcomes that which is hard. Everyone knows this but no one dares to live by it."

—Lao Tze

notic score portrays a frantic world on the move. And on the brink. The word *koyaanisqatsi* in the Hopi language means 'life of moral corruption and turmoil, life out of balance'; and the film implies that modern humanity is living that way: Highways, lit at night with streaming cars, resemble coursing arteries; clouds scud across a landscape painted in successive shades of gold, ochre and deep indigo in a wild light show, similar to my nightmare.

I also thought of Charlie Chaplin's frenzied scene in the giant clock of *Modern Times* and the hilarious scene of Lucille Ball struggling on the conveyor belt as chocolates speed by in the chocolate factory episode of the *Lucy Show*.

More and more, writes Masaru Emoto, the individual feels increasingly delegated to a miniscule piece of a vast machine that is moving ever faster. "The great steps forward can often be made by becoming smaller instead of bigger, by going slower instead of faster,"[26] Emoto counsels in his book *The Secret Life of Water*.

This wisdom is reflected in the artisanal culture and the slow-food movement, which embraces a creative cooperative model and focuses on individual expression and creativity. I gave several examples of this in Chapter 9.

Economist E.F. Schumacher advocates the notion of "small is beautiful" in his human-centred economic model.[59] His philosophy is one of *enoughness*, which advocates the appreciation of human needs, our limitations, and appropriate use of technology. Schumacher's philosophy grew out of his study of village-based economics, which he called *Buddhist economics*. Questioning the appropriateness of using gross national product to measure humanity's well-being, he emphasized that "the aim ought to be to obtain the maximum amount of well-being with the minimum amount of consumption,"[59] and promoted the values of justice, harmony, beauty and health over materialism.

We are witnessing a major shift in peoples' choice for wellness, such as selecting organic foods, eco-friendly products and activities, com-

plimentary medicines, self-education, and self-expression. The latter is evident in the major shift in the consumer model of the music industry and now the same shift is occurring in the publishing industry, where indie publishing now makes up the majority of books published, both in print and online.

"Some argue that the people who can inspire us to improve our quality of life, to laugh, to enjoy beauty, will become the most admired people in society, not those who earn the biggest salaries,"[60] writes Alain Ruche, strategist and policy maker for the Secretary General of the European Union External Service. "For now, artists and cultural actors can only aspire to this new kind of economy."

Cultural literacy goes beyond teaching our children and teens about others' cultures, says Ruche. "The pace of cultural interaction and change is so fast that it implies making real-time choices to navigate through diverse situations with a capacity to actively interpret, rather than simply build on knowledge." Ruche further argues that, "creativity is becoming the critical factor of this century."[60]

It comes down to balance. We all knowingly or unknowingly strive for balance in our daily lives—that sacred but sometimes messy place where yin and yang joyfully collide: a place and time where the heavenward strain for perfection is tempered with the ponderous scent of soil and dirt, where dark and light blend in a chiaroscuro of infinite possibility. We strive for balance because it is wholeness—the mandala—and wholeness brings us peace, joy and understanding. So, why do so few of us achieve it? I think that is because, ironically, balance incorporates paradox, which is difficult for us to embrace. Balance is complex; it requires creativity, innovation, and an open mind.

Because balance is always shifting and redefining itself—like water. Water is a mentor.

Photo 11.22: A kayaker paddles Ashbridges Bay on Lake Ontario, Canada.

Photo by Merridy Cox

The Wisdom of Symbiosis & a Case for Altruism

"If you really want to study evolution, you've got to go outside sometime, because you'll see symbiosis everywhere."

—Lynn Margulis

Evolutionary biologist and microbiologist Lynn Margulis contends that evolution proceeds through *cooperation*, not *competition*: "Life did not take over the globe by combat, but by networking."[61] Examples of such networking, including interspecies cooperation, mutualism and altruism abound in Nature.

"Sit in a park at dusk and watch a group of swallows dive and swoop, and you enter into a profound mystery,"[62] writes Philip Ball in his book *Flow*. "Watch schools of fish evading their predators off the Great Barrier Reef, or herds of wildebeest crossing the savannah, or even observe a culture of bacteria proliferate and spread under a microscope and you begin to understand that biological organization does not stop at the level of the individual organism. All these groups display motions that hint at some grand scheme, some sense of coherence and even purpose that governs the collective behavior of the community."[62]

In Chapter 3, I talk about how turbulent flow, though seemingly disorderly, chaotic and unpredictable, retains a propensity to organize into distinct and coherent patterns of motion that spawn vortices. In Chapter 6, I mention the coherent behaviour of fireflies, birds, and fish and how "disturbance" propagates like a wave. This brings us to the *fractal* nature of all things: how every part carries the whole and the whole defines the part. It also suggests the deepest of reasons for the wisdom of altruism, compassion, forgiveness and other acts of kindness. And why these are, in fact, so prevalent in the universe.

From endosymbiosis in multicellular organisms to the selfless behaviour of the vervet monkey crier (see below) or the mutualistic behaviour of bottlenose dolphins with the fishermen of Laguna, Brazil, Nature has demonstrated amazing and heroic instances of cooperation and altruism.

Altruism has puzzled philosophers and scientists for many years.

In a 2007 article in "Suite 101" Rebekah Richards writes, "Morality, integrity, generosity, honor—these are concepts our society esteems, rewards, and expects. They are principles embodied by our cultural heroes, and values which we strive to develop in our children. But where do these qualities originate? Are we taught to be good, or do we possess innate virtue? Are we condemned to a constant battle against our 'lower nature'?"[63] Is altruism a matter of nature or nurture?

Richards cites scientists and philosophers from the 5th century to the present day (Augustine of Hippo, Michel de Montaigne and Thomas Henry Huxley to name a few) who had in common the notion that humankind's goodness was just a veneer over a morality that was rotten and self-serving at its core. Some suggest that no act of "unsolicited pro-sociality" can be characterized as wholly unselfish. There is always something to be gained from the act, they insist, even if it is only to "feel good."

Photo 11.23: Raindrops on a hosta leaf, Mississauga, Ontario, Canada.

Photo by Nina Munteanu

At the other end of the spectrum of prejudice, some anthropologists argue that morality and true altruism are qualities limited to humans, as a result of learned behaviour and cultural ethics. The inference here is that those qualities humans share with animals are base and those we do not share with animals are elevated.

Other scientists argue for an alternative to anthropocentric hubris. They argue that altruism is an ancient impulse and an empathic instinct; something more primitive than culture and, in fact, considerably more ancient than the human species itself. They posit that altruism is deeply innate, predating the phylogenetic split that occurred six million years ago. According to them, selflessness is as natural as appetite.[64]

It was the grace of altruism that allowed it all to happen in the first place.

It started with nineteenth-century scientist Edward Westermarck who argued that morality involved both humans and non-human animals and both culture and evolution.[64] Of course, he was met with much skepticism. In 1999 zoologist Brenda Bradley wrote, "Altruism is difficult to explain within traditional models of natural selection, which predict that individuals should exhibit behavioral traits adapted to promoting genetic self-interest."[65] She has a point; so why limit ourselves to a traditional model then? In Chapter 9, I discuss how microbiologist Lynn Margulis explored a non-traditional paradigm based on cooperation. I also discuss how scientific discoveries are made by stepping outside tradition.

Scientists have been demonstrating for years that cooperation among organisms and communities and acts of pure altruism (i.e., not reciprocal altruism or kin/group selection) are, in fact, more common in Nature than most of us realize.[66,67,68,69,70]

Decades of experimentation suggest that moral or altruistic qualities exist in non-human primates and also provide support for the idea that human morality is innate. A 1964 study found that rhesus monkeys who could pull on a chain to acquire food would refuse to pull for days, if doing so delivered a shock to another monkey; they were "literally starving themselves to avoid inflicting pain upon another."[64]

Chimpanzees, unable to swim, have drowned attempting to save the lives of their companions.[66] Human children as young as one year old were observed comforting others; household pets have also demonstrated a response to distress in people by attempting to comfort them.[64,67,68]

On the other hand, some researchers in recent lab studies with chimpanzees, suggested a potential absence of "other-regarding preferences" (altruism) in test animals and concluded that their studies confirmed that such preferences are limited to humans, who alone are sophisticated enough for cultural learning, theory of mind, perspective taking and moral judgment to convince them to perform an altruistic act.

These primate studies, which based their measures of altruism on food allocation, may have failed to demonstrate altruism due to the measure, compounded by the laboratory setting. Animals do not behave the same in their natural habitat as in a laboratory; their priorities are different. I found it interesting that true altruism was demonstrated more in life-threatening, real-life scenarios over less life-threatening ones, (e.g., experiments conducted in the lab using food exchange). My opinion is corroborated by scientists Felix Warneken and his collaborators, who concede that the distinction between food exchange and life-saving help is a potentially crucial one.[67,68]

Valid examples of true animal altruism in the wild do exist. The vervet monkey is one example. This species evolved a complex community that fosters the existence of an altruistic individual: the crier monkey.

Vervet monkeys travel in groups, and the criers give alarm calls to warn fellow monkeys of the presence of predators, even though by doing so they attract attention to themselves and increase their chance of being attacked. Biologists argue that the group that contains a high proportion of crier monkeys will have a survival advantage over a group containing a lower proportion, thereby encouraging this trait to continue and evolve among individuals. The vervet monkey crier is Nature's hero. And Nature's heroes are our real altruists.

In Chapter 9, I talk about the dolphin as example of interspecies cooperation (i.e., mutualism and altruism). Aubrey Manning writes in the Daily Mail of a female dolphin who selflessly saved a beached mother whale and her calf off Mahia Beach in New Zealand.[69] In Laguna in Brazil, the bottlenose dolphins pursue a cooperative relationship with the local fishermen. Local artisanal fishermen rely on the assistance of cooperative dolphins to catch their fish. Researchers found that the most helpful dolphins are also particularly cooperative and social with each other.[70]

De Waal explains that "evolution favors animals that assist each other, if by doing so they achieve long-term benefits of greater value than the

Photo 11.24: Active Pass between Galiano and Maine Islands with a view of a ferryboat wake as another BC ferry passes, British Columbia, Canada.

Photo by Nina Munteanu

benefits derived from going it alone and competing with others."[64] The prevalent phenomenon of altruism is Nature's answer to the *Prisoner's Dilemma* (a canonical example in game theory, showing why two rational individuals might not cooperate, even if it seems in their best interest).

"Empathy evolved in animals as the main ... mechanism for [individually] directed altruism,"[64] said de Waal. And it is empathy—not self-interest—that "causes altruism to be dispensed in accordance with predictions from kin selection and reciprocal altruism theory."[64] De Waal further proposed that the scientific community has become polarized between evolutionary biologists on the one side and, on the other, a discrete group of economists and anthropologists that "has invested heavily in the idea of strong [in-kind] reciprocity," which demands discontinuity between humans and all other animals.[71,72]

"One of the most striking consequences of the study of animal behavior,"[73] says anthropologist Robert Sapolsky, "is the rethinking that it often forces of what it is to be human." He notes that, "a number of realms, traditionally thought to define our humanity, have now been shown to be shared, at least partially, with nonhuman species."[73] This makes some of us uncomfortable. To some, it threatens to make us less special. The corollary demonstrated is that we possess intrinsic virtue, not something "painted" on through cultural teaching or diligent personal effort. Of course, it also means that all other beings possess intrinsic value too. In the final analysis, what we generally "know" is coloured by what we believe and want to continue believing.

The growing knowledge and eventual acceptance that animals and very young children possess truly altruistic behaviour will have deep implications on how we interact with and treat each other, our animal world and Nature generally.

We tend to exclude the rest of animal and plant life from the notion of exhibiting the highest form of intelligence: that of cooperation and altruism. Many of us—if we even accept the existence of true altruism—consider it an exclusively human quality. This hubristic remnant of a "conquest" mentality, in which humanity identifies itself as separate

from Nature, blinds us from a reality that lies right before us. We cannot see what we don't look for; we can't know what we don't believe.

We have come to rely on science to answer questions we already "know" the answers to, because we have lost a sense of Unity. And as Goethe said of conventional scientists, "Whatever you cannot calculate, you do not think is real."[1]

Richard Tarnas (see Chapter 9) posits that the evolution of the Western mind has been driven by a "heroic impulse to forge an autonomous rational human self—a transforming self—by separating it from the primordial unity with nature."[74] In his book *Passion of the Western Mind*, Tarnas suggests that this "heroic impulse" began four millennia ago, with the great patriarchal nomadic conquests in the Mediterranean. Conquests that embraced "the repression of undifferentiated unitary consciousness and the *participation mystique* with nature; a denial of the *anima mundi*, of the soul of the world, of the community of being, of the all-pervading, of mystery and ambiguity, of imagination, emotion, instinct, body, nature, woman."[74]

Goethe and others like him believed that the human mind is ultimately the organ of the world's own process of self-revelation. In this view, Nature is not a separate, independent self-contained reality to be objectively examined by humanity from without; rather, its unfolding truth emerges only with the active participation of the human mind. Nature—and the Universe—is something that comes into being through the very act of human cognition.

Wisdom does not stand still. Wisdom flows. It doesn't flow in a straight line. Wisdom winds. Wisdom is wily. It transforms and transcends matter and energy with a subtle and patient hand. It erodes and deposits, from idea to emotion to philosophy. Wisdom tolerates. It forgives. It embraces and encompasses and—in changing—stays the same.

Wisdom is water.

Photo 11.25: Water slides off my hand as I dip it into the surging waters of the Credit River, Ontario, Canada.

Photo by Merridy Cox

References

1. Bartholomew, Alick. 2010. "The Spiritual Life of Water." *Park Street Press*, Rochester. 368 pp.

2. Bohm, David. 1989. "Interview with David Bohm." Interview on December 24, 1989 at the Nils Bohr Institute in Copenhagen. Online: https://www.youtube.com/watch?v=QI66ZglzcO0

3. Bohm, David. 1980. "Wholeness and the Implicate Order." *Routledge*, London. 284 pp.

4. Ho, Mae-Wan. 2006. "Two-States Water Explains All." ISIS Lecture, *Institute of Science in Society*.

5. Capra, Fritjof. 2010. "The Tau of Physics." *Shambhala*. 368 pp.

6. Ho, Mae-Wan. 2007. "Quantum Jazz: the Tao of Biology." ISIS Lecture, *Institute of Science in Society.*

7. Voeikov, V.L. and E. Del Guidice. 2009. "Water Respiration—The Basis of the Living State." *Water* 1: 52–75.

8. Popper, Karl. 1934 (1959). "The Logic of Scientific Discovery." Routledge Classics. 544 pp.

9. Schauberger, Viktor. 1934 (2010). In: Bartholomew, Alick (author). "The Spiritual Life of Water." *Park Street Press*, Rochester. 368 pp.

10. Ball, Philip. 2000. "H2O: A Biography of Water." *Phoenix*, UK. 400 pp.

11. Cameron, Julia. 2002. "The Artist's Way." *Jeremy P. Tarcher/ Putnum*. 237 pp.

12. Than, Ker. 2010. "Every Black Hole Contains Another Universe?" *National Geographic News*, April 12, 2010.

13. Kashlinsky, A., F. Atrio-Barandela, D. Kocevski, and H. Ebeling. 2008. "A Measurement of Large-scale Peculiar Velocities of Clusters of Galaxies: Results and Cosmological Implications." *Astrophys. J.* 686: 49–52.

14. Kashlinsky, A., F. Atrio-Barandela, D. Kocevski, and H. Ebeling. 2008. "A Measurement of Large-scale Peculiar Velocities of Clusters of Galaxies: Technical Details." *Astrophys. J.* 691: 1479–1493.

15. Goddard Space Center. 2008. "Scientists Detect Cosmic 'Dark Flow' Across Billions of Light Years." Press Release, September 23.

16. Jung, Carl. 1952 (1993). "Synchronicity—An Acausal Connecting Principle." *Bollingen Foundation*, Bollingen, Switzerland.

17. Gamow, George. 1966. "Thirty Years that Shook Physics—The Story of Quantum Theory." *Doubleday & Co.*, New York. 272 pp.

18. Limar, Igor V. 2011. "Carl G. Jung's Synchronicity and Quantum Entanglement: Schrödinger's Cat 'Wanders' Between Chromosomes." *Neuro Quantology* 09(2): 313.

19. Einstein, Albert. 1950. Letter to Robert S. Marcus, World Jewish Congress. Online: http://www.lettersofnote.com/2011/11/delusion.html

20. Fullerton, G.D. and M.R. Amurao. 2006. "Evidence that Collagen and Tendon Have Monolayer Water Coverage in the Native State." *Cell Biol. Int.* 30(1): 56–65.

21. Ho, Mae-Wan. 1994. "Coherent Energy, Liquid Crystallinity, and Acupuncture." ISIS Lecture, Institute of Science in Society.

22. Hiley, Basil. 2009. "David Bohm, Wholistic Universe, Quantum Physics." Interview with Basil Hiley, Emeritus Professor of Physics in Birbeck College. Online: http://www.youtube.com/watch?v=wayQn0uVlvE

23. Willard, Terry. 2012. "Coherence and Fractals." Online: http://www.drterrywillard.com/coherence-and-fractals/

24. Devail, Bill and George Sessions. 1985. "Deep Ecology: Living as if Nature Mattered." *Gibbs Smith*. 267 pp.

25. Schwenk, Theodor. 1965 (1996). "Sensitive Chaos." Rudolf Steiner Press. 288 pp.

26. Emoto, Masaru. 2005. "The Secret Life of Water." *Atria Books*. 178 pp.

27. LaViolette, Paul. 1997. "Earth under Fire." *Starlane Publications*. 405 pp.

28. Waldrop, Mitchell. 1993. "Complexity: The Emerging Science at the Edge of Order and Chaos." Simon and Schuster. 380 pp.

29. Story, David. 2014. "David Bohm, Implicate Order and Holomovement." *Science and Nonduality*.

Online: http://www.scienceandnonduality.com/
david-bohm-implicate-order-and-holomovement/

30. Cajete, G. 2000. "Native Science: Natural Laws of Interdependence." *Clear Light*, Santa Fe. 352 pp.

31. Ferguson, Elizabeth. 2005. "Einstein, Sacred Science, and Quantum Leaps: A Comparative Analysis of Western Science, Native Science and Quantum Physics Paradigm." Master of Arts Thesis, University of Lethbridge. 135 pp.

32. Alford, Dan Moonhawk. 1993. "Dialogues between Western and Indigenous Scientists." Presentation at the Annual Spring Meeting of the Society for the Anthropology of Consciousness, November 4, 1993.

33. Knudtson, P. and David Suzuki. 1992 (2006). "Wisdom of the Elders: Native and Scientific Ways of Knowing About Nature." *Greystone Books*. 272 pp.

34. Whorf, Benjamin Lee. 1956. "Language, Thought and Reality: Selected writings of Benjamin Whorf." Carrol, J.B. (ed.). *MIT Press*, Cambridge, MA. 290 pp.

35. Maryboy, N. 2004. "Exploring Indigenous science." *Shift: at the Frontiers of Consciousness*, March/May, 2004.

36. Peat, F.D. 2002. "Blackfoot Physics and European Minds." F. David Peat website. Online: http://www.fdavidpeat.com/bibliography/essays/black.htm

37. Rael, Joseph. 2002 (2011). "House of the Shattering Light: Life as an American Indian Mystic." *Millichap Books*. 216 pp.

38. Begaya, David and N. Maryboy. 1998. "Sharing the Skies: Navajo Astronomy." *Tucson Rio Nuevo Publishers*.

39. Maryboy, N. and D. Begay. 1999. "Living the Order: Dynamic Cosmic Process of Diné Cosmology." *California Institute of Integral Studies*. 594 pp.

40. Rael, J. and M.E. Marlow. 1993. "Being and Vibration." *Council Oak Books*, Tulsa, OK. 224 pp.

41. First Rider, A. 1994. "Sweetgrass Visions: The Combination of

Trickster and Theatre for the Transmission of Culture." Master of Fine Arts Thesis, University of Calgary, AB. 98 pp.

42. Freeman, M.M.R. 1992. "The Nature and Utility of Traditional Ecological Knowledge." *Northern Perspectives* 20(1): 9–12.

43. Pritchard, E.T.1997. "No Word for Time: The Way of the Algonquin People." *Council Oak Books*, Tulsa, OK. 259 pp.

44. Talbot, M. 1993. "Mysticism and the New Physics." *Penguin Books*, London. 208 pp.

45. Capra, Fritjof. 1984. "The Turning Point: Science, Society, and the Rising Culture." *Bantam Books*. 464 pp.

46. Sutcliffe, Joan. 2014. "Theosophy." Personal communication.

47. Blavatsky, Helena Petrovna. 1888 (2009). "The Secret Doctrine." *Tarcher*. 288 pp.

48. Campbell, Joseph. 1949. "A Hero with a Thousand Faces." *Pantheon Books*. 432 pp.

49. Wald, George.1964. In: Ball, Philip. 2000. "H2O: A Biography of Water." *Phoenix*, UK. 400 pp.

50. Kirill, Metropolitan. 2006. In: "Water, The Great Mystery." Julie Perkul and Anastasiya Popova, directors. *Intention Media*. 87 min.

51. Native Counselling Services of Alberta. 2015. "Water, the Sacred Relationship." Video documentary. 52 min.

52. First Rider, A. 2002. In: Ferguson, Elizabeth. 2005. "Einstein, Sacred Science, and Quantum Leaps: A Comparative Analysis of Western Science, Native Science and Quantum Physics Paradigm." Master of Arts Thesis, University of Lethbridge. 135 pp.

53. Murdoch, Isaac. 2015. "Rock Paintings: The Quest for Medicine and Knowledge." In: Online: *Ojibwayconnections.com*. 85–101 pp.

54. Ford, D.C. 2006. "Karst Landform." *The Canadian Encyclopedia*. Online: http://www.thecanadianencyclopedia.ca/en/article/karst-landform/

55. Gunn, John. Year. "Encyclopedia of Caves and Karst Science." *Routledge*. 960 pp.

56. NOAA. 2007. "Exploration of Submerged Sinkholes in Lake Huron." National Oceanic and Atmospheric Administration (NOAA) Great Lakes Environmental Research Laboratory, Ann Arbor, MI. Brochure, September 2007. Online: http://www.glerl.noaa.gov/pubs/brochures/Sinkholes_GLERL.pdf

57. Phys.Org. 2009. "Great Lake's Sinkholes Host Exotic Ecosystems." *Phys.Org News*. Online: http://phys.org/news/2009-02-great-lake-sink-holes-host-exotic.html

58. Oosthoek, Sharon. 2009. "Sinkholes below Lake Huron Hold Strange Ecosystem: Researchers." *CBC News*, February 25, 2009. Online: http://www.cbc.ca/news/technology/sinkholes-below-lake-hu-ron-hold-strange-ecosystem-researchers-1.801422

59. Schumacher, E.F. 1973. "Small Is Beautiful: A Study of Economics as if People Mattered." *Blond & Briggs*. 288 pp.

60. Ruche, Alain. 2014. "International Cultural Engagement—Part One: Are We at the Tipping Point?" *Kosmos*. Spring/Summer.

61. Margulis, Lynn and Dorion Sagan. 1986. "Microcosmos: Four Billion Years of Microbial Evolution." *Summit Books*, NY. 301 pp.

62. Ball, Philip. 2011. "Flow." *Oxford University Press*. 208 pp.

63. Richards, Rebekah. 2007 (2010). In: Nina Munteanu (author), "What Altruism in Animals Can Teach Us about Ourselves." *The Alien Next Door*. Online: http://sfgirl-thealiennextdoor.blogspot.ca/2010/06/what-altruism-in-animals-can-teach-us.html

64. De Waal, Frans. 2009. "Primates and Philosophers: How Morality Evolved." Stephen Macedo and Josiah Ober (eds). *Princeton University Press*. 232 pp.

65. Bradley, Brenda. 1999. "Levels of Selection, Altruism, and Primate Behavior." *The Quarterly Review of Biology* 74(2): 171–194.

66. Goodall, Jane. 1990 "Through a Window: My Thirty Years with the Chimpanzees of Gombe." Boston: *Houghton Mifflin*.

67. Warneken, F. and Tomasello, M. 2006. "Altruistic Helping in Human Infants and Young Chimpanzees." *Science* 311: 1301–1303.

68. Warneken, F., B. Hare, A.P. Melis, D. Hanus, and M. Tomasello. 2007. "Spontaneous Altruism by Chimpanzees and Young Children." *PloS Biology* 5(7): e184.

69. Manning, Aubrey. 2008. "Animal Magic: Why Species Give Each Other a Helping Hand (or Flipper)!" *Daily Mail*. Online: http://www.dailymail.co.uk/news/article-533571/Animal-magic-Why-species-helping-hand-flipper.html

70. Veigas, Jennifer. 2012. "Cooperative Dolphins Help Fishermen Catch Fish." *Discovery News*. Online: http://news.discovery.com/animals/whales-dolphins/helpful-dolphins-120502.htm

71. de Waal, F.B.M. 2008. "Putting the Altruism Back into Altruism: The Evolution of Empathy." *Annu. Rev. Psychol.* 59: 279–300.

72. de Waal, F.B.M., K. Leimgruber, and A.R. Greenberg. 2008. "Giving Is Self-rewarding for Monkeys." *Proc. Natl. Acad. Sci.*, USA 105: 13685–13689.

73. Sapolsky, Robert M. 2006 "Social Cultures among Nonhuman Primates." *Current Anthropology* 47(4):641–656.

74. Tarnas, Richard. 1993. "The Passion of the Western Mind: Understanding the Ideas that Have Shaped Our World View." *Ballantine Books*. 560 pp.

12.
Water
is
Joy

Photo 12.1: Water patterns form as sunlight dances over pebbles in the shallows of the Credit River, Ontario, Canada.

Photo by Merridy Cox

"Environmental sounds may be among the most sacred on the planet, for they are the sound of the Earth, rejoicing in itself."

—Jonathan Goldman

When I ponder my many joyous moments from childhood through motherhood and now wandering traveller, water has been there, my everlasting companion, nurturing me from the subtle spray of a Quebec spring rain to the gushing celebration of my child being born in Vancouver British Columbia to the sound of bracing waves of the Atlantic Ocean surf.

I am water rejoicing.

Joyful Childhood

"Forget not that the earth delights to feel your bare feet and the winds long to play with your hair."

—Kahlil Gibran

Photo 12.2: The author and her mother and siblings visiting the Mohawk First Nation village of Caughnawaga in Quebec, Canada.

Photo by Ilie Munteanu

I was born in a small town in the Eastern Townships of Quebec to German and Romanian parents. The youngest of three children, I started writing and drawing as soon as I could hold a pencil. Even before I could read, I wanted to become a "paperback writer," like in the old Beatles song.

I'm a bit of a bohemian and enjoy wandering the world in search of the strange and wonderful. I come by my gypsy lifestyle quite honestly: forty percent genetics (from both my passionate philosopher dad and my *wanderlustich* artist mom); forty percent my upbringing (they were very supportive of my artistic pursuits) and twenty percent God's Will. I loved both parents dearly. They let me be who I was, and because of that they helped shape what I now am: a loving mother; courageous artist; creative scientist; wandering explorer; everlasting child, trickster and storyteller; faithful student and enthusiastic teacher; judge and fierce advocate for the oppressed—the ridiculed—and the silent; lover of all living and inanimate things and God's humble servant.

I grew up, as the youngest child, following my brother and sister on adventures to the forest or the nearby fields or a local stream, where we exercised our imagination. We stirred twigs, soil, flowers, moss, lichen, seeds and other interesting things with water. These fuelled our "magic potions" that we then used on some poor insect or little beast. Hemlock cones became projectiles in "forest wars," catapulted at each other using tiny saplings that we mangled into effective siege engines. Yes, I was a bit destructive as a child—but I learned the value of creation too; through my art and through sharing and helping others. Respect and compassion are gifts we must learn to hone.

My fondest memories include playing outside in the woods, listening to the birds, and playing cars in the dirt with Mark and Bruce, the neighbourhood boys; hearing my mother's soprano voice singing in the kitchen as she baked her German sugar cookies; riding my bicycle and exploring the streets with my dog, Foxie. My father was always bringing home stray cats and dogs to my delight.

I spent a lot of my childhood days close to the ground, observing, poking, catching, prodding, destroying and creating. Perhaps it was this early induction to the sensual organic fragrances of soil, freshly cut grass, rotting leaves and blooming flowers that set my path, in later life, to enjoy gardening with the kind of joy that transcends. In his book *The Holy Order of Water* William Marks shares how many gardeners and farmers regard the earth as a natural form of aromatherapy.[1]

My mother kept a garden in our back yard. It was large and thrived with flowers and vegetables. I remember rows of bright dahlias with their button-faces and elegant gladiolas of all colours, tall like sentinels. Her vegetable garden had a diverse texture and fragrant earthy aroma of sweet peas, tomatoes, onions, and lettuce. My brother and sister and I used to filch rhubarb stalks from her large patch and eat them with sugar, our faces puckering from the sweet-sour burst of flavour. In the winter, my mother would flood the garden with water to create a huge ice rink for the neighbourhood to use for hockey. Somehow, I always ended up being the goalie, dodging my brother's swift pucks to the net.

My brother was my hero and my sister my partner in imagination. My birth family shares a common "bloodline"—all that we experienced since childhood has been mingled with the nature of our birthplace. Ultimately, we are connected in family and community through the watershed of our home. I will always feel connected to my birthplace, as to no other place. Its water is my water.

Photo 12.3: The author, age 3, pretending to read, Granby, Quebec, Canada.

Photo by Martha Munteanu

Joyful Motherhood

"A man sees in the world what he carries in his heart."
—*J.W. von Goethe*

When I gave birth to my son, Kevin, I felt a miracle pass through me. I felt divinity touch me with a kind hand and whisper its joy. I was humbled, awestruck and so overjoyed. A little miracle emerged out of me, completely formed and so beautiful! And so wet!

Kevin became my doorway to wonder. His curiosity was boundless and lured me into a special world of transformation.

I took time off work to spend with Kevin when he was young. We went on great trips, from the local mall, where we had a hot chocolate and played with Lego, to the local beach on the Fraser River, where we explored the rocks. When he was no more than three, I took him on endless adventures in the city and its surroundings. We didn't have to go far. The mud puddles of a new subdivision after a rain were sufficient to keep our attention for dozens of minutes. We became connoisseurs of mud. The best kind was "chocolate mud," with a consistency and viscosity that created the best crater when a rock was thrown into it.

Kevin and I often explored the little woodland a block from our house. We were explorers. Hunters. Gatherers. Magicians. We made "magic potions" out of nightshade flowers, fir and pine needles, loam and moss; then we fuelled our concoctions with the elixir of water from a stagnant pool.

We were blessed with "our own" slough; a large irrigation ditch that flowed along to the agricultural land reserve behind our property and flushed continuously with fresh input from the Fraser River. My husband Herb had built an impressive dock, and we had a fleet of boats, including several kayaks and a canoe. Trips down the slough, which included paddling through several culverts with heads bowed to avoid the spider webs, were common in the summers. Resourceful Herb had also created a rope swing that hung off one of the large cottonwood

Photo 12.4: The author and her son enjoying an exploratory hike in Nature.

Photo by Herb Klassen

trees lining the slough. Kevin and the entire neighbourhood used that rope swing to refresh themselves, plunging into the murky waters on hot summer days.

Our property was a short drive away from the Pacific Ocean. We spent hours on the expansive sands of Centennial Beach, wading for miles along the low tide waters, exploring the life that crawled and wriggled among the seaweeds. Herb shared a twenty-eight-foot cruising boat with his family; every other weekend, we had the opportunity to explore the west coast of British Columbia.

When Kevin was almost five, we spent a week boating around Cortes Island.[2] Our first anchorage was in Squirrel Cove, where we investigated a derelict ship on shore, played catch-me-if-you-can with an inlet stream to the big lagoon, and discovered a hidden lagoon that appeared behind a small waterfall at low tide. Here Kevin and I played the dangerous game of "sharks." Dangerous, because Mommy always lost and got eaten by the sharks. The idea was to jump from one seaweed-covered rock to the next, arms stretched out for balance. You were not allowed to walk on the sand or mud. Oops! Mommy slipped and fell on her you-know-what and got "slimed" by *Fucus* seaweed and sea water.

Photo 12.5: The author's son points out a starfish on the intertidal rocky shore of the Pacific Ocean, British Columbia, Canada.

"You're dead," Kevin said simply as I got up gracelessly. "The sharks ate you."

Dad kindly suggested that the game was over and Kevin had won. But Kevin insisted the game must continue because to really win you had to reach the *big* rock! I smiled. There were so many *big* rocks …

Photo by Nina Munteanu

Joyful Journey

"Better to lose count while naming your blessings than to lose your blessings to counting your troubles."

—**Maltbie D. Babcock**

Photo 12.6: The author's son Kevin and Herb walk the country street of Denman Island, British Columbia, Canada.

Photo by Nina Munteanu

In 2007, I created my first blog, *The Alien Next Door*. It featured my observations and thoughts as a writer and aquatic ecologist. My profile recounted my favourite things; one of them was walking in the rain, hearing its rhythms and the smell of the Earth after a rainstorm. I was connecting with the liberating and energizing nature of rain and water vapour. And how joyful it was!

In truth, I was reconnecting with my own nature. And inhaling the scent of a shifting breeze. Aside from creating my first blog, which was to herald my first published novel—my eco-thriller *Darwin's Paradox*[3]—I was to experience many other significant precedents. Through my blog, I encountered a force that would herald a great change in my entire perception of the world, of life's transcending nature, and even of my own destiny. As my wise sister Doina Maria once said to me: *Nothing can come into my experience without first coming into my consciousness, and when the inner is ready to express itself, it will express in the outer.*

The year 2007 heralded the beginning of a journey that would eventually lead me to the far corners of the planet, to encounter perceptions and dialectics that challenged the inertia of my soul. I would leave my hometown and my family to travel alone, meet archetypes who would lead me through swamp, quagmire and salty ocean, as well as crystal lake and rushing brook. I travelled on a fertile breeze, both warm and bracing.

I pursued my art with a fierce passion, flowing with the synergistic co-evolution of my interests in ecology and storytelling. Ultimately, where I put my attention, that I became. I am gypsy. I am knight. I am summoner. I am maid, mother and crone, transcending time and space.

More and more, I've become fascinated by the interrelatedness of things in space–time, particularly in ways that can't be explained. Coincidence, precognition, déjà vu—these all appear to play a shadow-dance with each other. Quantum mechanics shows us that not only is "solid" matter made up mostly of energy and "empty" space, but also what makes a solid a chair (versus you sitting on it) is the vibration of its energy. Quantum science has demonstrated that light and matter are made of both particles and waves that can exist simultaneously. *Schrödinger's cat* is mystical and quantum entangled. That mystical cat braved the notion that particles can be linked in such a way that changing the quantum state of one instantaneously affects the other, even if they are light years apart. What does it mean when solid flows, ghost-like, through itself under certain conditions? In my trilogy *Splintered Universe*, one person's past is another's future. And where do they meet? Perhaps in dreams?[3,4]

Water is the bold light of change. Water is the deep purity of soul.

As we enter the seventh golden age, the nirvana of my soul consciousness rejoices with the water of my birth. I soar with thoughts of returning to the plenum. Reborn, I rejoice.

Water is the abiding mother.

Photo 12.7: Older Kevin swimming the Pacific Ocean in Georgia Strait, British Columbia, Canada.

Photo 12.8: Younger Kevin rides a belly boat as he fishes in Fish Lake in the Chilcotin Plateau, British Columbia, Canada.

Photo by Nina Munteanu

Photo by Nina Munteanu

Water Rejoicing

"Environmental sounds may be among the most sacred on the planet, for they are the sound of the Earth, rejoicing in itself."
—Jonathan Goldman

Photo 12.9: Saltwater marsh near Mahone Bay, Nova Scotia, Canada.

Photo by Nina Munteanu

Now, as I roam the world as writer itinerant—travelling and teaching and learning—I find myself grateful for all that I have experienced and learned. Even the "bad" stuff, for even it has gifted me with blessings and opportunities.

Travelling the world has helped me realize that I was blessed with an abundance of water. I lived my entire life in a country of plentiful and healthy water. Canada holds one-fifth of the world's fresh water in lakes, rivers, and wetlands, as well as in our underground aquifers and glaciers. Canada's wetlands, which cover more than 1.2 million square kilometres, make Canada the largest wetland area in the world.[6]

Perhaps it is no coincidence that Canada is steward of the world's largest wetlands. Wetlands include marshes, swamps, fens, and bogs, all irreplaceable habitat for a huge diversity of nesting, feeding and staging waterfowl, reptiles, amphibians and mammals—many at risk. Wetlands provide a major filtration system, removing contaminants, improving water quality and renewing water's vitality; wetlands serve as reservoirs, controlling and reducing flooding toward a more balanced hydrological cycle. Wetlands are a source of oxygen and water vapour, serving a vital role in our global atmospheric and climatic cycles. As ecotones—transitional areas—wetlands protect coasts from erosion and provide exceptional opportunity for boundary interaction and the emergence of vitality. Like a good metaphor, wetlands "recognize" and encompass similarities between dissimilarities. Wetlands powerfully connect. Canada's strong multi-cultural policies and its open tolerance in embracing and celebrating diversity makes it the "wetland" of the world.

When I turn on the water tap in my house in Canada, it is pure drinking water. I don't need to boil it or filter it or test it for impurities and toxins. I am confident that it will nourish and hydrate me like water should. I can bathe without restriction. I can play with it. And I am grateful.

When you live in gratitude, you live in joy.

The search for true happiness has been going on for millennia and remains the subject of discourse for philosophers. Yet, it continually seems to elude many of us the more we pursue it.

American author, Bill McKibben wrote in *Ecology Magazine*: "Climate change isn't just a threat. It's an opportunity for us to live happier, more fulfilling lives."[7] What he's getting at here is that one person's happiness can't continue at the expense of others. If one person finds wealth, success and "a sense of well being" by cheating or polluting, that kind of satisfaction will harm the Earth, others, and ultimately themselves. It is the opposite of altruism. And altruism lies at the heart of true happiness.

Mattieu Ricard, a Buddhist monk and French biologist and philosopher, says that "pre-occupation with the self leads to detrimental urges."[7] According to Ricard, one of the primary ways to attain happiness is to flow with compassion by practising altruistic love. In his book *Happiness: A Guide to Developing Life's Most Important Skill*, Ricard adopted the perspective of the Dalai Lama called *secular spirituality*, to assist people in embracing what the French call *joie de vivre* and what Aristotle described as "human flourishing."[8]

Photo 12.10: Jack Russel, Reggie, enjoys the water, fetching sticks on Cherry Beach, Lake Ontario, Canada.

Sharon Betcher of the Vancouver School of Theology suggests that in our consumer culture the mass media stimulate people toward "immature desires." She further asserts that happiness needs to be linked to ethical action. She believes that "an understanding of [true] happiness will turn the planet away from environmental degradation."[7] Douglas Todd of the *Vancouver Sun* adds, "changing our understanding of happiness could set the stage for a truly ecological age."[7] McKibben says, "We know, after the long experience of the 20th century, all the things that don't work for human satisfaction (centrally planned economies, endlessly repeated ideologies, even more accumulation). We know, from what the scientists now tell us weekly, what doesn't work for the planet (burning hydrocarbons). Environmentalism is now the art of put-

Photo by Nina Munteanu

ting those two sets of facts together."[7] Echoing McKibben's approach, Betcher says: "In our current context, living within constraints can be more creative and fulfilling than merely satiating desire."[7]

The danger of self-preoccupation was illustrated by a chilling experiment conducted on laboratory rats in 2007. The experiment consisted of giving electrode-fitted rodents the opportunity to press three levers: one provided food, the second provided water, and the third stimulated the pleasure centre in their brains. The rats kept juicing up on the brain's pleasure synapses and forgot to eat or drink. They died—euphorically—of dehydration and starvation.[7] The lesson is obvious: hedonism and addiction to drugs, sex, gambling or food may provide short-term bliss, but we will end up in long-term misery. Satisfying desires motivated by vanity, fear or a hunger for self-esteem will never lead to contentment or happiness. Happiness is a state of mind and requires one to "work at it," according to Ricard. Like anything worthwhile in life, it requires effort.

Heesoon Bai of Simon Fraser University suggests that happiness is found in feeling connected. She describes happiness as the "spirit of vitality," which can be witnessed in those who display openness, aliveness and warmth. "Happy people are charged," she says. "They're fuelled by clean-burning energy."[7]

In the end, there is no magic stick to achieve happiness. We are most happy when we make others happy. We are happy when we are in touch with an inner spark, follow an ethical path, feel connected to humans and the natural world and contribute to the wider community.

Photo 12.11: Sammy, the family cat, enjoys a winter hunt.

Photo by Nina Munteanu

The Little Stream Called to the Sea—A Sufi Tale

Once there was a little stream that dreamed of flowing to the sea. The stream started in an aquifer, a huge pool of water underground, but the call of the ocean was so strong that the stream pushed its way through nooks and cracks, up through the earth until it burst forth into the air and began its journey toward the sea. As its waters bubbled to the surface they ran down the hill carving the streambed into the earth. Sometimes the stream babbled as it travelled, sometimes it gurgled, some times it roared. At times the stream traveled alone. Its waters were so clear you could see the pebbles that lined its bed. At other times the stream ran through great lakes, or tumbled over a cliff, or joined other streams to form a river, and then split again to travel alone, but always, always the little stream yearned to flow into the sea.

Sometimes the stream would run fast and deep, eager to reach the sea. Fish swam in its waters as it carried them swiftly on its journey. Sometimes the stream would grow wide and slow, and it would carry boats on its back as it continued its journey. But always, always the little stream yearned to flow into the sea.

One day, just as the call of the ocean seemed to grow a bit stronger, the stream found itself growing sluggish, its waters grew thick with mud, until sadly it pooled into a brackish mudhole right on the edge of the desert. "Woe is me," thought the little stream, "now I'll never get to the sea." It tried going around the desert—but the desert was too wide. It tried going under the desert—but the desert was too deep. Still (even with mud in its "ears") the little stream heard the call of the ocean and

Photo 12.12: Footprints in the snow at Port Credit on the shores of Lake Ontario, Canada.

Photo by Nina Munteanu

yearned to flow to the sea. After what seemed like a long time, as the stream just pooled there in the sun, it began to hear a second voice. "I can take you to the sea, little stream," whispered the wind. "Come with me, I'll carry you to the ocean shore."

"How could you do that?" scoffed the stream. "You are only made of air."

"I can carry you on a breeze," whispered the wind, "But you must be very brave, for you must let go of yourself and change."

"I've changed many times," said the stream.

"But this will be different," said the wind.

The little stream paused, but deep within, the stream still yearned for the sea. The stream let go… and the wind picked it up particle by particle. At first the stream was scared, for it felt lost, it was no longer a stream but was turned sort of inside out and had become moisture swirling in the sky. The view was like nothing the little stream had ever seen before. Not only was the whole world laid out below it, but it was surrounded by sparkling jewels. Then what had been the stream realized that all those sparkling jewels were parts of itself. Molecules of water, droplets of moisture, sparkling in the light. What had been the stream realized that it was truly beautiful on the inside.

Next, the stream-turned-moisture saw that it was not alone, for the wind had whispered to other streams, and ponds, and even to the morning dew upon the oasis. All had turned into moisture. And all their parts were also sparkling in the sun. Together they were even more beautiful, for the sunlight had changed them into all the colours of a rainbow.

Then the little stream-turned-rainbow felt itself falling, and falling and falling. All the other droplets were falling too, until plop, plop, plop, plop—all the droplets ran together into a mighty river which rushed down the mountainside, across a coastal plain, and into the sea, where the waves pushed it back and pulled it forward and the currents carried it far out into the pulsing depths. The little stream was content.

Photo 12.13: East Queen Street in the Beaches during a snow-storm in Toronto, Canada.

Photo by Nina Munteanu

But I understand that every now and then, the wind would breeze by, whispering to the currents in the sea … "Come with me, come with me…" and that the moisture would rise up into the wind and be carried away to start all over again.[9]

Photo 12.15: Clothes left on the line in a winter snow, Vancouver Island, British Columbia, Canada.

Photo by Nina Munteanu

Photo 12.14: Skier in Whistler Village looks forward to fresh powder, British Columbia, Canada.

Photo by Nina Munteanu

Water's Prayer

Ecologist Garrett Hardin's 1968 paper entitled "The Tragedy of the Commons"[10] was required reading for ecologists like me. The paper explored the unfortunate result of a situation where the pursuit of self-interest results in collective ruin. Farmers who share a common pasture, for instance, will increase their herds little by little until they destroy it through overgrazing. This is essentially the "prisoner's dilemma," a hypothetical game theory, which concludes that self-interest ultimately undermines the mutual benefit of unselfish acts.

"Water is the ultimate commons," writes Barbara Kingsolver, who adds that watercourses were once deemed boundless and "the notion of protecting water was as silly as bottling it."[11] Things change, don't they?

According to the Natural Resources Defense Council, more than half the American population drink bottled water and at least a third consume bottled water regularly.[12] This is water that was taken from one watershed and effectively sold to another. We pull water out of the ground; we bottle it and truck it away or confine it in pipes and send it hundreds of kilometres from its watershed.

Throughout all this, water has remained what it is. All-giving.

Water is an altruist.

Ultimately, water will travel through the Universe and transform worlds; it will transcend time and space to share and teach; water will do its job to energize you and give you life, then quietly take its leave; it will move mountains particle by particle with a subtle hand; it will paint the world with beauty, then return to its fold and rejoice.

I am water. I am joy.

"Be excellent to one another, and party on, dudes!"[13]

Water Is Joy

References

1. Marks, William. 2001. "The Holy Order of Water." *Bell Pond Books*. 296 pp.

2. Munteanu, Nina. 1997. "A Week Around Cortes Island." *Pacific Yachting*, May Issue.

3. Munteanu, Nina. 2007. "Darwin's Paradox." Dragon Moon Press. 320 pp.

4. Munteanu, Nina. 2011–2014. "The Splintered Universe Trilogy." *Starfire World Syndicate* and *Pixl Press*.

5. Munteanu, Nina. 2012. "Interview with Nina Munteanu." Derek Newman-Stille (interviewer). *Speculating Canada: Canadian Horror, Science Fiction, and Fantasy*, November 27, 2012. Online: http://speculatingcanada.ca/2012/11/27/interview-with-nina-munteanu/

6. Environment Canada. 2015. "Water." Online: http://www.ec.gc.ca/eau-water/

7. Todd, D. 2007. "Changing the World." *The Vancouver Sun*, July 7, 2007. Online: http://www.canada.com/story.html?id=32bcebaf-3e4b-4f1e-b3e1-f4ec2bd55dce

8. Ricard, Matthieu. 2007. "Happiness: A Guide to Developing Life's Most Important Skill." Little, Brown and Company. 304 pp.

9. Sufi Tale. 2015. "The Little Stream Called to the Sea." Provided by Pamela Smith-Loeters, Unitarian Congregation in Mississauga, ON. Online: http://cuc.ca/archive/canuue/CANUUE%20SUMMER%2002.pdf

10. Harden, Garrett. 1968. "The Tragedy of the Commons." *Science* 162 (3859): 1243–1248.

11. Kingsolver, Barbara. 2010. "Water is Life." *National Geographic, Water Special Issue*, April 2010.

12. Natural Resources Defense Council. 2013. "Bottled Water: Pure Drink or Pure Hype?" Online: http://www.nrdc.org/water/drinking/bw/exesum.asp

13. Herek, Stephen, Director. 1989. "Bill & Ted's Excellent Adventure." Orion Pictures. 90 min.

Afterthoughts

Photo 13.1: A nest of water wavelets form in the shallows of the flowing Credit River.

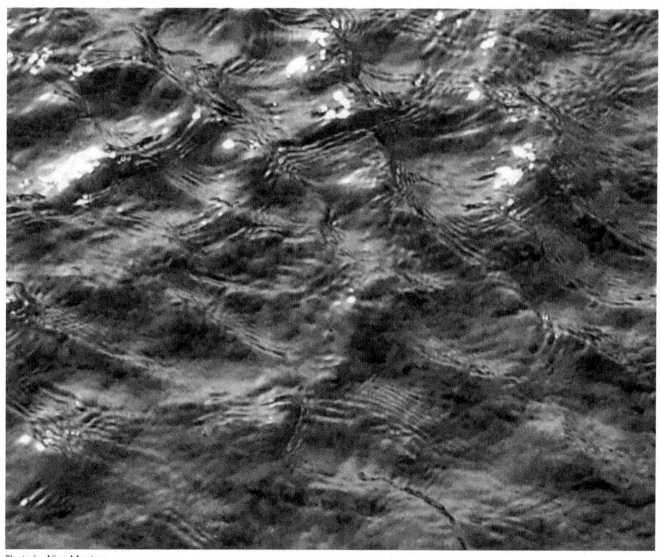

Photo by Nina Munteanu

"I only went out for a walk and finally concluded to stay out till sundown; for going out, I found, was really going in."

—John Muir

Do you believe in serendipity or destiny?

The pursuit of this book has been oddly serendipitous ... influenced by what quantum physicist David Bohm would call "Implicate Order", what Jung would call "synchronicity", the Vedas would call "akasha", Goethe would call "the ground of all being", Rudolf Steiner would call "cosmic intelligence", and biochemist Mae-Wan Ho would call "quantum entanglement."

Early on, during the research and writing of this book, I discovered that this project on water had become a gestalt watershed for all the important moments in my life. Places I've been. Things I've learned. People I've met and with whom I'd had surprising discussions and realizations. All spanning many years. And many of them totally unrelated. And yet, now, with a sudden flood of context, their significance has transcended into a new fabric of meaning through surprising connection. Like puzzle pieces cooperatively arranging themselves into a symbiotic pattern of synchronicity: from a strange discussion with a fellow student in college to a learning moment in motherhood to meeting a mysterious stranger on the Internet or serendipitously reading an article that resonated and set in motion a new adventure.

It's truly humbling.

I've had watershed moments like this before, but none as all-encompassing. Over a decade ago, when Karen, my publishing friend, suggested I write a book on how to write fiction—a brash idea, given it was still early in my own writing career—I embraced the task and wrote and researched the textbook in three short months. The research came fast and easily. The Universe provided everything I needed. The format and content came to me in bursts of "genius". It came out of me like someone else was directing me and I was simply transcribing. *The Fiction Writer: Get Published, Write Now!* has been praised for its content and style. It was translated into Romanian by *Editura Parallela* and is currently used in universities, colleges and high schools all over the planet and considered a useful tool by a full range of writers from new and young to old and established. It remains my bestselling book. To this day, I know that my fiction-writing textbook arose from a universal collaboration. I had help. The book, in turn, has helped many budding writers of all ages and all over the world write better.

And from that regard, it has fulfilled my prime directive to help make the world a better place and to give voice to those who would otherwise remain silent or be silenced.

It starts with the word. And that word is water.

I taught limnology and served as an environmental consultant for over twenty-five years. During that time, I waded—and stumbled—through northern muskeg, avoiding bears and moose. I scrambled up—and down—the talus slopes of acid mine tailings ponds. I sampled the tannic water of a rural dystrophic lake. I took sediment core samples from the bottom of a northern reservoir. I hiked through logged old growth forest in search of fish-bearing streams. I sampled water over a 24-hour period along a working river impacted by industrial effluent. I collected and studied surface algal blooms—as part of a limnological

Photo 13.2: Heritage house covered in fresh snow, Lunenburg, Nova Scotia, Canada.

Photo by Nina Munteanu

study—of an urban eutrophic lake to create a community restoration plan. I replanted hectares of marsh with indigenous plants to restore its functionality. As a limnologist, environmental consultant, mother and naturalist, I was blessed with the opportunity to see water in so many identities, circumstances and places around the world.

My mission is simple with *Water Is…*

I hope that somewhere among these pages, you have emotionally connected with water, as I have. It's that simple.

Water Is… has incorporated a synchronicity that defies space-time. I have no doubt that it's the result of quantum entanglement.

Water is the singularity.

Photo 13.3: *The author (and feline friend) enjoys the splendor of Desolation Sound on the west coast of British Columbia, Canada.*

Photo by Herb Klassen

When Science Tangos with Art—Synchronicity

Imagination is more important than knowledge

—Albert Einstein

I tell stories. I'm also a scientist. I use the scientific method in my research to seek truth; I also find truth presented to me through the symbols of intuition.

A few years ago, I was introduced to Krista Fogel, a University of British Columbia masters student, who was investigating the use of creative art in high-ability scientists. She named her thesis: "The Self-Perceived Experience of Investigating Science with an Artistic Spirit: A Hermeneutic Phenomenological Study of High Ability Scientists Who Also Engage in the Arts."[1] *Hermeneutic*, by the way, is the development and study of theories of the interpretation and understanding of texts (I had to look it up) and *phenomenology* is an approach to philosophy through the study of phenomena.

Krista wanted to interview me as part of her project. I was flattered, of course. Me, a *High Ability Scientist*? Who'd told her that? Once I got past my own humble angst, I found Krista's questions bracing; they reopened a world of compelling ideas I had carried with me for some time. The concept of using art to do good science has dwelled inside me since registration day at Concordia University when I quit my fine arts program to pursue a science degree only to come full circle and write fiction. I got my Masters Degree in Ecology and Limnology and was then working as a scientist for an environmental consulting firm (I now write and teach writing full time). I did research, drove boats, collected samples and analyzed data, then wrote up my findings and made recommendations. I wrote science fiction novels on the side.

"History shows that eminent scientists, such as Leonardo da Vinci, also engaged in the arts,"[1] said Fogel. She went on to cite 400 other famous scientists who also practiced art at a high level. "If not entirely engaged in the arts, scientists throughout history have at least engaged in science with an artistic spirit. Scientists and artists use common tools for thinking such as intuition and imaginative processes."[1]

Krista and I met several times at the local Starbucks, where I "toked" on coffee as she fumbled with her notes. A young gal with a direct but unassuming gaze and a gentle smile, Krista asked me to share my personal experience of mixing art with science. Every good scientist is an artist at heart: science is the tool and art is the process.

Fogel concludes that when conducting scientific investigations with an artistic spirit, the scientist holds her heart central, from which the artist springs. This "allows us to connect with serendipitous occurrences, which breed discovery,"[1] Fogel adds.

You can train your mind as both artist and scientist to become more aware of serendipitous occurrences around you. I call it being in sync and wrote about it in several articles for various magazines and mentioned it here.

When I'm working on a story, for instance, I find that events, opportunities, actions and resources directly germane to my project present themselves: watching an applicable movie that a friend chose for us to see; picking up a newspaper (which I seldom do) and reading a relevant article; looking for something on the Internet and finding something totally different (OK; that happens to me all the time); a friend out of the blue introduces a pertinent topic, or someone you haven't seen in a long time bumps into you with significant news. As though the universe was providing me with what I needed. Of course, my mind was focused on anything to do with my current piece. It was as though I had donned a concentrating filter, one that would amplify relevant details. I'll go further: I was unconsciously acting in a way that was bringing me more information relevant to my project. Ask and you shall receive.

Often, when I'm researching a novel, I pick up things serendipitously. Something will come up that just fits with what I was searching for. An article pops up in the news. Or I'm talking to someone and they bring up just the topic I am researching. These things always happen to me. This occurs not only in my fiction writing but in my scientific pursuits. Some years ago, I was doing a pollution study using glass slides for colonizing algae to compare communities of an urban stream to those of an agricultural stream. I was really looking to see the difference between communities of these different stream environments when I discovered that the algae were colonizing the glass surfaces according to the current. Compelled with more questions of why, how and what if, I pursued this new line of research (which turned out to be far more interesting than my original research premise) and wrote several ground-breaking papers on it.

Indeed, questions like "why" and "what if" are germane to both art and science; the 'what if' question is the science fiction writer's premise, which comes from the artist part of you: imagination and an inquisitive and open mind. The idea of seemingly unrelated events intersecting to produce meaningful patterns has spawned new notions of thought from the scientific study of spontaneous order in the Universe (synchronicity), to *synchromysticism*—the discovery of convergent archetypal symbols in pop culture (e.g., books, music and film).

Writer and philosopher Jake Kotze suggests that, "Synchronicity happens when we notice the bleed-through from one seemingly separate thing into another—or when we for a brief moment move beyond the mind's divisions of the world."[2] Synchronicity and serendipitous discovery, like metaphor, appear when we change the way we look at things.

Serendipitous discovery comes to us through peripheral vision. Like our muse, it doesn't happen by chasing after it; it sneaks up on us when we're not looking. It comes to us when we focus outward and embrace our wonder for this world. When we quiet our minds and nurture our

souls with beauty. It is then that what we had been seeking naturally comes to us. Like a gift.

Author Sibyl Hunter tells us that, "Sync operates as an undercurrent of divine awareness personified through the myriad processes and symbols that make up the building blocks of our reality. Within that current, we spin our modern-day myths into books, fairy tales and movies, subconsciously retelling ourselves the same story over and over."[3] This also holds true in the models and metaphors of scientific genius, which often spring from the creativity of an intuitive heart and imaginative mind.

According to Mark A. Runco at California State University, "creativity depends on originality, while accomplishment and achievement reflect other problem-solving skills. Creative thinking involves at least three things: 1) the cognitive capacity to transform experience into original interpretations, 2) an interest in producing original interpretations, and 3) discretion." The title of Piaget's monograph, *To Understand Is to Invent*, reflects the fact that we do not have an authentic understanding of our experience until we construct that understanding for ourselves. In other words, "it is one thing to memorize some datum; it is quite another to discover it for one's self; only then do we understand,"[4] says Runco. Fogel concurs: "what Piaget called *invention* is a kind of creation, a creation of personal meaning. Piaget tied assimilation to imaginative play into creative interpretation."[1]

According to Dean Keith Simonton at the Univeristy of California and author of *Scientific Genius: A Psychology of Science*, even the most illustrious creative geniuses of history have careers riddled by both hits and misses, both successes and failures. He uses Albert Einstein as an example. A man who has achieved almost mythical status as a genius, Einstein's career "was plagued by terrible ideas, false starts and surprising disasters."[5] Simonton tells the story of Einstein's debate with Niels Bohr over the implications of quantum theory, in which Einstein offered a series of arguments that Bohr countered. Bohr once even pointed out that Einstein failed to take into consideration the theory of relativity! According to some, Einstein wasted the final years of his career working on a unified field theory that was almost universally rejected by his colleagues. Einstein defended his missteps by noting that errors can advance science so long as they are not trivial; the greater the error, the greater the opportunity for new perspective and discovery.

It is left for us to simply recognize the dance.

Photo 13.4: Youth enjoying a scenic walk in Vancouver's Stanley Park as a cruise ship passes under the Lions Gate Bridge, Canada.

Photo by Nina Munteanu

Singularities, Gravity and Love

Speaking of singularities and black holes ... I recently watched Christopher Nolan's science fiction epic *Interstellar*.[6] Critical reception was widely mixed. Reviews ranged from being dazzled and awestruck to thinking it utterly ridiculous and silly. Much of the range in opinion had in fact to do with the hard science: hard science that Nolan insisted he get right by hiring theoretical physicist Kip Thorne to best approximate what a black hole and a wormhole would look like and behave. Science so good that it generated a discovery worthy of reporting in a scientific journal.

To accurately portray a black hole in the film, Thorne produced a new set of equations to guide the special effects team's rendering software. A black hole apparently spins at nearly the speed of light, dragging bits of the universe along with it. Based on the notion that it was once a star that collapsed into a singularity, the hole forms a glowing ring that orbits around a spheroidal maelstrom of light, which curves over the top and under the bottom simultaneously. The team then discovered that "warping space around the black hole also warps the accretion disk," explained Paul Franklin, senior supervisor of Double Negative (the visual experts). "So, rather than looking like Saturn's rings around a black sphere, the light creates this extraordinary halo."[7] Thorne confirmed that they had correctly modelled a phenomenon inherent in the math he'd supplied and intends to publish several articles in scientific journals, based on these findings. In Chapter 11, I talk about some of the latest theories about black holes that suggest that these "singularities" may in fact be tunnels for spiralling matter (or energy) falling into them between universes in a multiverse.

"The creation of something new is not accomplished by the intellect but by the play instinct acting from inner necessity. The creative mind plays the objects it loves"

—Carl Jung

Interstellar begins in the near-future on a post-climate change Earth, plagued by dust storms and failing crops in a society reverted to parochial superstition. Cooper (Matthew McConaughey), once a NASA pilot and now a farmer, laments: "We used to look up at the sky and wonder at our place in the stars, now we just look down and worry about our place in the dirt."

In a scene reminiscent of present day schools removing cursive writing from the curriculum or the controversy of teaching evolution (e.g., in favor of creationism), Cooper's daughter's teacher, Ms. Kelly, informs him at a parent-teacher meeting that the history textbooks have been rewritten to make known the "truth" about the moon landing: "I believe [the moon landing] was a brilliant piece of propaganda," attests Ms. Kelly, "that the Soviets bankrupted themselves pouring resources into rockets and other useless machines ... And if we don't want to repeat the excess and wastefulness of the 20th Century, then we need to teach our kids about this planet, not tales of leaving it."

The danger of turning away from scientific exploration—particularly space exploration—in times of great social and economic insecurity is a theme that runs deep in the film. Not only are scientists and engineers portrayed as whole individuals, both smart and compassionate, but they are also marginalized in a future world looking more to blame than to fix. "We didn't run out of planes and television sets," the principal of the school tells Cooper. "We ran out of food."

When a gravitational anomaly leads Cooper and his daughter Murph (Mackenzie Foy) to a secret NASA base in the middle of nowhere, an old colleague, Professor Brand (Michael Caine), recruits him to pilot the interstellar *Endeavor*, NASA's "Noah's Ark", into the far reaches of outer space to repopulate the human race.

Equipped with a bank of human embryos, Cooper and his team follow the trail of the 12-ship exploratory *Lazarus* mission sent out earlier, led by Dr. Mann, an intellectual without connection who believes that "we can care deeply, selflessly about those we know; but that empathy rarely extends beyond our line of sight."

What saves *Interstellar* from sliding into patriarchal colonialism is its subversive theme. And because of it, the movie transcends into artistic commentary.

I speak of love.

Love embodied by two of the main characters—both women: Cooper's daughter, Murph, and his shipmate, Amelia Brand. Love that is irrational. Love that is unscientific. Love that is inexplicable. And love that is all powerful. Inviolate. Eternal. And, I believe, our salvation.

Aspects of "imperialist expansionism" and "patriarchal rationalism" interplay through Cooper, who embodies both in his "cowboy" science. Love propels his evolution to transcend them. In Cooper, we see the tension between rationality of science and the "irrational" faith of love. Related to this, Cooper must continually choose between the personal and the whole in defining his humanity and ultimately his hard choices. First with his daughter and her "ghost", then with Amelia Brand in their mission to another galaxy.

After a botched mission, Amelia appears to abandon the very tenets of hard science to ask the defining question: "Maybe we've spent too long trying to figure all this out with theory. Love is the one thing that transcends time and space." She describes love as a cosmic force, a kind of empathic drive that provides the very basis for humanity's survival: a link to our wholeness as living beings within a breathing multi-dimensional universe. When Cooper challenges Amelia's unscientific notions, she responds with, "Love isn't something we invented. It's observable, powerful … Maybe it's evidence, some artifact of higher dimensions that we can't consciously perceive." Amelia nails it when she, in turn, challenges Cooper: if the second choice turns out bad, they will have enough fuel to do only one of two things: go on to the third planet in hopes of distributing the seeds of humanity OR go back home to his children. Which will he choose? It's interesting what he does end up choosing: he chooses love. Love drives him to do impossible feats, like dock his shuttle with a damaged and recklessly spinning *Endeavor*.

Photo 13.5: Water patterns emerge on the surface of flowing Credit River, Ontario, Canada.

Photo by Nina Munteanu

Love for Murph drives Cooper into the black hole … and out of it. Love directs him to that precise quantum moment where his love for Murph transcends into love for all humanity: to save the world.

This is the secret. The secret Mann in his intellectualized definition of what it means to be human could not touch. The window for connection to the whole is through a single tiny grasp of it. The glimpse into Eternity is through the lens of love. I am reminded of a quote in David Mitchell's *Cloud Atlas*: "What is any ocean but a multitude of drops?" In Spielberg's *Schindler's List*, Itzhak Stern quotes the Talmud: "Whoever saves one life, saves the world entire."

So what is love, then? Is it gravity? Does it communicate through the God particle in the fractal fabric of the Higgs field? What other phenomenon grows from nothing? What other phenomenon is not lessened but in fact grows by giving it away? What other phenomenon provides the very weight and structure—the meaning—of our existence? What other phenomenon is like a whisper heard in a crowded room; and when combined creates the most beautiful symphony? Is it that simple?

If gravity is a plane of existence—a fifth dimension that can exist across space-time—is a black hole simply a doorway? Like death? Is love the fuel of evolution, lifting us up into a higher state?

Catholic theologian and author of *The God Who Loves You* Peter Kreeft shares a new worldview based on love: "…Gravity is love on a material level. In fact, [gravity] has two movements: one is towards union, back to the center, the big bang, the past by gravity. And the other is to give itself out to all other beings, out into the future, the expanding universe, by energy and by entropy, which is energy giving itself out to the empty places."[8] This is reminiscent of Goethe's polarized systole and diastole. Similarly, not only does God love everything, but everything loves God. The acorn, electron, tomcat, human and angel. God loved these differences into existence and each loves back in its own way, says Kreeft.

"When we think of gravity," says Kreeft, "we do not think of it as the body of love or the material expression of love … We do not see God's love at work in the very structure of matter … Why does that funny little electron in a hydrogen atom keep doggedly orbiting around its positively charged nucleus rather than zooming off orbit in a straight line? The scientific answer is: because its angular momentum, which tends to move it straight away from the nucleus, is exactly counterbalanced by its electromagnetic attraction to its oppositely charged nucleus." Kreeft asks, "Why do negative and positive charges attract?"[8] The electron loves its proton because it's a proton, he says. We can see the same principle at work on every level, Kreeft argues: gravity and electromagnetism on the inorganic level; a plant's attraction to the sun and to water and nutrients in the soil; animal instinct; human intuition and love.

Water is love.

Photo 13.6: Young Kevin enraptured by giant pumpkins grown in fertile Richmond Island on the Fraser River, British Columbia, Canada.

Photo by Nina Munteanu

References:

1. Vogel, Krista. 2008. "The Self-Perceived Experience of Investigating Science with an Artistic Spirit: A Hermeneutic Phenomenological Study of High Ability Scientists Who Also Engage in the Arts". *The University of British Columbia Master of Arts Thesis.*

2. Kotze, Jake. 2011. Quoted in: "The Sync Book: Myths, Magic, Media, and Mindscapes: 26 Authors on Synchronicity". Alan Abbadessa Green (ed). *CreateSpace.* 368 pp.

3. Hunter, Sybil. 2011. "The Individual Journey of Sync". In: "The Sync Book: Myths, Magic, Media, and Mindscapes: 26 Authors on Synchronicity". Alan Abbadessa Green (ed). *CreateSpace.* 368 pp.

4. Runco, Mark A. 2014. "Creativity: Theories and Themes—Research, Development, and Practice". *Academic Press*, 2nd ed. 520 pp.

5. Simonton, Dean Keith. Year. "Exceptional Creativity and Chance: Creative Thought as a Stochastic Combinatorial Process". In: "Beyond Knowledge: Extracognitive Aspects of Developing High Ability", Ch. 4. Larisa V. Shavinina & Michael Ferrari (eds). 258 pp.

6. Nolan, Chris (director). 2014. "Intersteller". *Paramount Pictures.* 169 min.

7. Rogers, Adam. 2014. "Wrinkles in Spacetime: The Warped Astrophysics of Interstellar". *Wired Magazine*, October Issue. Online: http://www.wired.com/2014/10/astrophysics-interstellar-black-hole/

8. Kreeft, Peter. 2015. "Love Sees with New Eyes". Peter Kreeft website. Online: http://www.peterkreeft.com/topics/love-sees.htm

Acknowledgements

No work of merit and relevance is a truly isolated endeavor. At the very least the writer invokes her imagination and her muse—which surely reside in the greater fabric of the divine. This work is a culmination of many decades of observation and experience. It is also the result of some splendid and fulfilling collaborations.

I thank Costi Gurgu and his great eye for graphic design and interior layout. I extend my gratitude to Merridy Cox for superlative and detailed editing and indexing. I thank Kerste Voute for her diligent scientific eye and artistic spirit.

I thank Elmar C. Fuchs of WETSUS in the Netherlands; Andreas Wilkens, Michael Jacobi, and Wolfram Schwenk of the Institute of Flow Sciences in Germany; and Dr. Bernd Kröplin at the University of Stuttgart, Germany, for both suggestions on the manuscript and for permitting me to use their excellent images. I thank Isaac Murdoch of the Serpent River First Nation community in northern Ontario for sharing his tales of wisdom of the Ojibway with me. I am also grateful to Dr. Elizabet Sahtouris, Professor in Residence at Chaminado University, Hawaii, for her kind advice on the manuscript and to Finnish writer Emmi Itäranta for kindly reading an earlier version of this work. Gratitude goes to all whose work I cite in the chapters of this book, particularly those who took the time to spend some time with me—in a local coffee house or on the Internet—talking about water. I thank you all; you know who you are.

Any errors within these pages are mine, no one else's.

My heartfelt gratitude goes to my family: Mom, Dad, Doina, Cornel, Herb and my bright star, Kevin, whose light shines a brilliant beacon in my life; as well as others who have become my "family" and who are nurturing me toward my singularity: Merridy, accomplished naturalist and blithe colleague on field trips along the Credit River and beyond; Margaret, co-conspirator on wild adventures and wise "trick-ster" mentor; Anne for providing a nurturing and creative environment for much of the writing of this work and a willing partner on explorations of discovery; and finally Karen—as always my muse and my source—thanks for getting those seats on the 50-yard line.

Photo: Boats in Steveston Harbour, Richmond, British Columbia, Canada.

Photo by Nina Munteanu

Contributors:

L.C. Di Marco, B.A., M.E.S., is a Toronto artist-writer-instructor with a special interest in the environment, disability and animal welfare advocacy (www.liana.biz). Her poem *Re-Wilding the Sacred* is published here for the first time.

John Ambury is a Toronto poet living in Mississauga, ON. His poem *Moving Waters* was previously published in *Canadian Voices, Vol. 1* (Bookland Press, 2009) and *The Courtneypark Connection 2013* (In Our Words Inc.).

Merridy Cox, B.Sc., MMsl, is a Toronto-based editor and photographer, specializing in technical and scientific works and the natural sciences. An amateur field naturalist, Merridy is managing editor of Lyrical Leaf Publishing and has published two e-books, *Shapes of Swan* and *Edwardian Pets and How to Keep Them*. Her poetry and photography have appeared in three anthologies. http://www.englishmanual.wordpress.com

Costi Gurgu is an Art Director with Superpixel Design (superpixeldesign.com) and RootPM (http://rootpm.com). He has worked for Playboy Magazine, the French fashion magazine Madame Figaro, the women lifestyle magazine, Tabu, Investment Executive and many other publications and publishing houses (http://illustration.costigurgu.com). He is also an awarded speculative fiction writer (costigurgu.com).

Nina Munteanu, M.Sc., R.P.Bio., is a Canadian ecologist / limnologist and author of over a dozen non-fiction books, novels and short stories. She consulted in the aquatic sciences as senior scientist for over twenty years and conducted aquatic research at the University of Victoria and Concordia University. Nina teaches writing at the University of Toronto and George Brown College in Toronto, Canada. www.ninamunteanu.ca

In the index, the page numbers in italics are for images and those in bold are for definitions. Page numbers preceded by a Q are for quotes, and those with a T are for tables.

E

Schmandt, Brandon, 65

Scholes, Gregory, 26

Schrödinger, Erwin, 26, 94, 326–327, 440

Schrödinger's cat, 26, 531

Schumacher, E.F., 508

Schumann, Winfried Otto, 309

Schumann Cavity, 309–310, 327

Schumann Resonance (SR), 113, **113**, 302, 309, **313**

Schumpeter, Joseph, 281

Schweitzer, David, 248

Schwenk, Theodor, 66, Q77, 135, 150–151, 156, 164–165, 179–180, 261, 292, 485

Schwenk, Wolfram, 135

scientific method, 408, 412

Scientific Revolution, 403, **405**

Sebaldus, patron saint of Nurenberg, 360

secular spirituality, **533**

sefriot (energy centres), **317**

self, 285, 411

selfish gene, 286, 410

self-referral state, transcendental consciousness and, **440**

serendipity

    breeds discovery, 546–548

    properties of, 543

serpent tunnels (north shore, Lake Huron, Ontario, Canada), karst formations, 504

Shakespeare, 28, Q48, Q262

shapes

    of crystals, 362

    icosahedron, 361–362

    of Platonic solids, 362

symmetry and creative process, 87

    vesica piscis and, 364

    of water splash, 349

Shaviro, Steven, 287

Shaw, George Bernard, Q181

Sheldrake, Rupert, 194–196, 235, 239–240

Shintoism (Japanese religion), **306**, 447

    and Nature, 306

Shiva (Hindu god)

    and *Anahad Nada* (the unstruck sound), 316

    or Nataraja, 283–284

    statue of, 284

    subatomic matter and, 284

    three states of, 284

Shiva, Vandana, 395, 445, 457

Shrine of the Black Stone (Mount Arafat), *Zemzen* (sacred well) at, 446

shrines, 446, 446–447

Shri Yantra, **366**

Shu, F.H. (see Lin, C.C.)

Sikhs, use of holy water, 453

Simonton, Dean Keith, 549

Singapore, water management in, 119

singularity, 551

    technological, **409**

sinkholes, 404, 504

Sirkeci Railway Station (Istanbul, Turkey), 168

Skinner, L.B., 51

Small, Jacquelyn, Q438

small is beautiful, 508

smart materials, **244**

Smith, Adam, 411

Smith-Loeters, Pamela, 451

snakes, Ojibwa legend about, 503

snow, 354, 354–355, 355, T357

snow avalanches, non-random order of, 137

snowflakes, 249, 321, 354–358, 355, 356, **356**, *356–357*, 357–358

snow ghosts, 355

societal shifts, choices toward, 508–509

society

    autopoiesis and, 326

    patriarchy and, 399

    relationship with water, 399

Socrates, 217

solar system, creation of, 55, 60–61

solitons, **315**

solute, 98

solvent, water as, 94

Soubirous, Bernadette, 454

soul, 347, 420, 421, 497

soulmates, 198

sound (*see* also, vibration)

    of animals, 302

    effects on plants, 302

    and language, 496

    as language of mind, 328

    and universal energy, 496

sound waves (see also, vibration)

    dolphins and Schumann Resonance, 310

    expressed in various materials, 266

    healing, 267

    movement through water, 266

space

CPSIA information can be obtained
at www.ICGtesting.com
Printed in the USA
LVOW03s1607190117
521538LV00006B/358/P